O'HIGGINS AND DON BERNARDO

O'Higgins and Don Bernardo

By

EDNA DEU PREE NELSON

E. P. DUTTON & COMPANY, INC.

New York, 1954

My deep gratitude to Marchette Chute, for her invaluable criticism of the manuscript of "O'Higgins and Don Bernardo." And my thanks to Margarita Yglesias, for Spanish translations. All research for this book was done at the New York Public Library, an institution which I thoroughly appreciate.

E. D. P. N.

CONTENTS

Part I
THE FATHER

CHAPTER I

KING CARLOS the Third of Spain stopped before a mirror decorated with gold garlands and pomegranates. He saw behind him dark red velvet window draperies fringed heavily with gold, a portrait by Velasquez, a painting by Murillo. Black tables held marble and alabaster busts of Spanish monarchs. On both sides of the great doors were kneeling statues of saints and apostles and, high above, a ceiling was resplendent with eagles, lions, shields, emblems of Castile and Aragon. Proud Spanish nobles peered from the paintings, as if asking about the colorless face, the spare figure, standing before the mirror.

King Carlos studied the bony frame in black brocade, thin legs swathed in black silk. It was, he thought, a figure that would be happier wearing the robe of a monk.

But since he was King of Spain, he had dedicated himself to the rule of righteousness. His subjects were children who needed wise and disciplined guidance. To help them overcome evil he had banned temptations: bullfights, games of chance, gambling, theaters and dancing. He preached wisdom, the value of diligence and thrift, the rewards of prayer.

He turned from the mirror and went to his chapel.

Before the marble altar, covered with lilies embroidered on the gold cloth, he knelt. The pyx which held the consecrated wafers, a golden vessel in the form of a cross ablaze with gems, glittered under the light of many tapers. But the crown to be given the righteous would be brighter, he thought.

He finished his prayers.

11

Rising, he went to his sitting room where his chocolate was served each morning. At a table holding his model of excavations of the antiquities of the Roman Caesars, to which he had contributed thousands of Spanish pesos, he sipped the hot drink, and fitted miniature columns and paving stones into a courtyard.

An archaeologist, he thought, had a good life.

But pleasure must end and the work of a monarch begin. Opening a blue-enameled box, he took a pinch of snuff, enough to last the entire day, and since the hot chocolate had not warmed him through he held his thin fingers over the coals of a silver filagree brasero.

It was nearing nine o'clock. Each morning at nine he conferred with one of his ministers. Today, it was the Marquis of Sonora, Don Jose de Galvez, Minister and presiding officer of the Council of the Indies. The Council directed all affairs of the Spanish colonies and Galvez was the most conscientious of his officials. Under Galvez, the income from the colonies had increased. He kept the good will of the colonial administrators as no other minister had. And he was forthright in his opinions and honest with the Crown's finances. Galvez was an exceptionally fine minister. There were few like him.

On the stroke of nine Galvez was announced.

He entered quickly, a smile on his genial countenance, a lock of hair dropping over his forehead. All of his motions were swift and exact. Everything about him suggested directness—the straight eyebrows, the fine, definite line of chin and nose.

The simplicity with which he greeted His Majesty was refreshing. He wished the King good morning, prayed God to spare him many years, and without delay opened a map of North and South America. He spread his chart over the table. On it the possessions of Spain were marked boldly in red crayon, and in a corner was the date when the map was made, February, 1787, less than a month ago.

Minister Galvez laid a finger on Chile.

The King studied the map. He had forgotten that Chile had such an extensive coastline. It must be two thousand miles at least. With that long exposed coast open to enemies, the forts should be well strengthened.

"Brigadier Ambrosio Higgins de Vallenar has finished repairs to the forts in north and south Chile." The voice of Galvez was easy and confident. "At present he is working on the enlargement of forts St. Augustin and Galvez, here at Port Talcahuano." He moved his finger a few inches south along the map.

His Majesty was pleased with Brigadier Higgins. The alert Irishman had accomplished another important mission. He thought again how competent Galvez was at getting the co-operation of these colonial officers.

"Brigadier Higgins has never failed us." Minister Galvez looked earnestly at the King.

Once more his Minister was giving Brigadier Higgins the credit. Time after time that had happened. Galvez praising him, asking honors and better positions for the Brigadier.

King Carlos stared at the map. It was true. The Brigadier never failed the Crown. Neither had he failed to remind His Majesty of his untiring, constant labors for Spain. Nothing was omitted from his long detailed letters, which always began with profuse and humble words of gratitude for past favors, and continued with a graphic portrayal of his achievements. Long ago he had constructed mountain houses across the Andes, giving Chile mail service throughout the year instead of only during good weather. The Crown received a vivid picture of the hazards he took and of the sickness incurred by him as a result.

He was untiring in his labors for Spain. But he was an ambitious officer who wanted promotions and asked for them.

Over the years King Carlos had advanced him from Captain of Dragoons to Brigadier-Commandant of the Frontier. He had appointed him Intendente-Governor of the Province of Concepcion at the time the Crown had divided Chile into two territorial districts, one north and the other south. On Higgins His Majesty had bestowed the Order of Carlos the Third, and other honors. Once, the King had thought seriously of making Brigadier Higgins a member of his expedition to excavate Roman cities. But Higgins had been needed in Chile where he had influence with the barbarian Indians. With these promotions and honors had gone monetary rewards. And now he would want something more.

Without raising his voice, Minister Galvez managed to convey a question as to what additional honor King Carlos planned for Brigadier Higgins, in his opinion the most competent of all colonial administrators.

At the moment His Majesty had no answer. He would have to think the matter over.

Galvez continued to speak of conditions in Chile: the Governor, Benavides, was sickly and old. Soon the King might have occasion to consider a new Governor-President for Chile. He smiled his friendly smile. "Don Ambrosio Higgins, perhaps."

King Carlos was shocked. His Minister was asking the Crown to name the Irishman Higgins to the highest post in Chile. Impossible! The position had always been given to deserving Spaniards of good family born in Spain, with long records of service. Already King Carlos had three applicants, all natives of Spain.

"The Crown needs a Governor in Chile who knows the English well. Brigadier Higgins, being Irish, dislikes and distrusts them. You know, Your Majesty, how the Irish Catholics serving in your Royal Forces feel about England. Never a good word for the British or the English King, George the Third." He smiled broadly, as if the idea amused him. "Brigadier Higgins would keep the English from getting a foothold in Chile either for contraband trade, or for conquest."

The English! Always the English.

King Carlos thought of the years the English had been smuggling slaves and merchandise into Buenos Aires from the Portuguese colony of Sacramento. For years they had taken valuable metals out of the Spanish colonies. Spain had tried without success to stop the outrage. He wondered how many millions in metals the English had taken out?

Now, they were hoping to establish a similar trading center on some island near Chile, or in Chile itself. And perhaps they were considering conquest of that colony.

He sighed. It had been a mistake for Spain to join with France to fight with the North American colonists against England. That was in 1779, eight years ago, and at the time King Carlos had hesitated. He should have realized then the outcome if England lost its American colonies. Looking around for other lands to colonize, England would turn naturally toward South America and would consider the action justified.

But to appoint an Irishman as Governor and President of Chile because England was prowling in the South Sea! That, it seemed to King Carlos, was not necessary. It was asking too much. He looked hard at the long coast of Chile on the map before him.

Minister Galvez had circled with a crayon the islands within reach of Chile.

There were so many! King Carlos left off counting because the number was alarming. There could not be that many!

But there they were, looking up at him from the South Sea, a great number of large red eyes, asking what he could do about defending Chile without a capable official like Don Ambrosio Higgins de Vallenar. And the long finger of Chile at the mercy of enemies except for the forts, a very few forts scattered along those thousands of miles of open sea.

The forts of Talcahuano were vitally important. They had been reinforced with guns, enlarged, staffed with more dragoons. And quickly, by Brigadier Higgins.

"The Brigadier has never married," Galvez said. "He might have married a native-born Spanish woman. He might have had children. He has not. His devotion to his adopted country is complete. No ties."

All this His Majesty already knew. Before the Irishman had been appointed Governor-Intendente of Concepcion, his record and his personal life had been investigated. Spain strictly forbade the marriage of her colonial officials with native-born women. It divided the allegiance of an officer. Instead of thinking only of what was important to the Crown, he wondered also how a measure would affect his wife, his children. If a man had children born in the colonies, immediately he became concerned with what he considered injustices by the Crown against their rights.

The Crown had to discriminate against those born in the colonies when it came to making appointments to government posts. The native-born might sometime attempt to take over the colonies.

An official who withheld information from the Crown about a colonial-born wife or children would be instantly dismissed. It was an ancient and a necessary rule. It had always been strictly enforced.

The King said, "We will write the Brigadier a letter of commendation. The appointment must wait. But it will have our serious thought. Send me your file on Brigadier Higgins."

For an hour they discussed colonial commerce, the output of Chile's mines, improved agriculture for the Indies, the construction of highways and higher impost duties.

Don Jose de Galvez prepared to leave. He took a paper from his portfolio. "You have probably seen this, Your Majesty," he said.

The King smiled. Galvez always assumed that the King knew about everything. It was a compliment. He glanced at the sheet, saw it was a copy of the London *Political Herald*, which he had not seen. He wondered how it was that Minister Galvez learned about these matters ahead of his ambassadors. "Leave it with me," the King said.

His Minister folded the map, shut his portfolio. He said again that God would be with His Excellency many years. The door closed behind him.

The article from the London paper was a long one and it was written with that casualness of which the English were masters. The success of North Americans in winning their independence from a foreign King, it ran, had encouraged South Americans to think of liberating their countries from the grip of Spain. A number of Spanish colonials were at present in London with a plan to free their homelands.

King Carlos read the article through to the end. Thoughtfully, he laid it down.

These colonials, he told himself, were Jesuits, perhaps a half dozen, smarting from having been exiled from the colonies long ago. It had happened before. The secret police of Spain would know about them. Soon they, like the others, would be discovered and brought to Spain and given prison sentences until their ardor cooled, or until they died in prison. His police had their instructions to keep the Jesuits divided. They were impoverished, scattered to the four winds. Some were in Italy, others in various parts of Europe, some in the United States, and these in England.

This flare-up in London would die out. A revolution could not be started without the help of governments and great amounts of money and ships and men. And then, too, the rebels would have Spain to deal with. The ringleader would be spirited out of England. The only thing the King feared was that England would attempt to seize some territory near Chile.

England must be watched.

He was interrupted by the arrival of his son Carlos.

The King wished Carlos would not dress like a fop of the Puerta del Sol. The hours and years he had devoted to trying to impress upon his son the responsibilities of a monarch, the importance of keeping state matters to himself, the need to avoid the influence of his wife Luisa Maria and her favorites.

Now looking at the weak face of his son, the King once more felt despair.

But he would try again to direct his son, try to make him a righteous monarch. Once more he would warn him against that wicked, undisciplined woman, Luisa Maria, and her friends.

For an hour he talked with his son.

The clock reminded King Carlos that it was time for dinner.

At table he thought of deep forests beyond Madrid. There he would be uninterrupted. There with dogs and gun he could hunt, think quietly and make important decisions. He would consider well a suitable applicant for Governor and President of Chile.

CHAPTER II

GUARDING the bay of Talcahuano, two forts looked toward Cape Horn and the sea. From the rampart of Fort Galvez, Brigadier Don Ambrosio Higgins de Vallenar peered south. The air ruffled his graying hair and tugged at his white and black poncho.

If there was a sail, his eyes would discover it with more exactness than a telescope, he told himself. For had he not always been able to see better, farther, with more precision than telescopes or the eyes of younger men?

Nor had his sixty-odd years lessened the endurance of his body, the energy of his mind. Since the order had come from Spain, requiring the forts to be strengthened against the English who were again on their stealthy hunt for a foothold on this coast, had he not worked tirelessly day and night to enlarge fortifications, adding quarters for additional dragoons, installing more cannon, never thinking of himself, or whether he should rest, and at the end of a day still looking less than fifty years old?

Now the forts were ready. The coastline was prepared.

Minister Don Jose de Galvez would be delighted. He would inform King Carlos. God keep His Majesty many years!

Turning, the Brigadier left the rampart, mounted his black horse and rode along a narrow path which circled the bay.

A herd of sea lions, grown indolent and fat in these quiet waters, sunned themselves on the island of Quiriquina at the entrance to the harbor. From the rocks came the melancholy lament of pelicans.

Offshore a whale spouted. They sometimes entered the bay. But there was not a whaling vessel in all of Chile, nor fishing craft, to haul in the barracuda, dolphin and tuna. Only a few small coastal ships arrived in Talcahuano yearly to provision the forts of Valdivia and Chiloe to the south.

Once a year four or five Spanish vessels came from Callao, the port for Lima, a voyage of almost a month. The ships brought limited cargoes of wool and velvet trousers, velveteen waistcoats, some earthenware, buttons and clasps, silk hose, table and altar cloths. And sugar and Paraguay herb. From this herb a drink was made called maté. A Chilean would go without clothing or food, but never without maté, which he took morning, noon and night.

For scanty imports Chile paid dearly with vast amounts of wheat, the finest in the world, which she sold at ridiculously low prices. A suit which the Brigadier could purchase in Madrid for fifty pesos cost six, seven or eight times that amount after five handlings in the ports of Spain, Lima and Chile.

There were riches for Lima and Spain but little income for poor Chile. Spain held the monopoly on products that could be grown better in Chile—olives, grapes, limes, apples, figs, apricots, pecans and walnuts. But Chile was forbidden to ship these products to Spain or other countries, and her ports were closed to foreign vessels. No article could be manufactured in Chile without permission of Spain.

Sometime the Brigadier would change things if he could, introducing products on which Spain had no monopolies. He wanted a better and a richer life for Chile.

He glanced back along the beach of Talcahuano. Whenever the ships arrived from Callao, the port came alive. Shippers dashed about on fine horses, handsome vicuna ponchos whipping like banners, in brimmed hats, giving orders and expecting instant obedience. They reminded Higgins of the Irish lords of his youth, when he had worked at any labor for bread and tea. He had despised that poverty. Had not his family descended from the O'Neils of Ireland? He was better than they.

Had he not reminded himself of the superior O'Neils time without end while he saved a pittance to get himself out of Ireland? Had he not left his homeland that day with scarcely enough money in his shabby suit to buy a meal, a bed? Had he not sworn as he watched the seacoast vanish that he would prove himself better than any Irish lord?

He had traveled thousands of miles from Ireland searching for fortune and titles, wanting to be greater than they.

But he had not escaped them.

For here in Chile were Spanish lords, worse than the tyrants of Ireland. The Brigadier hated them with the same fierceness.

In Chile, the slaves from Africa, the creole, mestizo, mulatto, cholo, zambo, danced to their tunes. You saw them here when the Callao ships were in port, ordered about, beaten if they moved too slowly, hungry, crawling to please the lords in return for a little food and drink.

Those that were paid gambled away their mean pay before it was earned, perhaps. Drinking too much chicha. Trying to forget their poverty. They accepted their lot, being taught by the priests that it was the hand of God. Often hungry, yet they contributed to the Church excessive fees for baptism, marriage and for burial in consecrated ground. The priests must be paid and the peasant borrowed the money or else donated to the priests eggs, fowl, bread, vegetables that should have fed himself and his family.

The Brigadier stared at a flock of wild geese.

There had been lean days for him in Spain. But in the city of Cadiz, as throughout the peninsula, Irishmen had the status of citizens. He had worked at various jobs. He attended school. He studied Spanish, Greek, geography, mathematics. It was as a bank clerk that he first realized the opportunities in the Spanish colonies. No other country could ship goods into Spain's colonial ports and consequently fine satins, brocades, wools, porcelain, the manufactured wares of other nations, poured into Cadiz, passing through the warehouses of local merchants before being reloaded onto Spanish ships of the line and transported to the colonies.

Into the bank where Higgins worked flowed the pesos. And

along the narrow streets of the city were erected magnificent homes by men who held trade monopolies.

Higgins, totaling up the daily balances, had been amazed.

He, too, would become a merchant!

For weeks he haunted the offices of a merchant. He was more weeks persuading the trader to send Higgins and a cargo of merchandise to South America. They agreed that he would open a branch store for the merchant in Chile. They both would prosper.

The voyage to Buenos Aires took three months. Higgins recalled his first sight of the sluggish Plata winding like a yellow serpent, a hundred and fifty miles wide at the mouth, and the houses of Buenos Aires, flat, white, like dominoes on a table. It was winter but the air was warm and humid.

A gaucho guided him across the thousand or more miles of uninhabited pampas to Mendoza. In Mendoza, near the Andes, he was warned against crossing the mountains. It was winter. There would be delays and storms. He would not get through. Higgins and the mules carrying his merchandise would be swept over a precipice.

He refused to wait. Before he was two days out of Mendoza, he regretted his rashness. He struggled to climb one mountain, only to see higher mountains ahead. It was a nightmare.

The Brigadier glanced toward the Andes, thinking of the risks he had taken, of paths where death hung, of plunging cliffs that dropped straight as a plummet into hell.

And then, coming out of the mountain passes, twenty-five miles along a valley, Santiago, the capital of Chile. Drinking at the fountain in the Plaza, he caught sight of the handsome lime and brick palace of the governor. He stared. To the west was the cathedral, east the eminence called Santa Lucia. He saw shops. He would lease a store and start his business.

The location he wanted was owned by Don Juan Albano, a successful merchant who was being hounded by Spanish authorities because he was Portuguese. All Portuguese were suspected of being smugglers.

If Higgins was to make a profit on his wares, the kind Don Juan Albano Pereyra explained, he must peddle in the provinces. In Santiago were skilled and rich competitors. Many people in the provinces seldom came to the capital.

His pride almost choking him, Higgins became a peddler. He walked. One mule for his merchandise was all the could afford.

He sold everything. He emptied his packs and rode back to Santiago. From now on, he told himself, he would succeed as a merchant. Because now he had learned how to sell. You laid a trap, you flattered, complimented, the customers.

He would return to Spain to buy a large consignment of merchandise. In Chile, he would operate as a wholesale merchant. Soon he would be living in a mansion on Rey Street.

Something more he learned. Every government official in Chile also managed a business on the side. A position with the Crown lent both prestige and dignity. While he was in Spain buying goods, he would apply for a government position. It would guarantee business. It would pay for his living.

In Santiago, Don Juan Albano Pereyra, the Portuguese, approved of Higgins' plan. He encouraged him, applauded his enterprise and gave him needed and invaluable advice about the sort of merchandise Higgins should buy. He even advanced him pesos.

Back in Cadiz Higgins borrowed large quantities of money. He purchased linens, shirts, brocades, velvets. A Lima merchant who was momentarily in Cadiz agreed to handle Higgins' business in Lima.

He also looked for a government position. For weeks he waited for a decision from the Council of the Indies, in Madrid. At last he was named assistant to Captain Don Juan Garland, an army engineer and newly-appointed engineer to Chile. Captain Garland was an Irishman. He was authorized to pay engineer-surveyor Higgins five hundred pesos a year.

Only five hundred pesos a year. And he was already forty.

Juan Garland was a friend from the beginning. He asked eagerly for a share in the mercantile venture. He knew nothing about business, he had never been to South America, and he accepted Higgins' word.

Upon his return to Santiago, Higgins rented a store and began unpacking his stock. Before the work was finished an order came from the governor for Juan Garland and Higgins to travel to southern Chile and repair the forts. Higgins had either to resign his position or go at once. He needed the salary of five hundred pesos, and the prestige.

They left their business in the hands of an agent, Diego Armida. When the Lima merchant refused to accept the merchandise as agreed, Armida disposed of it at a great loss, leaving Higgins and Garland deeply in debt.

Then Garland started for Spain, promising to return. With a feeling of hopelessness Higgins watched him sail, knowing somehow that he would not come back. Garland died aboard ship. To Ambrosio Higgins, friend and companion, he bequeathed seventy-four hundred pesos.

It was then Higgins saw in an Indian uprising an opportunity to get a commission quickly. He trained peasant-dragoons into fighting men capable of competing with savage Indians. The outbreak was quelled. Spain gave him a captain's commission. Soon he would be a colonel. Then would come higher ranks.

Five years later Higgins was only a lieutenant-colonel! Those were bitter, bitter days.

The Brigadier glanced toward Concepcion, touched the flank of his horse and galloped for a mile. Then a mule train appeared.

The packsaddles of the animals bulged with potatoes, fowl, plump red grapes, skins of wine and wheat and other provisions for Higgins' troops at the forts of Talcahuano, where an additional force of dragoons had been installed.

In the distance was Concepcion, beyond it the mountains, and swinging around the city, like a silver scimitar, the Biobio, the greatest river of Chile. Below Concepcion the river emptied into the South Sea and marked the boundary line between Spanish and Indian lands. A line of forts extended around the Indian territory, beginning with San Pedro Fort and ending over three hundred miles south, at Valdivia.

The houses of Concepcion, of whitewashed earthen bricks, the cathedral, the churches, four or five cloisters, a nunnery, slept in the afternoon sun among tufts of palms, wild walnut, cedars and maytenus. The roofs were of faded red tile. Surrounding the city was an adobe wall covered with moss and tall grass.

In Concepcion and beyond on large haciendas dwelt wealthy Spanish, whose roots and hearts were in Spain. They lived like the lords of Ireland, using their workmen far worse than the African slaves.

A bell tolled.

It was the opinion of Brigadier Higgins that Bishop Don Francisco Jose Maran controlled the bells from his study. Unfailingly, the bells rang whenever Higgins returned to Concepcion after an absence.

Bishop Maran disliked Higgins for being foreign-born and particularly for being an Irishman. He resented having to share honors with the Brigadier as ordered by the Crown after Higgins had been named Intendente-Governor of Concepcion. The Bishop had tried hard to have the ruling changed.

Recently, wanting to go to Valdivia to administer communion, the Bishop had asked permission to travel through Indian territory. This request Higgins refused. He explained that the Indians were disturbed over talk of placing Spanish missionaries in their midst. The powerful Indian chiefs had promised Higgins to bring all their people into agreement with the plan. But until this was accomplished, it would be dangerous for any Spanish resident to pass through Indian territory.

Without permission the Bishop entered the forbidden territory with his priests, servants, slaves and mules carrying rich vestments and the Church jewels.

His people were murdered by the Indians. The Bishop alone escaped with his brief shirt to cover him.

Hastily, the Brigadier conferred with his chieftain friends and sent troops after the Indian culprits. The Church valuables were recovered. The Indian leaders of the outrage were hanged from trees along the Valdivia road. Another Indian uprising was narrowly averted.

The incident might have inflamed the entire frontier, bringing death to Spanish men, slavery to their women and great destruction to towns and haciendas.

A delegation of the Bishop's friends came to Higgins' residence a few days later. Instead of thanking him they demanded that he declare war against the Indians and subdue them.

When he refused they sent letters to the Crown from Bishop Maran and his friends, denouncing the Brigadier. Special messengers scurried across the Plaza at all hours of the day, with yet another draft of another scathing letter to the Crown about Higgins.

Even faster raced Higgins' couriers to the ships with letters to Minister Galvez which denied enemy charges. While a letter was being prepared by the Bishop, Higgins, having learned its contents from his spies, would hasten to write the facts. His pen rushed words onto pages about his reasons for transferring fifty dragoons to Valdivia, about the praise of Indian chiefs for Higgins' actions in the Maran matter and how it had averted a violent war. About many other unjust criticisms, Higgins wrote.

The Brigadier knew that in his residence next to the cathedral his enemy Maran was praying the Crown to name the Spanish Don Tomas Alvarez Acevedo when the time arrived that Chile needed a new Governor and President.

The hate increased.

On April twenty-seventh, Governor Benavides died.

This was the opportunity Higgins had been waiting for over long years! He could be Governor and President of Chile!

The Brigadier penned a letter to Galvez urging that he recommend him to His Majesty Carlos the Third.

Minister Galvez knew everything there was to be said about Higgins.

Except one thing.

Galvez did not know about the boy Bernardo. He did not know that Higgins had had a son and by a native-born woman.

And he must never know. The Crown must not learn that secret. For Higgins would not be named Governor of Chile if the Crown learned that his son was a Chilean.

CHAPTER III

BRIGADIER HIGGINS rode toward his house in Concepcion, thinking of a time ten years ago.

He was then a lieutenant-colonel of cavalry, returning to the frontier village of Chillan after a bloody but successful campaign against the Indians. Coming toward him were villagers singing and strumming guitars. It warmed his heart, knowing that the people of Chillan appreciated his efforts to make peace at council tables with the chiefs, or, that failing, to campaign against the barbarians.

The Crown had ignored his successes and his requests for advancement in rank. His future looked dark.

He saw the stately Don Simon Riquelme de la Barrera y Goycochea ride toward him. In all Chile there was no more noble Spaniard. He always entertained Higgins when he visited Chillan.

Don Simon swung in beside him. A man of perhaps fifty, he appeared older. He spoke gratefully of the success of the campaign: once again Higgins had risked his life to protect the Spanish. Tonight, at the Riquelme home, the hero would be entertained.

Then he smiled broadly. "I consent to your betrothal to my daughter. Dona Isabel is waiting for you."

A delirium of joy seized Higgins. Many times he had asked to marry Dona Isabel. Each time Don Simon had refused. But now he withdrew his objection.

This was wonderful news.

The beautiful, slender face of the girl. Dona Isabel welcomed him eagerly. Her dark eyes were tender, and she whispered softly, "At last, you have come."

For a moment he held her gently. Although he was long past his youth, he now was a youth again.

The small hands of Dona Isabel stirred hot maté. She sipped the liquid as was the custom, then passed the silver cup to Higgins. At eighteen, her dignity was that of an older woman. Her eyes were compassionate, the unspoiled look of the generous young. She warmed his tired heart, long deprived of gentleness. Her fingers were like petals falling against his sleeve.

He sat beside her at supper but he could not eat. The silver dishes filled with mountains of food, he refused. He needed no wine. His happiness made him giddy enough to dance the fandango and a country dance called the cuando.

She sang, as they danced, her voice clear, sweet. The words he would never forget. Nor her good-night kiss.

That night he was wakeful, thinking of her. He would not wait months for a license from the Crown to marry Dona Isabel. He would go to Santiago to ask the help of the Governor of Chile in obtaining an immediate license. The Governor was well satisfied with Higgins' services. Let him show his appreciation for an officer who long ago should have received promotions and honors.

Higgins had ridden to Santiago.

At the Palace entrance were dragoons resplendent in red and gold.

The Governor received him at once in the tiled audience room. He opened the interview with compliments. It was fortunate, Higgins' arriving in Santiago at this time, he explained, because the Governor wanted to pass on to him letters commending his services. The letters were from Don Jose de Galvez, Minister of the Council of the Indies. In the name of King Carlos, Galvez praised Higgins' military and administrative conduct, his construction of the mountain houses to provide better mail service.

Higgins was advanced to the rank of colonel of cavalry and his salary was increased. The Governor's eyes smiled his own commendation and pleasure.

Stunned by the sudden and unexpected promotion, Higgins was

speechless. The shocked feeling passed. He realized with a soaring of spirit that the long hoped-for advancement was his.

"From now on, your advancement should be rapid." The Governor spoke with confidence. He praised Higgins as the best officer and executive on the frontier, the only officer capable of maintaining peace with the Indians, the one man, during two hundred and fifty years of Spanish rule, who had subdued the savages without fail.

"Spain has been slow to recognize your ability," he said. "But now you have been noticed by the Crown. Work as tirelessly for Spain in the future as in the past, and you will have any position you desire."

Above the Governor's head, the Spanish colors stirred.

Any position Higgins desired? The Governor was not given to speaking carelessly. Higgins' heart seemed to stop. It moved again with a great surge.

He might even become Governor of Chile!

All his proud hopes were reborn in Higgins. He could have the authority he had always wanted. He could help the poor of Chile. He could change barbarous laws.

His power would be greater than that of the Spanish lords! And the Irish lords!

At last! Rising, he managed to thank the Governor. He walked from the room, feeling that it was *his* palace, passing the glittering guards—*his* dragoons.

Back across the Maipú plain he rode, across a rushing ford and toward Chillan, dreaming of the future.

He was already colonel. Soon another promotion to brigadier. Then, perhaps, Intendente of Concepcion. And then Governor of Chile! It might take two years, or three, or four.

Now he had something of value to offer Dona Isabel.

Dona Isabel! The license! He had completely forgotten the license!

He pulled on the reins to turn and go back to Santiago, and then he remembered.

Dona Isabel was native-born. If he married her, he could never aspire to be governor of Chile. He could not have both.

The light went out of the day. He struggled on over the road between Santiago and Chillan. Darkness swept into the valley. His spirit was buried in shadow. He could not choose.

There were two rooms in his heart. In one was Dona Isabel, in the other the post of governor and the Spanish lords bending the knee to him. And peons looking up with happy faces to thank him.

Indeed, how could he choose?

In the end, he compromised. He would speak to Dona Isabel. She had wisdom and fairness far beyond her years. Together they would decide.

He rode on to Chillan.

When he entered the Riquelme residence that evening the words were on his lips.

Dona Isabel put a hand over his mouth. He was to speak only of love. The other speeches could wait until morning. Taking his arm, she walked with him into the patio.

Moon whiteness lay on lime trees, on the fountain. Now and again one of the linnets called softly. The night was heavy with fragrance of jasmine, oleander, ginger flowers; they were sweeter that night. How her heart-shaped face entranced him, and the light in her young, eager eyes. Her skin was like white roses.

Holding her, he felt hunger sweeping through him, all the longing of a man for his love.

She sang softly a little song, lying in his arms, her figure pliant and yielding. She had missed him, she said, and being betrothed meant belonging to him. She would be his forever.

A few steps away, beyond the archway, was her bedroom. He could see the white-draped bed.

His desire had stormed within him, blinding him to everything but his need of her. He lifted her in his arms, held her close, carried her across to her room and laid her gently upon the bed. And he had lain down beside her.

Behind Brigadier Higgins the cathedral bells clanged solemnly and without melody.

The license to marry Dona Isabel had never reached Chile, for the license had never been requested by Higgins. And the Riquelme family thought the Crown had refused to grant one. Higgins had let them think that.

The bells ceased ringing. There was quietness.

At his residence he went along the corridor thinking of the promotions that had followed. First, colonel, and letters of commendation and increases in pay. With each advance, Higgins had written to the King and to Minister Galvez immediately of his deep gratitude.

In his bedroom, Higgins poured water from a silver pitcher into the bowl.

His child and Dona Isabel's was born at her father's house in August of 1778, more than nine years ago. And for hours and days after Higgins learned of it, he tried repeatedly to write to Dona Isabel. He could not. How could he ask forgiveness?

He pushed the memory away, but it persisted.

His son had been named Bernardo.

Higgins laid the towel on the rack, thinking of another day when Dona Isabel married Don Felix Rodrigues.

After that marriage, Higgins took Bernardo, as indeed he had always planned to do when the child was no longer an infant. For does not a father take fierce pride in an only son, wanting for himself the direction of the young life? And had not Higgins' heart always turned with tenderness to the lad? It was a bitter thing not to be able to acknowledge a son.

With the help of steadfast friends, the change had been made. Higgins' faithful officer, the loyal Don Domingo Tirapegui, made the journey to Chillan to fulfill the mission. Tirapegui was a noble from the Spanish province of Navarre. If the need arose, as God forbid it should, he would die for his chief. He had delivered the four-year-old Bernardo to Don Juan Albano Pereyra, in Talca.

Long ago, Don Juan Albano had retired to Talca where he had

a hacienda outside the town. He had had Bernardo baptized and christened Bernardo Higgins by the priest of Talca. The certificate of birth and baptism said boldly that Higgins acknowledged himself as father, but the mother's name had been omitted. In all fairness Higgins could not name the mother. A copy of the certificate was in Higgins' strong box.

But to the world the child was Bernardo Riquelme. That was was the name he must use throughout the whole of his life.

Among all those children racing over Juan Albano's acres, who would suspect that one belonged to Don Ambrosio Higgins de Vallenar? The secret would never be revealed. For the few to whom the secret had been entrusted were loyal friends.

Higgins' secret was safe.

CHAPTER IV

FROM his window facing the Plaza of Concepcion, Bishop Francisco Jose Maran glanced up from his maté to see Brigadier Don Ambrosio Higgins de Vallenar passing.

It reminded him that tomorrow was a feast day. Brigadier Higgins had returned to the city. He would attend Mass. The Bishop would be forced to receive him. Since Higgins had been appointed Intendente-Governor, the Bishop no longer ruled supreme in his own domain.

More and more the Irishman was usurping what had once been the prerogatives of the Bishop alone. His own position in the community was no longer pre-eminent. It was almost unbearable. Once, he had addressed his troubled heart to the Governor of Chile for a ruling in his favor. He complained that Higgins lacked confidence in the Bishop, consulting him only occasionally and then only about some ecclesiastical matter. The answer from the Governor had been unsatisfactory. He reminded the Bishop of his Christian duties. He reminded him that harmony was important between prelates and state officials.

But the Brigadier would strip the Church of everything but faith. He wanted less fees for the priests. The marriage fee, Higgins believed, was excessive. And he wanted baptisms and burials to cost the people less.

His softness with the Indians made them bold. The Brigadier sided with them. Recently Higgins walked into this room, dust on his boots and the scarlet carpet freshly cleaned. He had told the

33

Bishop that on the prelate's head was the murder by the Indians of his people.

The Bishop had been outraged. He spoke sharply to the Brigadier. You did not consult barbarians about introducing missionaries into their land.

He studied the silver bombilla in his maté cup.

Higgins turned everything to his own use.

When the French navigator, La Perouse, was expected to reach Talcahuano with his ships, Higgins, called to an Indian conference on the frontier, asked the Bishop to receive the French navigator, to apologize for Higgins' absence, to tell him that the safety of the people of Chile depended upon Higgins' keeping the peace.

The Bishop had been delighted to serve. For once he would not share honors with Higgins. La Perouse would report the official reception both to his government and to Spain. The Bishop would be commended. He would be given honors by the King.

He ordered a costly robe. He wrote his speech. From a window he saw Higgins ride off for the frontier.

La Perouse and his officers reached Concepcion, the residence of the Bishop. Seated in his brocade chair, the Bishop received the important guests.

He explained at length the necessity for Brigadier Higgins' absence. He actually heard himself tell La Perouse that only Higgins of all men in Chile could keep peace with the barbarians.

How foolish of the Bishop to praise Higgins!

Before Maran had begun his welcoming speech, a messenger brought word that the Brigadier was returning from the frontier! And soon Higgins made a dramatic entrance into the Plaza on a horse caparisoned as if for the King himself.

The Bishop's residence was emptied as if infested with the plague.

To the French government and to Spain, La Perouse praised Brigadier Higgins for everything. He made one mention of Bishop Maran. But he spoke disrespectfully of the priests, calling them the worst subjects in America.

The Bishop thought he knew where La Perouse got that information. More than once Higgins had criticized the friars. And Higgins' purpose was clear to the Bishop. He wanted La Perouse to commend him to the Spanish Crown.

The Bishop studied the ring on his finger.

Higgins' hopes of being governor of Chile were doomed. Spain would never appoint a foreigner to the highest position in the colony. And besides, Bishop Maran and his friends had bombarded the Spanish ministers and the King with criticism of Higgins. They would continue to tear him down until he was stripped of offices and honors and driven from Chile!

For no mortal was without his indiscretions. The confessional had taught the Bishop that. By endless searching for unfavorable evidence against the Brigadier, some offense against the Crown would be uncovered, and Higgins would then be at the mercy of the Bishop. And he would show Higgins no mercy!

From an outer room came the voice of a young priest in prayer. The devoted prayed too constantly, like children crying for light in a darkened room.

Bishop Maran stirred impatiently.

The prayers ceased. There was an apologetic cough.

Turning, the Bishop saw the young priest in the doorway, hands clasped, his bloodless face all humility, his robe clinging to his bones. Worshipfully, he looked at Bishop Maran. "Captain Don Vincente Carvallo y Goyeneche, Your Reverence," he whispered.

The Bishop was annoyed. He did not wish to speak with Carvallo. The Captain wanted to become a priest, because, as he explained to Maran, it would give him leisure to work on a history of Chile that he was writing. But it was, doubtless, only an excuse to escape from the supervision of the Brigadier. For if Carvallo had despised Higgins before he spent that six months in prison, he must hate the Brigadier now!

Once, after the Captain's arrest, the Bishop had tried to intercede for him, both with Higgins and the Governor of Chile. It did no good, for here on the frontier the Brigadier was master.

When Carvallo had served his term, he came to the Bishop and vented his spleen. He would find a means of bringing disgrace upon Brigadier Higgins, he stormed.

The Bishop had attempted to silence him. Unless Carvallo had proof of his statements against the Brigadier, he advised, it would be well not to spread them for he might find himself in even more serious trouble.

And now, Bishop Maran recalled some of the wild accusations made by Carvallo against Higgins. He said the Brigadier had an eye for the ladies and if Carvallo named all the women in the life of the Irishman, it would be a list as long as his sword. And, he said, what about scandals on the frontier, about trade in illicit arms and liquor to the Indians? Perhaps, he had inferred, Higgins had been mixed up in it. And what about Higgins' farm, Las Canteras, which was said to be stocked with cattle and oxen from the Indians? Why should the Araucanian chiefs want to make gifts to Higgins?

The Bishop had again cautioned Carvallo about his wild statements.

Thoughtfully, he now stared at the young priest.

Yet, if Carvallo could unearth some scandal against the Brigadier, it would be useful in ridding Chile of Higgins, their common enemy. The Captain was interested in writing a history of Chile. It would be an excuse for his asking permission to examine the archives of the country, and to be absent from his military post at Los Angeles on occasion.

For the Church and the Crown, he thought, he must do everything possible to rid the country of the enemy Higgins!

He would speak with Carvallo. Gently, he would lead him on with compliments and flattery. "Send Captain Carvallo in," he said.

Carvallo entered with his peculiar gait that always reminded the Bishop of a crab hurrying for cover. He carried a package wrapped in his poncho. "A dozen fat quail." He threw back the folds of the garment. His usually boastful voice was almost humble.

Feathers glossy, bodies rounded from feeding on wild grain, the quail were temptingly plump.

The Bishop could not remember the last time when fat quail had looked at him from his dinner plate. His dinners lately had been most unsatisfactory, the fowl scrawny. "It am delighted to see you." Bishop Maran managed a smile. "What brings you all the way from Los Angeles?"

He had come to see the surgeon, Carvallo explained. Perhaps the Bishop recalled that while he was unjustly imprisoned here in Concepcion, there had been an illness?

The Bishop nodded. An elusive sickness which the surgeon could not locate. Still, perhaps a sickness had developed since. One must be fair.

Carvallo looked at the Bishop with pious eyes. If he could not be received by the Church, then he wanted a transfer away from the frontier and the Brigadier. The Bishop had friends in Santiago. If the Regent, Don Tomas Alvarez de Acevedo, would intercede for Carvallo, then perhaps the Brigadier might transfer him.

Acevedo! He was the Spaniard the Bishop and his friends wanted as Governor and President of Chile.

If the Captain would help to find evidence against the Brigadier that could prove him disloyal to the Crown, then the Bishop would use his influence to assist Carvallo.

And Carvallo would help. His hatred of Higgins was, like the Bishop's, so great it could not be contained by a book. Between them they would destroy his power!

The Bishop leaned forward in his chair. His voice low, cautious, he began to outline a plan.

CHAPTER V

Leaving his bedroom, Brigadier Higgins went toward his office along the covered walk bordered with native herbs. They had been planted by Spanish botanists sent to Chile a year ago to tabulate Chilean flora and to experiment with trees, shrubs and fruits.

At the door to his office, Captain Domingo Tirapegui was speaking with a cholo woman. Her Indian ancestry showed in her straight, coarse, black hair, but her features were Spanish. About her neck hung an Indian necklace of silver that covered the front of her white blouse. Her red skirt was full and long.

Tirapegui saluted. His honest eyes were disturbed. The woman had a complaint against Carvallo, he said. He had bought a dozen quail and a fighting cock from her. Now he refused to pay until after the cockfight today. "She wants her money at once."

Brigadier Higgins felt the old annoyance. Carvallo absent from the fort at Los Angeles where he was needed. Other officers forced to do his work. They would complain, and rightly. And here he had bought a fighting cock, planned to enter it in some backyard arena, when there were laws against gambling. "What is he doing in Concepcion?" he said.

"A visit to the surgeon. The old ailment."

That frayed and dishonest excuse, Higgins thought. There was no infection or illness. Carvallo used it for sliding out of disagreeable duties. Carvallo's trouble was his lack of discipline.

The patience with which Higgins had labored to make Carvallo a good officer! But when he spoke with the officer, asking him to keep away from evil companions and drink, from women, he only looked hurt, like a scolded child.

Even imprisonment had done Carvallo no good. He pretended he did not understand why he had been arrested, when he knew it was for insolence to his commander, Captain Jose Maria Prieto.

This time, the Brigadier told himself, he would not spare Carvallo. He might even throw him into prison again and for longer than six months. "Find Captain Carvallo," he ordered, crisply. "Bring him to me."

"He is with Bishop Maran." Tirapegui glanced toward the Bishop's residence.

Then the quail were for Maran. Fat quail for the Bishop, Higgins thought. Carvallo and the Bishop were plotting something against the Brigadier. He said, "Bring him when you can."

Higgins entered his office with its white plastered walls, dark ceiling, framed letters of commendation, his own map of Chile and the stuffed dispertadores, a bird known as "the awakener" because it signaled danger. It chattered like a parrot, or perhaps like a magpie, and roused the other birds. He had seen flocks of birds soar off at the warning call of the dispertadores. The beady eyes of the bird stared at him. The awakener, he thought.

He went to his desk. He thumbed through the letters eagerly and quickly.

He saw the letter from Madrid. It was from the Crown. The important seal danced in the sunlight. His pulse raced.

This might be the appointment! It might tell him that he, Brigadier Higgins, had been named Governor and President of Chile.

Tirapegui passed through the ample gate of the quadrangle. It was pleasant to stretch his legs after a long ride in the saddle. The day was sunny.

The cholo woman walked beside him. She stared hungrily at the fruit for sale by country people.

Tirapegui bought two peaches and gave her one. "Come after five tonight," he said, kindly. "You will get your fighting bird back again."

"*Gracias, Senor Capitan.*" She darted off.

Sitting on the edge of the fountain Tirapegui broke the peach and ate slowly. From here he could watch the residence of Bishop Maran. He kept an eye on the house and listened to the chatter of market people, braying of mules, the shouts of the water carrier.

For Tirapegui, rounding up the Captain was an old story. It was not a pleasant assignment. But today he had one advantage. He knew where the Captain was. Usually, he searched taverns and gambling spots, to find him with a questionable female on each side of him, reciting his own bad verses.

Today, Carvallo would leave the residence of the Bishop and start for the cockpit back of the nearby tavern.

He studied the peach in his hand.

There was no more honorable man, no person Tirapegui revered more, than his brave Brigadier who risked his life for Chile. More than once, he had watched unhappily as the Brigadier rode alone into Indian country to speak about peace with some chief who refused to sit at a council table with the other chiefs. "And don't come after me," he would order. "I'll come back."

The Brigadier was just as courageous when it came to fighting the Indians. He would try for months to make peace over the council table, but if it failed and the Indians began depredations, he could be as ruthless as they. He could trail an Indian band like a good hunting dog after a fox.

Tirapegui turned the peach in his hand.

Honorable, braver than any person Tirapegui had ever known, the Brigadier would receive Tirapegui's loyal service as long as he lived. Never had Higgins failed to keep his word. There was no smirch against his honor.

Far-away the voice of a woman singing drifted back to him.

Once, only once, the Brigadier had not been fair. That was when he had been betrothed to Dona Isabel Riquelme. The Brigadier had told him of the betrothal in confidence.

It was long ago. Tirapegui had still been a lieutenant.

Later, the Brigadier had ordered him to Chillan to bring a child from the Riquelme house to the hacienda of Don Juan Albano at Talca. "He is Bernardo, my son," the Brigadier said. "And it must never be known that he is my son."

A great sadness filled Tirapegui. After all the years he could feel that small body against him as they rode toward Talca. It was like holding his own boy.

Tirapegui watched the water that gushed into the fountain.

He had bathed Bernardo's face in mountain streams. How much older than his years he had seemed! How serious and unhappy his large blue eyes. The boy had a gentleness extraordinary in one so small. He was proud, too. Wanted to comb his own hair, thick and shining. And intelligent. And obedient.

When Tirapegui lifted him down from the horse and gave him into the keeping of Don Juan Albano, the boy had thanked him.

How quickly a child can find your heart.

Tirapegui rose from his place on the fountain's rim. The memory was too painful.

About him was a stirring. The time for the cockfight was near. He walked toward the Bishop's residence.

Carvallo appeared through the gate and turned south. Tirapegui hurried past a priest and called to Carvallo. "Brigadier Higgins wants you." Tirapegui stopped beside him.

Carvallo looked startled. "I thought he was in Valdivia," he said.

"He is waiting in his office to speak with you." Tirapegui glanced across the Plaza to Higgins' residence. "Where is the fighting cock?" he asked.

"Look." The arrogance was gone from Carvallo's voice. "I've placed a heavy bet on that cock. It can win me a great amount of money. My children need food and clothing. I have to have money."

Carvallo's children were always in need. And Tirapegui could not bear to think of any child lacking anything. Carvallo did know fighting birds, and sometimes he won. Perhaps this would be one of the times. Another half hour or so and the fight would be over. The children would have what they needed and the cholo woman would have money for her bird. "This once," he said.

The tavern was deserted. A table was covered with bottles of liquor and fruit swarming with flies. They passed through the door at the back of the room and into the patio.

In the center of the court was a shallow pit and on a mound of earth two cocks were fighting. The spectators—countrymen, muleteers, soldiers—standing on benches placed around the improvised arena, were dancing in excitement.

Carvallo walked to his servant who stood holding the fighting cock. He examined the silver spurs which had been placed on the legs of the bird.

Tirapegui watched as Carvallo passed the bird to a handler. He walked slowly to the edge of the pit.

The handler had placed Carvallo's bird on the mound of earth at the center of the pit, opposite another fighting cock. The ruff of neck feathers began to rise. The feet of the birds lifted in a slow ritual. The dance moved faster. They cavorted like savages in a tribal rite, stepping high, circling. Each watched for an opening to attack.

A sudden flash of silver. The spurs of the black fowl buried themselves in the head of the russet, and blood spurted.

Captain Carvallo let out a howl, as if his own flesh had been pierced and torn.

Tirapegui stepped nearer. He wanted the cholo woman's bird to win. It had to win!

But the crowd pushed against one another, roaring for the black fowl to kill his opponent. Tear the russet bird into a hundred pieces, take his feathers from him one by one, strip him of his proud record! Cut him into ribbons.

Now the eyes!

Leave him no eyes!

Now the other eye, and leave him no sight with which to see his black opponent!

The birds spun dizzily, a mass of russet and black. For a game cock will fight even without eyes as long as the heart beats. And the heart dies hard.

They hung high in the air above the mound of the cockpit. They danced on the earthen heap, tearing through feathers and flesh with their evil spurs. They were bleeding badly. The pit was strewn with feathers.

Tirapegui felt sick. But he watched the vicious stabs of the black creature.

The shouting increased, went on for what seemed to Tirapegui an eternity. Then silence.

The russet bird lay limp. Once it tried desperately to raise its bloody head. Then it was quiet.

Carvallo's face was deathly pale. He looked as if he would collapse.

Someone laughed. It was a contemptuous sound.

Carvallo glanced around the pit, his sick eyes seeking the man who dared to laugh. He located him, made a lunge and lost his footing. He rolled into the pit, struggled to his feet, his uniform covered with blood and black and russet feathers. A button was missing from his coat.

Angrily, he climbed from the pit. He saw Tirapegui. "Tell the Brigadier I'm with the surgeon," he begged.

Now they were in for it, Tirapegui thought.

"Tell the Brigadier I've already ridden back to Los Angeles," Carvallo implored. He looked frightened.

And he had reason to be disturbed. For he would have his privileges taken away, and both the price of the cholo woman's fighting bird and the price of the quail would be deducted from his pay. He had been gambling. The Brigadier had warned him against it.

"Come along," Tirapegui said.

He would take his own punishment, Tirapegui told himself, for he deserved it. He should have known better.

Together, he and Carvallo entered Higgins' office.

The Brigadier glanced up. If he saw the missing button on Carvallo's coat, or the blood, he said nothing. This was astonishing, because the Brigadier would not tolerate the least untidiness in the dress of his dragoons.

"If you have visited the surgeon," he said, a great sadness in his voice, "get back to your post. Don Thomas Dolphin is riding to Los Angeles. You will go with him."

That was all.

Carvallo looked stunned. He walked off in a daze.

But Tirapegui gathered his scattered wits. Something had happened to the Brigadier. "You are ill, sir," he said.

With tired eyes the Brigadier looked up. "Yes," he said, "sick to death. The Marquis of Sonora, Don Jose de Galvez, is dead!"

CHAPTER VI

FROM OUTSIDE the window came ribald laughter, in this moment as shocking as levity in a death chamber. For with the announcement of the death of Don Jose de Galvez, the room in which the Brigadier sat had become a place of mourning. Sunlight fell on his table, but it was the light of the tomb. The chill of the sepulcher was here.

His protector who had never failed him with honors and encouragement and promotions, the loyal, steadfast friend, was gone. Together they had labored for Chile and for the Crown.

The shadow from the window grille was a black cross. He stared at it.

Black. Everything was blackness. The grave was victorious, the sting of death was here in this room, in his heart. He was walled in by suffocating darkness and all about him was shrouded death. He saw the black bier of Don Jose de Galvez carried high through shadowed streets, through lines of black-garbed mourners, and the drums spoke of death. "Death, death. Darkness and death," he said.

Already Galvez was a fading, dusty memory. Higgins, here in remote, bleak Chile, would be forgotten too.

Stiffly, he rose from his chair. "Ave Maria," he muttered, but the rest of the prayer escaped him. And yet, prayers always had helped at other times.

Taking his wide black hat, he walked into the gloom of the quadrangle. Clumps of dusty trees and the barracks room lay beyond. He passed slowly through the iron archway, like the dreary gates of a cemetery, his steps paced like those of a funeral cavalcade, avoiding the crowded Plaza, the cathedral.

A little farther on he saw a weathered cross in the garden of a cloister. It recalled the small church nearby.

Inside the chapel there were no organ, no violins, no chanting of a choir to beguile the senses. Only ghostly white walls, heavy black beams, the light falling weak and pale through the window openings. He was the only worshiper. For this he was grateful.

He knelt, feeling old and tired, his poncho flowing around him darkly like a grave. Words dropped on to his mind and lay there without meaning. Still he knelt, the stones hard against his bones, repeating words and feeling only blackness and grief.

At last, deep within him, the midnight gloom yielded a little. A prayer formed and revived his spirit enough so he could find meaning in scriptural passages: the Lord was mightier than the grave. Those that mourned were comforted.

Comfort Thy servant, Oh Lord, he prayed. Comfort the tired heart of Thy servant. If a servant asked for bread, he was not given a stone.

For long minutes he knelt, hearing the soothing promises.

There was a great quietness. The prayers had helped.

And the prayers would do more. They would not fail him. The human bridge had gone. His faithful Galvez had departed. But the prayers were here.

Reward was certain for the faithful. The worthy, tireless steward was blessed. Give, Oh Lord, give and withhold not!

His heart was refreshed. The will of the Lord would be done.

He rose and leaving the church walked rapidly back to his residence.

In his office he prepared the proclamation announcing the death of his friend Galvez.

Galvez had gone. He had passed to his rewards, God rest his indomitable spirit. The strong patron of Brigadier Higgins was no more on this weary earth. He had been gathered to the bosom of his Father. God rest his soul, Higgins thought, listening to the loud tolling of the bells.

Maran, listening to the bells, would gloat over the defeat of his enemy, the Irish brigadier.

As he listened he thought of his blighted prospects. If only there was something he could do to revive his hopes, some person to whom he could appeal in his extremity.

He thought, there are other ministers in Madrid.

The Brigadier pulled himself forward in his chair. He could plead his cause to others. He picked up his pen and began writing down the names as he recalled them: Count Floridablanca, the Prime Minister, and Don Manuel de Néstares. The Marquis del Campo, Ambassador to London, who was aware of Higgins' watchfulness of the English in these seas. There was the Count of Campomanes and Senor don Almerico Pini, Director of Mails for the Indies.

It was Don Almerico Pini who had approved Higgins' plan to improve the overland postal services between Chile and Buenos Aires. He had been extravagantly grateful, Higgins recalled.

Rising, the Brigadier went to the cabinet with the huge lock where he kept his official and confidential papers. He turned the key.

In neat stacks were the portfolios of leather which he had invented, each lettered with a subject, the papers lying in tidy piles within their receptacles. He found the portfolio that contained the correspondence, the contracts, the letters of commendation on the building of the mountain houses.

At his desk he opened the folder. On the top was the King's letter of approval written from Ildefonso, Spain. Beneath it was the letter from Don Almerico Pini, commending Higgins for conserving the Royal funds in building the houses. Another letter expressed Pini's interest in the construction plans, and in the materials used.

The houses had been built of brick and limestone with arched roofs. They had been stocked with jerked beef, chocolate, maté, tobacco, sugar. Each mail courier had a key.

One of the houses the Brigadier had located at Ojos de Agua where the least snow was known to fall. Another was at Alto de las Lagunas, protected by great rocks. The building of the house at the Cumbre at the highest point in the Andes had given him bad moments and mountain sickness. Blood had run from his nostrils. Near an arroyo he had placed the house las Cuevas, and another at Puenta del Inca on the bank of the Orcones River. Still another house was situated at the exit from the great canyon. From there to Uspallata one could travel safely. Later, there had been other houses built. The distance from the guardhouse in the beautiful Aconcagua valley a few miles from Santiago, across to Mendoza on the other side of the Andes, was at least a hundred and eighty miles.

Pini knew all about this work. He was familiar with the change in mail schedules inaugurated by the Brigadier. Six mails passed across the mountains during the year. No longer was Chile isolated in winter from the outside world.

Yes, Don Almerico Pini, an important Minister of the Crown, would remember the Brigadier.

But would Don Almerico prefer a native Spaniard to an Irish-born officer for Governor of Chile? Would he object to Higgins being advanced to the post ahead of Spanish applicants?

And if not Don Almerico Pini, to whom could he turn?

He stared at the shelf of the cabinet holding the orderly files. One after another he went through them, copies of letters, the original letters, maps and rough sketches of forts, all bound with tapes, all neatly tied, searching carefully each separate folder for names of important men in Madrid who might help him.

Here was thanks for the treaty with the Indians at Tapihue, where the Indians accepted nineteen articles of capitulation, agreeing if necessary to provide Valdivia with provisions.

And this was the record of the parliament at the Camp of Lonquilmo, which to the Indian meant "the place of good reasons," when the Brigadier and the Indians agreed on markets north of the Biobio River, to the prohibition of the sale of arms, to free passage over the road south to Valdivia.

The King himself had written his approval of these agreements.

How often His Majesty, at the suggestion of Don Jose de Galvez, had turned his thoughts kindly to Higgins, writing words of appreciation and commendation, giving the Brigadier promotions one after another.

Higgins needed only some minister who had the confidence of His Majesty to go personally, as Galvez would have gone, and present the Brigadier as the best applicant for the post of Governor and President of Chile. The King would listen.

He thought about it, staring at his quill pen, the silver inkwell.

After a moment, he began a letter to Pini.

Then, recalling that the letter would take months to reach Spain, he paused. By the time the letter was received, the appointment would already have been made.

Here in forsaken Chile, the Brigadier's hands were tied by distance, by miles of land and sea! He could not write and plead his worthiness. Because of distance and time, he could not reach out and speak with the King. In his hour of greatest need, he was helpless, forced to wait, without hope, without any crumb of consolation.

Like a heavy storm cloud, fear gathered within him. He tried to push through the bleakness.

Had he not prayed? Had he not asked the will of the Lord to be done, feeling confident that the will of the Almighty, and his, were one? And were not Christians commanded to pray, to trust in His will? Had he not told himself he would trust completely?

He sat quietly, trying to generate confidence and pour it into his heart. "I believe," he said, and reached for faith. But fear spoke louder. He thought, "Suppose it is not the Lord's will that I have this appointment? Suppose I am being chastened for being unfaithful to some trust, to some promise made long ago for an obligation not fulfilled?"

The room seemed too cold, suddenly.

A brisk wind fluttered papers on his desk. He watched, searching his heart.

The wrong done Dona Isabel he had always regretted. He had prayed for forgiveness many times, and he had confessed his wrong openly to a trusted friend. Only a short while ago when he had thought he was dying, he called his friend Don Thomas Dolphin to his bedside and again confessed.

Dolphin had left his mercantile business and hurried to Higgins. He entered his bedroom, placed a cool, firm hand on the Brigadier's fevered brow.

Death was near, Higgins had said.

Indeed, Dolphin said, death was far off. The Brigadier could not die. Not until Dolphin had repaid him for all his kindness and help over the years.

The smile, always in his eyes when he spoke of their friendship, deepened.

Had Higgins not secured for him a position as pilot of ships coming in and going out of Talcahuano? And remember all the times Higgins had stood with him during the early struggles and disappointments that went with starting a mercantile business. Was it not now one of the most prosperous in South America? Were they not Irishmen who understood the need of the Irish heart for friendship and for speaking openly what was troubling the mind? And what, indeed, lay so heavily on Higgins' heart? Whatever it was, it should not burden Higgins who would share his last peso, his only crust, his one coat with friend or stranger. "Tell, man, what troubles you," he said.

"If I am indeed facing death," Higgins said, "I want you to promise me something. For I cannot confess this matter to any priest."

Then he had spoken to Dolphin of his betrothal to Dona Isabel. Of his betrayal of the girl. He had spoken of Bernardo. Would Dolphin promise to take Bernardo when Higgins died, and educate him as Higgins would describe in his will? The will would be prepared at once.

Dolphin listened quietly. He had promised. "But speak not of dying," he said, "when your work is not finished. When you have the Spanish lords to deal with, the post of Governor of Chile ahead."

That time, Higgins had unburdened his mind and cleansed his heart. He had promised to set his house in order. And the Lord had touched him and he had recovered.

But had he made the will? Had he put into writing for Dolphin instructions about the boy's education? He had sworn, and he had not fulfilled his pledge. By their acts ye shall know them, the good book said.

Well, now he would delay no longer. He would make his will. He would indeed set his affairs completely in order.

A little peace came then. The fear lessened. He believed that he was working harmoniously with his Creator again, and his heart felt almost childlike as he walked to his bedroom where he kept his strong box in a chest.

He would prepare a will, and write a letter authorizing Dolphin to take the child and educate him, and he would place the documents in his strong box to be read when he died.

In his bedroom he unlocked the box. He took from it his copy of Bernardo's birth certificate and reread it again to be certain that all the facts were there:

"Pedro Pablo de la Carrera, priest and vicar of the town, and doctrina of San Agustin de Talca, certifies and gives necessary faith and right that the 20th of January, 1783, in the Parish church of the town of Talca, I put the oil and crisma and baptized sub conditione, a child named Bernardo Higgins who was born in the diocese of Concepcion the 20th of August, 1778, son of the Maestre de Campo General of this Kingdom of Chile and Colonel of the Royal armies of His Majesty, Don Ambrosio Higgins, unwed bachelor by a lady of high class of that diocese, also unwed, who to his credit and for her sake has not mentioned her name. The said child Bernardo Higgins is under the care of Don Juan Albano Pereyra, inhabitant of this town of Talca."

There was more. But it was repetition, a rambling on of the good priest about not knowing if the child had been baptized or who the godparents were. But it was in order, properly dated and signed.

At his table he began a letter to Thomas Dolphin:

"Senor, devoted friend and countryman: Upon my death, this letter will provide you and the executors of my will, with instructions about the care and education of my son, Bernardo Higgins, who is at present living with Don Juan Albano Pereyra, in Talca.

"I ask that my son be taught mathematics, Greek, English, French, ancient and modern history, political science, geography, literature and art, and the profession of engineering to enable him to earn a lucrative living when he is grown."

The Brigadier paused. He sat back against the hard straight chair.

Where, he asked himself, would his son be taught these subjects? In Chile no school gave instructions in anything more than bad Latin, theology, a smattering of art, a shred of literature. The Crown had already determined how Bernardo could be educated in Chile. What limited subjects Chileans could study was written into the law by Spain, and Higgins could add nothing. Nothing at all.

His son could not learn engineering in Chile. It was not taught here. There were no engineering schools.

Unhappily, he studied the letter he had begun. There should be more tolerance about education in the colonies, he thought, angrily. Too many young Chileans wasted their lives at the races; gambling; watching bullfights. They learned to strum guitars and play pianofortes, to sing, dance, serenade the ladies. They could tell stories well, were clever at mimicry. There were scarcely any books. Sometimes a Chilean youth wrote verses, or purchased a government office if he could afford it, or bought a title. The young men entered the Royal service and usually made poor officers, but they went about sporting their uniforms like brightly plumed cocks. And they married rich heiresses.

The Brigadier studied the design on the iron lock of his strong box, as he thought of the dreary fate of his son.

It was a sorry birthright he had bequeathed to the boy Bernardo!

With a disturbed heart, he tried to redraft the letter, but there was little to say that Spain had not already said for the boy. His son could be a priest. He did not want Bernardo to become a priest; not in Chile. Nor yet a lawyer, doomed to a clerkship, rising no higher than an adviser, an assessor at most.

After another attempt to form a letter, he tore up all the drafts, promising himself that on another day when he felt less depressed, after the mourning for Galvez was over, and after he learned about the appointment of Governor of Chile, then he would write a suitable letter. And he would wait until then to prepare his will. For today, with the grief and the fear hanging thick as a cloak over his spirits, he could indeed do nothing.

The Masses had been said for Don Jose de Galvez and the weeks of mourning were a thing of the past.

Still Higgins grieved for that lost opportunity with such despair and sadness that it threatened to engulf him. And the fear gave him no rest. He would think of another being given the appointment as Governor and his spirit would be depressed until he wanted neither to eat nor sleep, and had no desire to live or to die.

He decided at last that a change would help him recover. He would go south to Valdivia and open up the land, have it planted to wheat and orchards. He would send cattle. The land would supply Valdivia with food and make the residents of the walled city independent. Too long they had idled away the years, bringing their necessities by ship from Talcahuano. The Brigadier for years had wanted to end that annual payment from the Crown to support Valdivia.

He would go south. He would order his courier to bring word of the appointment to Valdivia.

All evening Higgins worked on his arrangements for the trip to Valdivia. He worked until his eyes were heavy and his mind tired, until he could scarcely lift his feet as he went along the passage to his bedroom.

Now, he would sleep, he told himself.

But he lay on his bed listening to the sad song of a far-off night bird, to the plaintive sound of a zither. The botanist Hipolito Ruiz had brought the instrument with him from Spain and had presented it to Higgins' mulatto Tasso. The servant played it well. But the tunes tonight spoke mournfully.

The Brigadier stared through the screened curtains of his bed at the hulking wardrobe, at dark lines on the white walls where his muskets hung.

He could hear the rising wind, the heavy tread of his guard outside his door. Tonight it sounded ominous. Deadness was in his heart and mind and the night was a torture.

At last he slept, exhausted by his thoughts.

He was wakened by the sound of a horse galloping on the pavement of the quadrangle. Then he heard the voice of his courier and he knew the soldier had come through from Santiago to bring him word of the appointment, as Higgins had ordered.

Quickly he sat up, pushed aside the netting, and stood.

He reached for his robe and could not find it.

There was a rap at his door, quick and hurried.

The robe. Where was the robe? At last he found it. But the sleeves eluded him and he could not locate the bell to ring for a servant.

Again the insistent knock, loud and hard.

He stumbled across the room to the door, and jerked it open and peered into the dimly-lighted corridor.

His courier held out the leather mail pouch. "It is an urgent message, sir," he said.

"You have ridden well," Higgins said. "The servants will give you supper."

His courier saluted. "Thank you, sir. I hope the news is good." He darted off.

Then, the taper would not light. Three times the Brigadier tried before the wick caught the flame. The yellow light snatched eagerly at the pouch lying beside the candlestick.

With shaking fingers Higgins found the key to the pouch. The key jammed in the lock. He tried to calm himself, attempted again to make the key work. At last the spring flew back. Hastily, Higgins removed the letters and sorted through them until he found the one he searched for. Then his knees buckled and he dropped onto his bed.

Sitting on his bed he broke the seal.

Large black script looked up from the handsome parchment. The taper wavered. For a moment dizziness seized the Brigadier. It passed. He read:

"Don Carlos, by the grace of God, King of Castile, of Aragon. . . . Due to the death of Don Ambrosio de Benavides the office of Governor and Captain-General of the Kingdom of Chile and President of my Royal Audiencia has become vacant, and giving attention to the merits and services of the Brigadier of my Royal Forces, Don Ambrosio Higgins Vallenar, commandant of the Frontier, has been appointed to succeed him. . . . "

Higgins sat frozen, stunned, staring at the golden words.

Then elation swept over him. It was the joy of victory after battle. It was victory over his enemies.

King Carlos had not forgotten!

The Brigadier repeated the good words again and again as if to reassure himself that it was indeed the truth. Then he fell to his knees and prayed from a full heart for the gracious King Carlos, the righteous and just King whom Higgins had always tried to emulate. The praise to God and King Carlos welled up with overflowing vigor, strong and refreshing. The King seemed to stand above the earth and the weakness and meanness of mortals. All was clear and light. The King was on his side and there was nothing that Higgins could not accomplish now he had been given this power. He rose, rededicated, certain and strong.

Now let Bishop Maran ring the bells! Let the bells shout the news. King Carlos himself had reached out and honored his servant the Irishman, the peddler whom the enemies called foreigner. Now the foreigner was chief over them. Let the enemies know!

CHAPTER VII

THE MORNING began quietly at the hacienda of Don Juan Albano Pereyra.

Bernardo and his playmate, Casimiro Pereyra, paddled their raft of inflated sheepskins along the Claro river that bordered the pastures to the west. As gently as a leaf the balsa bobbed on the stream. Peering over the side of the sheepskin, Bernardo saw his light hair and blue eyes in the reflection made almost as dark as Casimiro's. His rounded face, broken by the rippling water, looked older than nine. "Casimiro," he said, "how funny my face looks in the water."

His friend looked. Laughed. Then glanced at his own and laughed again.

Mooring the balsa, Bernardo and Casimiro crossed the meadow to the sprawling adobe house.

In the large entrance patio was the excitement of a fiesta. Two of the country wagons, great wheels bound with cowhide and pulled by oxen, moved across the courtyard. Servants were bringing in branches of laurel and myrtle. And Don Juan Albano Pereyra, in felt hat and black poncho, was leaving for Talca.

Don Juan Albano mounted the bay horse. He said gently, "In Talca he will have lavish entertainment and the kissing of hands which he dislikes."

Who was the important person who disliked entertainment, Bernardo wondered.

He watched the kind face of Don Juan Albano, hoping he would offer to take him along to Talca.

But Don Juan Albano reached for his lines. Leaning forward he studied Bernardo thoughtfully. His eyes twinkled. "Bernardo," he said, "tomorrow the new Governor and President of Chile is coming to visit us!"

Bernardo tried to speak but his voice was too small, his throat tight.

"His name is Brigadier Don Ambrosio Higgins de Vallenar."

It was as if an earthquake had struck. He heard Casimiro's shout of delight, saw him dart to spread the news. When he felt steady enough, Bernardo crossed the yard and went to his room.

"My father!" he said, softly. "I will see my father!"

For three years he had known the wonderful truth! Now he would see his father, whom he had dreamed about since that day. The secret overflowed his heart. He kept shouting to himself that his father was coming to see Bernardo, his son!

That day, three years ago, a friend named Rozas came to the hacienda. He had been brought to Bernardo's room by Don Juan Albano.

"This is Bernardo," Don Juan Albano said. "Bernardo Riquelme."

The visitor Rozas had studied Bernardo. "Can you read, Bernardo?" he asked. "What have you read? Do you like to ride? What is your favorite sport? What would you like to be when you are a man? Do you like music or drawing? Do you like it here at the hacienda?"

When all the questions had been asked and answered, Don Juan Albano thanked Bernardo.

Outside in the corridor Bernardo had stared at his closed door. Once long ago a stranger had taken him from home in Chillan and brought him to Don Juan Albano. Was another stranger going to snatch him from this new home?

He must know what was being planned for him.

Then he remembered the door between his and Casimiro's rooms. It was kept locked. The key had been removed because the boys talked when it was open, instead of sleeping. The door was made of small, carved panels. He and Casimiro had worked one panel loose. Through it they spoke softly to one another at night.

He hurried to Casimiro's room. Noiselessly, he removed the panel. The opening was about five inches square and hidden by the headboard of Bernardo's bed. Now he could hear clearly.

Don Juan Albano was saying, "Bernardo is the natural child of the Intendente of Concepcion, Brigadier Ambrosio Higgins. I am old like his father and may die soon. If necessary you can testify to this truth about the boy. His father asked me to tell you."

His father the great Brigadier Higgins! The brave Indian fighter. He was more fearless than the Indian hero, Lautaro!

But then Don Juan Albano spoke again. "No one must know that Brigadier Higgins has a son," he said. "If it becomes known the Brigadier will be expelled from the Royal service and exiled."

Bernardo's heart had beat fast. If he betrayed the secret, his father would be disgraced. He would be sent from Chile. Then, who would protect the people from the Indians?

Bernardo remembered the wonderful day clearly. And now another astonishing and magnificent thing had happened: he had learned that his father was coming to this hacienda to visit for three days.

He went to a window.

He could not tell his father's name. He could not shout to Casimiro or to anyone that his father was Brigadier Higgins. But his father was coming. And to see his son, Bernardo.

Suddenly, tears ran along his cheeks. He wept quietly, leaning against the window and thinking of his father.

Now he understood why he had been brought here from Chillan. It was to help the great hero. And that was the reason his name was Riquelme and not Higgins.

Riquelme was his grandfather's name.

He remembered the night he left home. His mother came to his bedside. Her face was pale and she was crying. "You are going to a beautiful hacienda," she said. "There will be other children."

He clung to her.

"Be brave, little one," she said. She held him close.

Then through the black night he rode with the soldier, trying not to cry, but crying a little.

Now he knew the reason for the secrecy. But nothing could change his being Bernardo Higgins. That was his name.

On the table was the paper kite he had been making. He would finish painting the Indian symbol.

For a long time he worked. He thought that when his father looked upon the kite and recognized the design, he would wonder what person had made it so skillfully. When he learned that Bernardo had painted it, he would be proud of his son and his work. Bernardo stared admiringly at the finished kite, thinking how his father would appreciate the Indian symbol. He listened to the pleasant stirrings, the preparations for his father's visit.

The thought was almost overpowering. His heart pounded faster.

The maid Amapa came with broom, pails, dust cloths.

His kite would be safe in the sala. But the sala was being cleaned also. Carpets, cushions had been removed and piled in the sunny patio. It was no place for his kite.

The servant Josue, dark cheeks bright as the pianoforte he was polishing, glanced at Bernardo and smiled. The big chief, the greatest man in Chile, was coming to visit, he said, and he would free them all. He was Governor of Chile. He had great power. There would be freedom and land for everyone, even the slaves.

Bernardo stared. His heart began singing. He had known the negro slaves could buy their freedom from their masters, if they had money. But where would Josue get two hundred and fifty pesos? Even with the little Bernardo had saved to give Josue, it would take many years to buy his freedom. And Bernardo wanted the slaves free, and land for them and the peons as he wanted nothing else. Except to know and speak with his father.

He could hear the hard thumping of his heart. Tomorrow, when Bernardo's father called him to visit with him, he would thank him for his goodness to the slaves and peons.

Josue shoved him gently toward the corridor, explaining that he had to hurry with the cleaning.

In the covered walk Bernardo saw that Dona Bartolina, wife

of Don Juan Albano, was talking to her brother who had just arrived.

Don Vincente de la Cruz, his cream vicuna poncho tied about his waist, was speaking about the arrival of the honored guest, Brigadier Higgins. "Why should he visit three days at your hacienda, when the people of Talca have planned a reception, a dinner and fireworks?" he asked.

"The Brigadier is an old friend of my husband." Dona Bartolina looked as distressed as if mules had again trampled her flower garden.

There was a better reason, Bernardo thought. His father wanted to know his son, Bernardo.

"Invite your important friends to dine with us," Dona Bartolina said. "You will be given an honored place near the Brigadier."

Don Vincente looked more cheerful. He would send over his portrait of His Majesty King Carlos the Third to be hung in the sala. And without glancing at Bernardo, he turned, sprang upon his horse and raced away.

Bernardo stood beside Dona Bartolina who was arranging roses and gillyflowers in a blue jar. He needed a place for his kite, he said. But she seemed not to have heard, and after a moment he crossed the courtyard and went to the meadow.

He unreeled the string to his kite. It rushed skyward like a bird freed from a cage.

Soon his beloved father would free slaves and peons!

The joy in Bernardo's heart was almost unbearable.

Tomorrow he would see his father. Would tomorrow ever come?

In the late afternoon he reeled in the kite and returned to the house.

The portrait of His Majesty King Carlos the Third had now been hung in the sala. Bernardo studied the tall figure. The eyes, sharply blue, looked down asking Bernardo's name, where he had been born and why if his name was Riquelme he was living here? The mouth of the King was tight, his cheeks thin and pale. The eyes stared through Bernardo.

This King must never know that Bernardo was the son of Brigadier Higgins, the new Governor of Chile.

He heard the clatter of wagons returning from Talca. He glanced anxiously about, looking for a hiding place for his kite. His eyes came back to the portrait.

He saw the perfect place.

Hastily, he slipped the kite behind the portrait of His Majesty. It would be safe under the eyes of the King. Then he ran toward the courtyard.

The oxcarts were being unloaded. Bundles were scattered about the patio and Don Juan Albano was speaking of Talca. "You should see the city," he said, smiling at Dona Bartolina. "Everything handsomely decorated. Brigadier Higgins will not approve of the Crown's money being spent so lavishly."

"My brothers will pay for everything." Dona Bartolina's chin lifted proudly. "They are disappointed that the Brigadier will not stay in Talca. I invited Vincente and his friends to our dinner for the new Governor."

Don Juan Albano looked distressed. "He wants no banquets and no guests."

"It is only fair," Dona Bartolina said. "And, Juan Albano, speak to him for my brothers. Vincente says the appointments come too slowly."

"I shall leave that to the Brigadier!" Don Juan Albano said shortly.

Bernardo thought that each would get justice from his father. The slaves and Don Vincente and the other Cruz brothers. For his father as Governor of Chile would do what was right for everyone. And Don Juan Albano knew this was true.

His friend saw Bernardo, and smiled. "Here is a new suit for you; and shirts. We must wear fine raiment for our honored guest."

How good and how kind. The thoughtful Don Juan Albano remembered everything, just as Bernardo's father did. He hugged the package to him, looking up happily at his friend.

The workmen had been arranging streamers, and now a red banner fluttered proudly. Then a gold streamer whipped out gaily.

All down the avenue of trees the colors flared. And in the court-yard wild, happy confusion as garlands of myrtle were strung and lanterns placed among the trees and a platform built for singers and dancers—in preparations for receiving the greatest hero in Chile.

Tomorrow was the day. Tomorrow was years away. Tomorrow, for the first time in his life, Bernardo would see his father!

He did not believe he could wait until tomorrow!

CHAPTER VIII

THAT MORNING as Governor Higgins rode into the courtyard he looked for the child Bernardo. He saw a handsome kite painted with a well-designed red and blue Indian symbol, and he stared at it, surprised that someone here was familiar enough with Araucanian Indian symbols to reproduce one. Then he saw the boy who was holding the kite, a lad of about nine with a mass of light curly hair, blue eyes large and shining.

Don Juan Albano riding beside Higgins said softly, "The child holding the kite."

Higgins would have known without that hint. "My son!" he thought, and his heart tightened, his hungry eyes studied the boy. The child was everything that Higgins had expected and more. He was handsome, he had dignity. "Look!" he told himself. "How proudly he carries himself."

The boy stared seriously at the Governor.

How fine his eyes. And what a kind expression for one so young. He must have a great interest in Indians to have placed that Araucanian symbol on his kite. That would explain his attraction to Higgins, the admiration in his eyes. He is fascinated by me because I have fought the Araucanians, Higgins thought.

That was the reason for Bernardo's steady gaze, like a quietly burning flame.

Here before the boy was the Indian fighter, who was reputed to throw a twenty-foot lance as well as any wild Indian. Here was the Brigadier-General, Master of the Camp, Commandant of the Frontier, Governor, Captain-General and President of Chile, arrived with all the glamor to inspire a young child, with glittering uniforms, many dragoons, swords in gleaming scabbards and all riding handsome horses covered with leather, velvet and silver. To the clanking of silver spurs and carrying banners of Spain, Higgins the Indian fighter had ridden into this quiet courtyard.

It was enough to entrance any boy; Higgins himself would have been entranced when he was nine.

Bernardo remained apart staring spellbound at Higgins while the other children darted among the dragoons, speaking with them and touching their swords.

Having dismounted, Higgins followed Dona Bartolina along the corridor where his son was seated. As he passed, Bernardo looked up with great, luminous eyes and so near that Higgins could have touched him. The temptation was almost irresistible to reach out and place a hand on the young head, a mass of curls.

Small, manly, stolidly the boy sat, clutching the kite and not stirring as the Governor passed. Except for the eyes, he might have been carved from stone.

Higgins glanced away, resisted the temptation to touch him.

His mind was on Bernardo as he listened to Dona Bartolina speak of her brothers and honors. She sat pouring boiling water over Paraguay herb in a silver cup.

Higgins took the maté, sipped a little and returned the goblet to Dona Bartolina, scarcely hearing her words.

He glanced toward the corridor.

Bernardo was not there. Higgins was disappointed. He looked about the room for the boy.

The child had laid the kite aside and was standing motionless before the portrait of King Carlos. His back was straight, head well placed on fine shoulders.

Higgins felt a glow of pride. The boy stood like a young prince. That was how Higgins had always stood. And his hair had been like Bernardo's. But hands and feet were small, as were his mother's, and although his blue eyes resembled Higgins', the expression belonged to Dona Isabel. The memory troubled him.

There never had been a handsomer child.

How Higgins longed to acknowledge the boy, keep him beside him!

But that was impossible. The secret could never be told.

✿   ✿   ✿

Dinner was served under oak trees in a patio. The children sat at their own small table. For hours the guests were served platters of partridge, quail, beefsteak, roast lamb, vegetables, pudding with a sauce from the sap of palm buds. The toasts had been constant.

Higgins had wanted only a quiet visit with Don Juan Albano. He had hoped to study Bernardo unobserved by prying eyes.

The bland face of Don Vincente de la Cruz smiled, as he rose to make a few remarks on the achievements of His Excellency, Governor Higgins.

Across the lace cloth, Higgins watched, hoping Vincente would make it a very few words. But five minutes passed; then ten. It had become an oration. He made Higgins' achievements sound dull indeed. What did Vincente know about Higgins' early struggles? Or how he fought for advancement? And it was news to Higgins that a title had been promised.

He would get the title. But he would fight for it. On his salary as Governor of Chile, Higgins could afford to pay a genealogist to trace his line. He would link himself with the ancient family of O'Neil and claim the title of Baron of Ballenary. The Spanish Crown would accept the statement of an accredited genealogist. Higgins would become O'Higgins.

No, no, my lad, the Governor thought, listening to Vincente, it was never as simple as that. And it was news to him that his construction of the mountain houses had been gratefully received by the people of Chile. The greater number of Spanish citizens ridiculed Higgins for attempting it, hoping that he would break his fool Irish neck by falling over a precipice.

He glanced along the table at the bored faces.

Vincente made it sound as if Higgins had rubbed a magic lamp. He mentioned that voyage which Higgins made at the urgent demand of the Crown, and how the ministers ordered Higgins to Madrid to make a report on Chile.

Higgins ran a hand along his cheek, thinking of that time. He tried not to smile.

The Crown, was it? It was Higgins pleading sickness, the need of consulting a specialist in Spain, that had got him to Madrid.

That was a long time ago. Before his betrothal to Dona Isabel.

And he had gone at his own expense, intending to demand recognition for his work on the houses. Indeed, he thought, when the Crown learned what he had accomplished for Spain, he would be advanced to a fine position.

After weeks, he got an appointment. He was to make a report on Chile.

Higgins had written the report, working day and night. He made tactful recommendations, withholding criticism of officials and clergy. He proposed that the Indians be placed in villages and taught agriculture and crafts.

He recommended that the Crown open a pass over mountains and pampas to Buenos Aires; establish ports in Patagonia to forestall the English encroachments; place two fortified ports on that coast; build six forts along the Biobio in Chile and three between Valdivia and Chiloe. He estimated the cost of forts at a hundred fifty thousand pesos.

He also made a map on which he marked rivers, Indian territory, mountains and volcanoes; the cities and towns of Chile. He gave it a title:

Description of the Kingdom of Chile, its Products, Commerce and Inhabitants. Reflections upon its Present Condition, with some Suggestions Relative to the Subjugation of the Infidel Indians, and Progress of the Dominions of His Majesty. 1767.

The Minister had scarcely glanced at the report. He had flipped a few pages and suggested that Higgins return to his old position in Chile. There was nothing for him in Madrid. Let the Governor of Chile recommend his services to the Crown.

Higgins was so disappointed he walked the streets all night. He told himself he could not give up.

But after weeks of hopeless trying he had to admit defeat. Greatly discouraged, he had sailed for Chile. How bitter he had been.

Five hundred pesos. That was his salary. He had learned a hard but valuable lesson in Madrid. To be given advancements, it was necessary to speak often about himself and his work to the most important minister and to the Governor of Chile. He told himself he could lose nothing by speaking up, and loudly. From that moment he began to write the endless reports of his labors for the Crown. Into the ears of Minister Galvez and the Governor of Chile, he shouted of his services, small or great. For the years were moving ahead rapidly. Higgins could not wait.

And now he was Governor and President of Chile.

If Don Vincente knew that already Higgins had decided to appoint him sub-delegate of the District of Maule, he would stop talking and sit down.

At last the tiresome oration was finished.

Higgins glanced at Bernardo. The child was applauding, too. His face was alive, as if he understood and appreciated the labors of Higgins for the Crown. An extraordinary child!

A friar rose, his face flushed with wine. He recited verses, as was the custom, of events in Higgins' work on the frontier.

They were tame, lacking reality. They should have been written in blood.

Higgins recalled the first skirmish with the Indians. He had been tempted to run for cover. He had never seen a twenty-foot Indian lance drive past him with the speed of lightning, never had seen horses rear above him until they looked mountain-high. He still could feel the sweating Indian bodies, naked and painted, hear the maniacal screams. Twice he was wounded. Somehow, in spite of his terror, he kept fighting, kept his musket firing.

That uprising and others had been quelled. All were bloody. But the first one would always be for him the most frightening. He ran a hand over the old head wound which still troubled him, and as he did he glanced toward the table where his son was sitting.

There was terror on Bernardo's face.

He hoped the good Don Juan Albano had not spoiled Bernardo and made him a little soft. Now, if Higgins could keep the lad beside him for a little time, he soon would toughen him until he was as daring as the Indian boys that rode fearlessly against the Spanish, tossing lances before they could sit a horse.

The friar ended the verses. There was loud applause.

Higgins wondered which at the table were friends and which antagonists. For the innovations he planned for Chile would rouse hatred and breed new enemies.

Later, above the patio the fireworks scattered into a hundred fantastic and colorful figures. The children screamed with pleasure.

All but Bernardo. He stood a little apart as if not quite belonging. It troubled Higgins. Why did the boy watch with such restraint? And why was he such a stoical little fellow?

His thoughts were interrupted by the farewells. The ladies billowed onto cushions upon the floor of the carretons, the men mounted horses. Off they moved, their laughter running back ribbon-like through the oaks, scattering like sparks of rockets.

In the deserted sala Higgins and Don Juan Albano smoked black cigars and sipped wine.

Now at last, Don Juan Albano said, his dark face lighting with a smile, at last they could visit. He hoped Higgins understood that the large company of guests, the elaborate entertainment, had not been to his liking. How did Higgins feel to have reached the pinnacle? How had the news of his appointment affected him after the long years of waiting?

Like being lifted by a great condor, Higgins said, and carried to unheard-of heights. It was like being transported with the speed of light from a valley to a towering point in the Andes, the peak of Las Caracoles.

A servant brought fresh wine, and departed. The candles flickered, lighting the furrows on the kind face of the Portuguese, the lines etched by sorrows.

"You have looked upon your son," Don Juan Albano said with quiet satisfaction. "What a fine boy he is."

Higgins said, "I am proud of him. And grateful to you."

"He is wise beyond his years. He is loving and thoughtful." Don Juan Albano's voice was gently boastful.

His affection could not be greater if Bernardo belonged to him, Higgins thought. The great heart of his friend overflowed to include his own, friends, strangers. Life had given him sorrows but no bitterness. He was all spirit. That was how Higgins had felt about him in the early days when as a peddler with no friends, no position or money, he had found in Don Juan Albano protection and affection.

"Bernardo can be trusted. He has almost too great a sense of loyalty. He will take any punishment as long as his friends, even the peon and slave children, are not punished."

Higgins was pleased that Bernardo could be trusted, that he defended his friends.

"We ride over the acres." Don Juan Albano smiled. "We talk crops. He thinks the workmen should have better living quarters, the same provisions that come to my table. He tells me about the plants and trees on my acres. The panque is for tanning leathers and the guayac has the heaviness of iron. This is flax, and this mustard. You should see the maps he has sketched of the acres, and the skillful hand he has for inventions. I want your eyes to see him as mine have."

The great heart, Higgins thought.

A servant slipped out of the darkness of the covered walk, bringing fresh candles. Silently, he replenished the burned stubs, and disappeared into the shadows of the patio.

"Bernardo wants the slaves to have their freedom." Don Juan Albano turned his wine cup. "My explanations do not satisfy him."

His own son. Higgins wanted Bernardo to be generous with the poor.

But the freedom of the slaves was another matter, Higgins told himself. In Chile there was a scarcity of labor of all kinds. The Negroes were better off than the peons, or the miserable Indians. The Indians had been a prey of unscrupulous Spanish traders and miners for centuries. They stole the Indian land and cattle, impressed Indians into service from which they never escaped until carried out in their coffins.

In a country of inequalities, Higgins thought, you first eliminated the worst and gradually you worked to end all unfairness. At present the Negroes had plenty to wear and plenty to eat. They looked down upon the peons. Here, the Negroes were better treated than in other countries, not even excluding North America that had won its freedom from England and had written into its Declaration of Independence that all men were created equal.

He glanced at his friend. He was certain he had explained the question to his son Bernardo better than Higgins could have done it.

"Tomorrow you will want a long visit with Bernardo," Don Juan Albano said.

This was indeed what Higgins wanted. No harm could come from such a meeting in this secluded hacienda. Perhaps he would never again see his son. To speak with him this once!

From the patio, or was it the corridor, came a shuffling sound, like a footstep.

Higgins glanced quickly toward the patio. He walked onto the covered passageway.

At the gates were his dragoons, guarding the entrance. He glanced along the walk to his left.

A figure was just passing through an archway at the far end where shadows gathered. Higgins saw the flutter of a skirt or perhaps a poncho. The corridor was long, with many rooms opening onto it. It might be anyone.

Don Juan Albano had followed to stand beside him. "Here there are only friends," he said. "Perhaps it was a servant wanting a glimpse of the new Governor of Chile." He went off down the corridor. His figure vanished into the shadows.

There were only friends, Don Juan Albano said. But Higgins knew that the enemy might be anywhere. Even within these quiet hacienda walls there could be an informer. A visiting priest, a servant hired for this occasion. Bishop Maran and the enemies had spies everywhere.

Don Juan Albano returned. He had found no one, he said. He looked disturbed.

The eyes sometimes played tricks, Higgins told him, wanting to be reassuring. When you were on the frontier you learned to suspect every sound, even an oak branch brushing the tiles of the roof. But Higgins himself had no doubt there had been someone lurking in the darkness, perhaps hidden by the trunks of oak trees.

"The leaves against the roof." Don Juan Albano looked happy again. "Tomorrow, we will ride over the land," he said cheerfully. "Perhaps Bernardo can ride with us. There are no eavesdroppers there."

In his room, Higgins removed his uniform with the brilliant epaulets, the glitter of gold braid, the fine shirt with the frill. In his nightshirt, he stood staring at the handmade lace cover.

Tomorrow, said the warning voice within, he must not visit with Bernardo. Not tomorrow, nor any day. It was too dangerous. The position which Higgins now held was higher, more exposed, the chances of discovery greater. He must watch more carefully all his actions. He must never be caught off guard.

He thought of the small face of Bernardo behind the kite this afternoon, of the eager eyes watching with such unchildlike control. And of the child now, lying in his bedroom somewhere along this corridor into which Higgins' door opened, his small body sprawled and relaxed in sleep.

To look upon his boy even in sleep would be a memory to keep and live with during the lonely moments. For there had been many desolate hours. There would be others.

Even that glimpse he must deny himself.

He stood thinking with great sadness that this son could be his only within his heart. And his heart cried against it. Cried out fiercely.

But Higgins turned the lock of his door. He let his hope of knowing Bernardo go reluctantly. Never to speak with this beloved child. It seemed too great a sacrifice.

At last, he let the hope go, knowing it could never be.

And suddenly, the night seemed bitterly cold.

CHAPTER IX

FOR THREE days Governor Higgins had been a guest at the hacienda of Don Juan Albano. Today he was leaving. He walked onto the terrace and glanced about the courtyard, saw the pack mules standing on three legs awaiting the loads. The muleteers were not about, nor the dragoons.

He saw Bernardo.

Higgins had not visited with his son. There had been no meeting, although the good Don Juan Albano had tried repeatedly to bring them together. Higgins had refused. But he had arranged with his friend to have Thomas Dolphin of Concepcion share the responsibility of educating Bernardo as Dolphin had promised.

The boy was flying his kite.

Higgins glanced once again about the courtyard and saw no one. He came back to Bernardo. How alone he seemed.

The boy was standing near the mules. If Higgins went over and pretended to examine the packs, he could speak quietly with the boy about the kite, the Indian symbol. He would hear the young voice answering. It would mean everything to Higgins to speak once to his son!

And the hour was early. No sounds came from within the house. There was no one about but himself and Bernardo.

He took a step forward.

"Senor, Your Excellency." A voice came from behind him.

Higgins turned quickly. His heart beat fast.

A black servant placed maté on a table and departed, his bare feet making no sound.

Higgins stared after the man.

Something in the walk of the slave was familiar. Could he have been the one who was listening outside the sala that first evening? Was he serving some Spaniard in Talca, or a priest? Bishop Maran had spies everywhere. A slave wanting pesos for freedom would spy.

How foolish of Higgins to have been tempted to speak with Bernardo when eyes were all about him. He sipped maté and watched the boy reel in his kite.

Bernardo was stroking the nose of a mule.

He glanced up and saw Higgins. For a moment he waited. Then he turned and walked slowly away.

Cold the pale sun, the morning deathly still.

Higgins stared at the cowhide trunks on the mules, at clumsy hinges and locks of brass.

A servant announced breakfast.

Higgins tried to eat. He could not.

The pack mules moved toward the entrance gate followed by the shouting drivers.

Higgins said his farewells. Dona Bartolina was grateful that he was thinking generously of her brothers.

Don Albano said, "May we meet again soon," with tears in his eyes.

"My faithful friend!" Higgins laid a firm hand on his shoulder.

Bernardo did not speak. It was not natural for a child to be that restrained. Why had he not shouted, "God with you," as the other children had? Except that he stood so immovable and stared so intently he might have been entirely disinterested. What thoughts was the boy thinking behind that calm mask? Why should he watch earnestly and yet say nothing?

Higgins thought about it, as surrounded by dragoons he rode toward the King's Highway. Horses reared, pranced, neighed. The singing of guests who rode with him rolled back, and the sound of castanets; the harness and spurs and swords rattled.

Don Vincente, beside Higgins, spoke of altar cloths, of gold and lace contributed by a brother in Spain for the church of Talca, of a hospital which Vincente and the brothers were expecting to contribute. He mentioned bridges to be built by them, of thousands of pesos given to the Crown by the Cruz family.

The Governor listened, but he was thinking of Bernardo.

He had not danced nor laughed as the other children had. Face pale, lips colorless, he had watched.

It was perhaps that he was overly excited. All children, Higgins told himself, straightening in his saddle, had pale faces and serious eyes when they were overwrought.

But he felt strangely disturbed and depressed.

He listened to Don Vincente, stared at the forests that hugged the highway.

It was natural to feel disturbed and pained at leaving an only child. He had looked upon Bernardo for the first time. Now he was lost to him forever. He would never see him again.

A hawk spiraled from a tree as swiftly as a kite hurrying skyward. He remembered the Indian design on Bernardo's kite, how the emblem stood out against the blueness when the boy was flying it this morning. How nice a lad. How gently he stroked the black nose of a pack mule. And helped a servant wrap fruit for Higgins. He sighed.

He tried to push the oppressive thoughts aside. He told himself that as Governor of Chile he had power to give Bernardo a happier country to live in. Was not that better than mourning because he could not again look upon him? Indeed any devoted father would have decided as Higgins had.

He roused himself. He listened to what Don Vincente was saying, he tried to enjoy the singing. Then he felt more cheerful.

With shouts of "Viva el Presidente!" the company of guests departed, leaving Higgins, his dragoons and servants to the quiet countryside, to cypress, oak, palms and maytens.

Higgins dashed ahead at a gallop. He thought of his plans for Chile. The reforms and improvements would begin. The power was now his!

For hours they rode at a rapid gait.

Near the highway some carreteros had unhitched their oxen.

The wooden wheels of the great carts were wrapped with hides. Over a campfire hung a cooking pot.

Higgins believed that every carretero in Chile knew him by sight. He often passed them as he traveled about the country. They would welcome him as protector, friend, as the new governor.

They waved sombreros of plaited palm leaves, and admiration was on their honest faces.

He rode on in high spirits, thinking of the indispensable carreteros. It was peasants like these and the muleteers that were important to Chile. They carried the cargoes to and from the ports. On them depended the distribution of exports and imports, of foodstuffs and building timbers, of army provisions. They could neither read nor write, but they never forgot an order nor confused it, no matter how intricate. Merchants entrusted them with large sums of money and never had lost a peso. They were poorly paid. And winter or summer, the carreteros walked beside the huge carts.

Higgins' first regiment had been selected from peasants like these. They could hang from a saddle by knee and ankle and racing at full speed, pick up a coin from the ground. They had terrified the Indians with their skill in throwing the heavy lances. The peasants also were dexterous in the use of the boleadores, a lariat attached to three leather balls and used by the Indians to hunt deer or ostrich, wild horses and cattle. Higgins had seen the peasants perform amazing tricks with the lasso, and some bad ones, like roping Indians in battle and killing them.

Governor Higgins studied the road ahead. What was it Don Juan Albano had said about Bernardo and the lasso? Oh, yes, the boy would not be happy until he had mastered the art of roping and tying a steer.

He would learn when he was older. Higgins was proud of Bernardo.

He had made the right decision about not meeting the child alone. And he had been protected from speaking with Bernardo this morning. If the slave had not brought maté at that moment, harm might have been done. Then the enemies would have had a clue. Suppose Bernardo, boasting quietly as children do, said to the wrong person that the Governor and President of Chile had spoken with him privately about his education, his future?

But he had not talked with his son. No one suspected. His secret was secure.

Higgins and his escort rode to the accompaniment of creaking leather, thud of hooves, rattle of spurs.

His officers discussed wheat and barley crops, the number of quintals of tallow shipped from Valparaiso last year. They wondered about the value of gold, silver and copper taken from the mines. They argued about the height of the Cumbre, high peak of the Andes.

Then began the tales. For every Chilean has a stock of them, either invented by himself, or passed down from generation to generation. The tales took the place of books. Spain restricted books in the colonies. There were no printing presses.

There were sagas of Pizarro, the Incas, the temples of gold. There were others of rivers where emeralds were found and of mountains that held lapis lazuli. And stories of Indians south of the Biobio, the human sacrifices; often Spanish prisoners. And of animals substituted now for human beings on the Indian altars.

Higgins had seen animal sacrifice. An opening was made in the heart of a living animal, the blood sucked by priests.

He would not rest until the Indians were civilized. He would not rest until south of the Biobio the land was waving with grain and green with trees. The heathen rites must be banished, Christian ideals practiced.

The stories of the Indians in Peru were certain to follow. About dying mules and damaged goods and razors forced upon the beardless Indians. Of unscrupulous priests and worthless traders misusing the ignorant natives.

But there were rascals and merciless men in all professions, Higgins thought, and Chile and Peru had more than their share. Now he was Governor, he would do everything that he possibly could to correct these abuses.

As Governor, he had power to begin reforms which would be accepted by other Spanish administrators. Thus, he would lead others to righteous government and bring happiness to the people.

Then Curico, where he was acclaimed. Here the peddler Higgins had once been requested to leave because he took business from the local merchants. Then followed Rancagua, near the River Cachapoal, where sometimes in the past he had been welcome, sometimes not so welcome. But always the peddler sold his wares, even when the Spanish looked down their noses at him.

A cold winter rain was falling as the Governor and his escort neared Santiago. He watched, his excitement mounting. He tried to think of the importance of rain to the country, of new forage for cattle and fine crops.

But instead his mind kept running on how all Chile now knelt to Higgins, as if to the King himself. For was he not His Majesty's representative and the greatest man in Chile?

And his kingdom began at the South Sea and reached to the Andes, mighty fortress that protected Chile from invaders to the east. His kingdom was protected by the impassable mountains that ran like a backbone the length of South America. Far north was the vast desert, a barrier to enemy attacks.

That meant that Higgins had only the coast and the southern frontier to watch to keep Chile safe.

And he would keep his kingdom safe.

He would plant the neglected land to sugar cane and cotton. He would try to break up enormous land grants from the Crown which the Spanish lords constantly refused to develop. He would gather the peasants into villages where they could league themselves against the lords.

There would be many changes.

With a light heart he watched the clean rain.

Ahead, a wagon loaded with hides creaked loudly, probably going toward Valparaiso. The oxen tugged stubbornly to keep the wagon moving through the muddy road. The countrymen walked, splattered to the knees with mud, shouting lustily a song about a girl named Rosa.

The words made little sense, but the men sang them as if they were going to a festival where there would be endless skins of chicha. Instead, at the end of their journey there would be only another load, the tiresome journey back along this poor road with cargoes for some rich hacienda.

They were the gayest people in Chile.

The Governor would give them better roads. With good highways they could travel faster and spend more time working their land. One of Higgins' first acts as Governor would be to consult with the engineers about a road from Santiago to Valparaiso to replace the bad road now in use.

Higgins and his party neared the Maipú River. The crossing would be made by a cowhide cable bridge of ancient Indian construction. The bridge spanned the river and was wide enough to take a carriage. Hanging forty or fifty feet about the Maipú, attached to bold cliffs on each side of the river, it was the only available crossing during high water when the stream became a rushing torrent spilling from the Andes until it spread in places to a fourth of a mile wide. As you crossed, the bridge began swaying gently. The sway increased and as you reached the center it pitched like a boat in a storm. If you glanced into the swirling waters you might become dizzy and lose your balance. It was better to fix your eyes on the opposite shore as you walked.

At the bridge, Higgins and his men dismounted.

Each led his horse, for sometimes a skittish animal became alarmed by the movement of the bridge, and gave trouble. It was better to walk and take no chances.

The cables of hide swung dizzily. Sixty feet below, the dark water seethed.

How many times as a peddler had Higgins crossed this bridge. And now he was crossing it to go to the highest post in the land!

He felt another kind of dizziness.

A little distance from the river, the Governor was greeted by deputies from the Santiago Cabildo, the Audiencia, the University, by leading citizens, by the Spanish lords. It was customary for the incoming Governor and President to be met and escorted to the

Country House, when he rested before proceeding to Santiago.

And although the Governor was received by the Committee with every appearance of friendliness, among them were enemies.

Don Juan Ignacio Goycolea rode beside Higgins as the senior regidor of the Cabildo. Later he would present to Higgins the keys of the city, and Higgins would go through the pantomime of opening the gates to Santiago. He said pleasantly that until the rain stopped, the party would be obliged to remain at the Country House. The residents of Santiago would be distressed to have His Excellency enter in bad weather. They were planning on elaborate decorations on all the streets, and until the rain let up the work could not continue.

The needless waste of money for festivities, Higgins thought in annoyance. But he must endure the ceremonies, the ancient formalities, all the foolish honors from the University, the processions and the Masses, the floats and entertainment.

It would have to be suffered. But he would like nothing so much as to enter the palace and go straight to his desk and begin the important work for his kingdom.

On May twenty-sixth, Higgins rode with a glittering company of picked troops and militia, officials of the city and the colony, entering the city along streets paved only in the center and with small stones. All the avenues of Santiago should be completely paved, Higgins thought, instead, of a space scarcely wide enough for a calesa.

From houses and gates were hung festoons of laurel and myrtle. Tapestries and banners covered the balconies, stretched across the streets. Everyone was in holiday dress, the ladies wearing their handsomest mantillas and tossing nosegays from balconies. The roadway was carpeted with gillyflowers, violets, lime and orange blossoms, carnations, anemones, the air sweet with fragrance. The great Plaza Real, on which the Governor's palace fronted, was filled with people. Drums throbbed, gitterns, guitars and triangles played gaily. The vendors of trinkets screamed their confections and flags and medals. Guns and cannon sounded a salute.

How sweetly the bells rang from the unfinished cathedral. Higgins thought it a pity that the beautiful structure had been years in this uncompleted condition. Long ago it should have been finished. In white garments a great company of nuns and priests clustered at the cathedral, preparing to begin a procession to honor the new Governor and President.

"*Viva* Higgins!" shouted the crowd, waving banners and tossing flowers. "*Viva el Presidente!*"

The countrymen teetered on the wheels of their carts which today were decorated with garlands of green and paper pennants and bright carnations. Ribbons trailed from their straw sombreros. Each muleteer wore a flower behind an ear, and silk streamers fluttered from every bridle. Small boys clambered into trees for a better look.

And the peddlers standing near the arcades which had been draped in the colors of Spain shouted louder than all, "Higgins, *Presidente!*"

Thick as poppies on a hillside, the flower sellers and musicians, the singers and dancers.

The mudholes, Higgins saw, were still in the Plaza. That he would change, and quickly.

A gaucho rose in his stirrups. He tossed a carnation to Higgins. "*El Presidente*," he called. "*Buena suerte!*"

Buena suerte, Higgins thought. He would need good luck, with all that he had planned.

Carrying in his hands the Royal Standard and surrounded by officials, he mounted a platform erected in the Plaza. He repeated the oath, "Don Ambrosio Higgins de Vallenar, Brigadier of the Royal Army, Governor and Captain-General, President of the Royal Audiencia, I swear and promise the King our Lord and his successors to the Crown of Castile and Leon, by God our Lord, and on this Holy Gospel, to obey and guard and comply with the orders which may be given me, defend your Lordship and the Royal patrimony and take care of its increase. . . . Amen."

His hand trembled as he laid it on the Holy Gospel. He would indeed protect and defend the Crown with his life. His Majesty had chosen him above the others. He would keep himself in this high place. He would never fail that trust.

Then Mass in the cathedral, the receptions, the state dinner, polite and brilliant toasts. Fireworks and dancing. How beautiful the ladies, the richness of their attire, and how like a thousand stars dancing, their fabulous jewels. And was ever there a more handsome view at night along the streets from Santa Lucia mountain on the east to the last house on the west, a more dazzling display of lighted candelabras?

And had ever a people been happier, Higgins thought, listening to the festivities far into the night. He could hear the music long after he had retired, and the sounds of revelry. The bells were still ringing. He thought of Bishop Maran and his bells, even felt compassion for the prelate who would be smarting under the disappointment of Higgins sitting in the place of the mighty.

Poor Maran!

The bells were pealing the victory of the Irishman, who stood now on the special eminence given him by King Carlos. The honors had been earned and none deserved them more, he thought.

He lay in a handsome room in the state Palace, and at the entrance were his guards in red and gold, protecting his Palace as he had dreamed it might be those long years ago. It had come to pass, the dream. He was Governor of Chile.

It would not be the end of the honors, the dreams.

For other soft, happy voices would sing praises of Don Ambrosio Higgins de Vallenar on another night filled with rich fragrance, and his heart would be even gayer with victory.

Before he died he would be Viceroy of Peru!

CHAPTER X

EARLY on a Monday, Governor Higgins rose and dressed in his plainest clothes. He took maté and hastened across to Government House for his first official meeting with members of the Santiago City Council.

The members were late.

Higgins waited, sitting in the crimson chair of state.

One by one and in pairs the members sauntered in. They were dressed in velvets and satins as if arriving for a levee at the palace.

Although they seemed surprised that Higgins had arrived ahead of them, his presence did not appear to disturb them. They bowed to him gracefully, smiled, took their time about finding their places, gossiped a little longer. "Time, time," they seemed to be saying. "We have all the time in the world." At last they settled back, comfortably and at ease.

When Higgins rose to begin his message, they applauded politely.

"Senores," Higgins began. "I am happy to be here."

The members applauded again. They smiled up at him.

"For an hour yesterday," he continued, "I rode about the city. To the east, I saw your fine haciendas stretching in beautiful order. Within the city I saw walls of your handsome and well-kept Santiago homes, the lavish gardens, the ornate, beautiful gates. Everything in order."

The Governor glanced toward a window grille.

"To reach these chambers, each of you must pass the Plaza Real. You ride on your fine thoroughbred horses, in your spotless clothes. It cannot be possible that you have not seen the pigs, the mudholes, the filth left by animals, the fountain filled with refuse, the rotting fish. The open sewers in the streets are a disgrace,

82

breeding disease and threatening the inhabitants of Santiago with epidemics. Gentlemen, your city is filthy. It is not policed and patrolled. You are not properly fulfilling your duties as Council."

A shocked gasp went around the room. They were sitting erect enough now! They did not applaud.

"Senores," Higgins said, and his voice was hard. "You have no civic pride! I deplore the indifference and negligence of the City Council. I want the Plaza cleaned. I want the entire city cleaned, the sewers covered. The streets must be paved and the city policed and patrolled."

Not a member moved. The air was quiet with their outraged anger.

"It is beyond belief," Higgins continued "that another break-water has not been constructed along the Mapocho River to protect the city against floods. The old dyke was washed away by that terrible flood five years ago. How can you justify such neglect? Daily, you jeopardize the lives of the residents of Santiago. You have failed in your responsibility. How would the Crown look upon such dereliction of duty?"

The members were too stunned or too furious to speak. But soon they would find their excuses. And Higgins would answer them.

"As for revenue," he said, "which is doubtless one of the excuses for not fulfilling these duties, if the Council has not sufficient revenue to finance the improvements, then the expense should fall upon persons, lands and products. You should tax wines, sugar and Paraguay herb. It is your duty to consider all this without delay, with zeal for the common good and in a spirit of magnanimity. In speaking to you thus," Higgins said, "I am only doing my duty, thus satisfying the high confidence which I have merited from His Majesty."

He paused, thinking one of them might have something to say. But the gentlemen remained in their places, forgetting to smile, forgetting to applaud, remembering only their indignation.

"I will conclude my remarks," he went on, "by saying that the Council must accept my proposals or I will refuse to be responsible for the city and environs being properly policed and made safe from floods, and for the well-being of citizens."

They understood well enough his meaning then: he would inform the Crown, and they would be in bad odor with the Madrid government.

Having finished, Higgins glanced at the colors of Spain above the crimson chair of state. In a deathlike silence he left the Council Chamber.

He returned to the palace. Leaving word with his secretary, Higgins mounted his horse and rode to the Mapocho River to inspect the breakwater that had never been rebuilt since the flood.

The intense light falling on the river was like the glow from an erupting volcano, the ugly light spreading over river, marsh, the road going toward Santa Rosa and the Andes, even over the Andes. It recalled the angry, flushed faces of the Council members.

But did they think Higgins would do nothing about cleaning up the city? Could he not see, from where he stood on the bridge, remnants of the demolished dam and the debris still lying where it had fallen during that flood years ago? It had rushed with thundering fury from the mountains, inundating a great part of Santiago. And the rubble had not even been carted away.

Back at the Council Chamber another sort of deluge threatened. The members would league others against Higgins.

Well, let them. This was only a beginning, he thought. He would upset them often with his plans for improvements. But out of the eruptions would come progress and happiness for the residents. Out of it would come the approval of His Majesty and the ministers of the Crown. And for Higgins, Lima and the post of Viceroy.

Leaving the bridge he rode along the river bank. A new breakwater would be built along the river front, a distance of at least a quarter of a mile. The wall should have a foundation fourteen feet below and as many feet above the river, and it should be wide enough for pedestrians to stroll along the top. He would plant the walk with trees and the residents would find it an agreeable place for recreation. He would have a parapet built to prevent accidents, and there would be stairs for ascending and descending. He seemed to see it now, a broad promenade with benches and willow or poplar trees for shade.

Higgins studied the river bank.

He estimated the cost would be at least fifteen thousand pesos a cuadra.

When things calmed down somewhat, he would announce his plan for improving the mountain passes of the Uspallata to Mendoza, and he glanced toward the peaks, thinking of the hazardous path, the cavalcades traveling slowly, one behind the other at the pace of a snail. Too many mules and loads were lost over the precipices where the road was scarcely wide enough for an animal to place its feet. Travelers and mule drivers could now travel only by daylight because of the danger of falling. Often it was necessary to dismount from the mules and walk where the path was too treacherous. From the bridge of Villarroel to the River of Uspallata the distance was more than seventy-five miles. This entire route Higgins would have repaired and widened in the worst places. Then, while it still would be dangerous, at least the risk of passage would be less.

The cost would be at least ten thousand pesos.

Then, Higgins would build a decent road from Santiago to the port of Valparaiso. A new one was urgently needed for commerce and should have been constructed years ago.

His kind but misguided old predecessor had started a Mint in 1784. The architect had planned a handsome structure, finer than any in South America. It was a perfect example of architecture, with columns and inner courts, balconies and living quarters for the officials of the Mint.

It was ridiculous to build such an impressive and magnificent structure, he thought. And was it not to cost many times the original estimate of five hundred thousand pesos, and had he not criticized the erection of an elaborate Mint? He was reminded by his predecessor at the time that it had been designed to mine fifty million pesos a year.

Higgins stared at the river.

There were not enough workers in all Chile to mine even half that amount of metal. The Mint was handsome, but it was rank extravagance. Chile was in need of a hundred more important projects.

But the building must be completed. What you began must be finished. Indeed, he would prosecute the work with zeal. And if the Crown would give him mineralogists like those soon to arrive in Buenos Aires and travel on to Peru, he could improve the output of Chile's mines and open up other developments. Don Pedro Rico, one of the engineers for Chile, had built a clever machine for mining mercury. Higgins had asked Rico to experiment with it in Higgins' apartment at the Palace, where he could help.

He had already written to the Marquis of Loreto, Viceroy of Buenos Aires, about having the mineralogists visit Chile. Then Higgins would have practical information for estimating the richness of Chile's mines. At present, because of lack of technical knowledge, there was no way of knowing what amount of minerals lay below the soil. But he was convinced it was tremendous. When he had proof, he would advise the Crown. His Majesty would be deeply gratified both for the information of the riches and by the astuteness of his new Governor.

His heart warmed as if already the King had commended him. The post in Peru seemed closer.

A dragoon was riding toward Higgins. When he was within hailing distance, he saw that it was Captain Tirapegui.

The Captain drew up alongside and saluted, apparently pleased to see his chief again after many days. "Your secretary told me that you were here," he said. "I had to see you."

God help us, Higgins thought, not trouble on the frontier?

Captain Tirapegui said, bluntly: "There is gossip in Talca about Bernardo. Don Juan Albano told me to advise you, as I passed through Talca coming to Santiago."

Like the clang of one of Bishop Maran's bells, the warning of danger went through Higgins. Then there had been spies at Talca. At this moment Maran might be on the scent. Higgins could not leave Bernardo at Don Albano's, hoping the gossip would die out.

If Bishop Maran in Concepcion heard of this, he would hunt ferret-like. He would plant more spies in Talca, for his tactics had always been ruthless. And now that Higgins had thwarted Maran's plan of being named the next Bishop of Santiago by asking the Crown to appoint another priest, the Bishop's hate for Higgins would be more malicious.

Bernardo must be removed from the hacienda of Don Juan Albano. Once the boy was taken from Talca, the gossip would cease for lack of evidence.

But where could he send the child? It must be a place remote from Maran and Concepcion and Talca, some far corner of Chile where few strangers came and where Higgins had friends that could be trusted.

Higgins began racing through names of isolated towns along the frontier, feeling as if already Maran was knocking at Don Juan Albano's door: Yumbal, Los Angeles, San Carlos, Chillan.

Chillan, Higgins thought, and paused.

There was an excellent Franciscan mission school at Chillan, one started by Higgins for training Indian children. At the head of the school was his faithful friend Padre Francisco Javier Ramirez. And except that Bernardo's mother was in Chillan, the school would be a place for Bernardo to live and attend classes.

Thoughtfully, Higgins stared at marshgrass near the river.

Would it be wise to have Bernardo near his mother?

The wind shook the grasses.

Indeed, Dona Isabel could be trusted. Dona Isabel had always wanted Bernardo nearer. Now that she was widowed and living again with her father, Bernardo would be a comfort to her on occasional visits from the mission.

Both Dona Isabel and her father had always been most discreet and guarded about the boy's birth and they would continue to be prudent. There were many branches of the Riquelme family in Chillan. Bernardo's surname would not attract any undue notice. He would be another Riquelme among many.

And there was now a young half-sister Rosa, born to Isabel of her marriage. Suppose she began wondering about Bernardo's relationship to her?

Higgins watched the loon among the grasses.

She would not ask questions about him. She was too young. She would accept him as a cousin, and happily.

And Higgins would ask his friend Thomas Dolphin to explain to Dona Isabel in his politic way the reasons for Bernardo's being sent to the mission in Chillan, the need for continued caution.

Higgins felt easier then. He glanced at Tirapegui. "I have an important assignment for you," he said. "When you have rested and taken some food, you will move Bernardo from Don Juan Albano's hacienda to the Franciscan mission school in Chillan. I will write messages for Don Juan Albano and Padre Ramirez."

A look of dismay swept over Tirapegui's face. One would have thought Higgins had ordered him to exile the boy to an uninhabited savage island. He was thinking, perhaps, that both Bernardo and Don Juan Albano would be desolate. He was thinking it cruel of Higgins to take Bernardo from a comfortable and happy home that the boy had learned to love.

But what was Higgins to do? Leave Bernardo with Don Juan Albano and let his secret be discovered by Bishop Maran and reported to the Crown? Wait, and let the ferrets hunt him out like a rabbit in a hole? Be expelled from Chile forever? Was that what Captain Tirapegui would have?

Indeed, was it not better for them all to have Higgins' secret protected so that he could continue to build a better country for Bernardo to live in, a better land for them all? He was not being cruel and heartless in taking the boy from Don Juan Albano. He was doing the best and wisest thing for his son. And for himself.

Higgins glanced off toward Talca. "There is great need for haste!" he said. "And make the journey to Chillan at nighttime when the roads are deserted."

CHAPTER XI

CAPTAIN DOMINGO TIRAPEGUI rode into the courtyard of Don Juan Albano late that evening, reluctant to carry out Higgins' order to escort Bernardo to the Franciscan mission in Chillan. And what sort of home was that after the warmth of the hacienda? Here he had playmates of his own kind. At the mission his friends would be Indian boys, a few friars.

Heartsick, he handed Don Juan Albano the letter from Higgins.

The old gentleman read the letter through twice, then he sat woodenly, his eyes sad. At last he spoke, his voice almost a whisper, "Bernardo must be told." He glanced at the darkening sky. "I suppose it is wiser if you travel at night. But it will be hard on the boy."

From the bench where he sat, Tirapegui said, "Would you like me to tell him?"

"I will go to him," Don Juan Albano said.

After a time Tirapegui saw Bernardo coming along the covered walk, a small, lonely figure. "Senor Capitan, good evening," Bernardo said.

Tirapegui tried to smile, not succeeding. "We will go, now."

Through the night they rode, into the shadowed forests which Tirapegui knew so well, passing neither beasts nor wagons, hearing occasionally the hoot of owl, the cry of a night bird, a stirring behind the underbrush as some animal scurried off to safety.

They reached Chillan early on a morning when the streets were deserted and before the country people were about. Even the house of Don Simon Riquelme was sleeping.

The child did not glance toward the house, as he did not remember that it was where he had been born.

At the mission, Padre Francisco Javier Ramirez greeted them. He read the letter from Higgins.

For a moment he looked searchingly at Tirapegui and the boy. Then he smiled. He called a servant and ordered Bernardo's trunk carried into the mission. "You will want rest and food," he said, glancing at Tirapegui.

"There is no time," Tirapegui said, thinking of the long ride back to Santiago, the need for him to report to Higgins as quickly as possible that Bernardo had been delivered to the mission.

Bernardo looked up at Tirapegui gravely, a little weary after the long ride. His eyes were wide and blue, and, Tirapegui thought, a little frightened.

Gathering up the lead-line of the mule, the Captain rode off, unhappy for Bernardo, but glad to be leaving. He never wanted another such assignment.

In Santiago, he found Higgins preparing for a journey into northern Chile.

Tirapegui made his report. "Everything went smoothly. There was no trouble of any kind. Don Juan Albano and the boy—"

"I am grateful to you," Higgins said, quickly, interrupting him. "I have many details to discuss with you about the journey to northern Chile."

The Governor was very brusque, Tirapegui told himself. Just thanks and no questions about his son, or whether he had been happy to leave the hacienda, or what he and Tirapegui had discussed on the way to Chillan, or even what Padre Ramirez had thought about the boy, or asked about him.

Still, with a thousand problems to worry him, there was no time for sentiment on Higgins' part, Tirapegui thought.

Then the Governor began speaking of matters connected with the trip to the north, and Tirapegui had no time to think about Bernardo.

Sitting at Higgins' desk, he listened to the plan. He recalled that no governor of Chile had ever visited northern Chile. There had always been too much trouble on the Indian frontier which lay south of the Biobio.

Higgins had been the first to keep an extended peace with the tribes. Now, he would be the first governor of Chile to visit the north country.

Tirapegui watched his chief listing the people who were to accompany him. He was taking an engineer, an assessor, a legal adviser, his secretary and a surgeon, a chaplain and many subordinate officials.

"Twenty-five dragoons. Fifteen servants," Higgins said. "You must arrange to be gone for at least six months."

Half a year, Tirapegui thought. Higgins must have really important plans for the north.

They left Santiago on an October morning and arrived at San Felipe the following day.

Tirapegui saw the town lying beyond an old Indian bridge near the Aconcagua River, a pretty village with a rambling main street and dusty poplars.

A number of city officials came to meet the party and they made polite speeches. They were delighted to have their new Governor as their guest. What was the wish of Governor Higgins? they asked, fawning, smiling a little too broadly. A puma hunt had been planned, if that would please him. Higgins replied that he had come on business, not for entertainment. He wished to inspect government buildings, the jail, convents, churches, the wine shops; pulperias. He would visit the mines in the vicinity, the dwellings occupied by peons who worked the mines, and the haciendas.

And he would begin at once!

If an earthquake had struck the town, the officials could not have been more startled. They were even more shaken when he demanded improvements.

The party remained several days in San Felipe where Higgins

ordered the town house, bridges and roads repaired. The jail, which he inspected, was crawling with fleas and vermin. He wanted it cleaned, whitewashed, swept regularly, supplied with running water for the comfort of the prisoners. All idlers and vagrants were to be arrested, sentenced for two years and put to work on the fortress of Valdivia. There must be an inn and an eating place built for travelers. The inn should be rid of fleas and kept clean, even though the floor was earthen.

A primary school was to be started.

Tirapegui watched the town officials as they looked helplessly from one to another. Finally, the Mayor said there were no funds for such lavish improvements. It could not be done, he told the Governor.

"The money will have to be raised," Higgins said, crisply. "We will tax produce."

There was a howl of protest from the wealthy hacienda owners and the merchants. But the Governor was adamant.

The priests were also delighted to see the last of the visitors. Higgins had questioned them minutely about their doctrines. Since no official dared step onto their ecclesiastical platform, they regarded these questions as blasphemy. About the number of parishioners they were hazy. They could consult the records. About marriages, births and deaths, these events went on regularly but these, too, would take figuring. But they could tell instantly to a peso the amounts due the churches and cloisters in tithes, taxes, royal patronage.

Town after town, and always the same thing over again.

And now Tirapegui rode beside Higgins as they went toward La Serena, second city of Chile, and even farther north.

After Santiago, the party had slept on the ground, taken their meals in tents beside the road, beneath trees, and they wished often for home and comfort.

But not Governor Higgins. The rougher it was, the more cheerful he became.

Ahead lay La Serena.

Tirapegui thought, what a perfect name for a town, and how beautiful the city after the long journey. To his left was the South Sea, a few miles away. If Pedro de Valdivia's native province of La Serena in Spain had been as charming, Tirapegui could understand his wanting to change the name of this Chilean city. Originally, it had been called Coquimbo. The port still was known as Coquimbo, as were the mines and the river which flowed through the valley where gold and copper mines flourished.

They stayed one week, two weeks, then three weeks in La Serena.

One morning Tirapegui mounted his horse and started for Coquimbo to arrange passage for the party to travel by ship to the last outpost of Chile, thereby saving an overland trip of three hundred miles across desert land.

He thought Higgins needed rest before attempting such a difficult journey.

The Governor's energy was boundless. He ignored fatigue. Tirapegui had never known Higgins to work so hard, so intensely, nor so long without rest. Feverishly, from morning until late at night, Higgins drove himself, as if work were all the pleasure left to him. It was as if he was working all over again for the position of Governor of Chile. Pushing himself, as if wanting to forget something that burdened him.

When Tirapegui was away from home he worked to keep from thinking of his family. Could Governor Higgins be trying to forget his son?

He rode down the straggling streets of Coquimbo. He saw on the harbor a balsa moving near the cliffs. The natives must be fishing for conger eels.

Conger eels! That was another of Higgins' projects.

Tomorrow, there would be a dinner at which conger eels would be served to demonstrate the food value of the huge eels that inhabited the waters along this coast, and members of the La Serena city government and some of the leading residents had been invited. Higgins had a plan about a fishing company for Chile. Here in the north the natives could fish for congers. In addition to providing an article of food, it would be an item for export. The Governor intended to place Don Thomas Dolphin in charge of the Chilean fishing industry. Ultimately, Higgins expected the Crown would permit Chile's fishermen to hunt whale.

Before that time, Tirapegui told himself, Chile would need ships and sailors. He would gamble his fine horse that the Chileans would make the best sailors in the world.

He tethered his horse to a rail near the fort, and walked to where a small boat waited to take him to the *El Aguila*, a Spanish merchant ship which was taking on copper.

With a favorable wind, the ship's master said, the trip to Caldera could be made in eight days. At the port of Caldera, Tirapegui could engage mules and drivers to transport the party across a hundred and twenty miles of hot, barren land to Copiapo. "In all the time I have been sailing to Chile," he said, "I have never heard of a governor visiting this north country." He glanced toward the balsa near the cliffs. "The Spanish in this part of the country boast that the Crown never interferes with their operations."

The Spanish in the northland were the most arrogant, the richest and the most heartless Spaniards in Chile.

"Governor Higgins will be a match for them," Tirapegui said.

The ship's captain moved his shoulders as if he doubted anyone could oppose successfully the ruthless Spanish mine operators. "Has he been able to stop the smuggling?" he asked.

Tirapegui did not answer.

But he was aware of the vigilance of Governor Higgins. With one small vessel from Lima to help patrol thousands of miles of Chilean coast, he kept the watch. One inadequate ship, and one dauntless and persistent Higgins tried constantly to close off the South Sea to foreign ships.

Governor Higgins had made progress, too. Foreign vessels were not allowed to enter Chile's ports for repairs or provisions. He had the nearby islands inspected regularly. Recently, to counteract illicit trade with foreign ships, the Governor ordered all cattle, sheep and horses that grazed near the coast to be moved inland, for animals were in great demand by the foreigners, and were used as barter.

A few days before, Governor Higgins had advised officials of La Serena and Coquimbo that if smuggling was not stopped, he would invoke the death penalty.

Tirapegui finished the arrangements for transporting Higgins' party to Caldera on the *El Aguila*. The day was warm. He stopped at a tavern for wine.

As he entered, three priests seated near the door glanced at his uniform.

He sipped his wine and listened to the priests' conversation.

"What nonsense to link the muleteer to the crime," one said. "He has not enough sense to plan so cleverly." He puffed at his cigar. "I got the muleteer off." He looked around the table at his brother priests and across at Tirapegui. "The officials are stupid," he said.

The priest kept on eying Tirapegui. He said, suddenly: "The Governor of Chile will never correct things in this north country. He orders the terror-stricken Indian workers to speak up against their oppressors. But the rich Senores smile behind the Governor's back. If the workers speak out against the mine and hacienda owners and operators, they know well enough that they will be punished the instant Governor Higgins has departed. The great Senores have unique and ingenious methods of punishment for those who protest."

He studied Tirapegui with bold, insolent eyes.

"The improvements will not be made," he said. "The evils will start again when Governor Higgins has gone. For here the great Senores do not stoop to co-operate with officials or with laborers. They are the untouchables, the titled monopolists who have been presented with grants by the Crown!"

The priests finished their wine, and departed.

Tirapegui called to the tavern keeper. "Who is the priest with the quick tongue?"

"Padre Don Clemente." The man looked distressed, as if he

thought Tirapegui might make trouble. "He always speaks out against everyone who displeases him. And many displease him," he added.

"Priests often speak too frankly." Tirapegui smiled, thinking of Bishop Maran and some of his priests in Concepcion, and how little their speaking out to their friends and the Crown against Governor Higgins had helped them.

The tavern keeper looked relieved and hastened to refill Tirapegui's glass to the brim.

Slowly, Tirapegui drank.

As the Padre Don Clemente said, the mine workers had been terrified. Tirapegui recalled a little fellow who had stood with one bare foot pressed hard against the other, trying to stop his knees from knocking together. He had not wanted to answer the questions which would incriminate the mine owners.

Tirapegui would always remember the starved workers taking muck from the mine in slopping, muddy cowhides, the slime running down their almost naked bodies, their few garments sticking to their sharp bones. From dawn until dark they worked. How frightened their hopeless eyes.

Abruptly, he rose, paid for the wine and left the tavern.

When he reached Higgins' headquarters, he found the Governor in conference with the great Senores. Tirapegui seated himself on the bench near the door while the meeting was in session.

So the Padre believed that the Governor was wasting his time, that Higgins would get no co-operation. And yet here beyond this patio, beyond the door to the Governor's apartments, the Spanish mine operators and hacienda owners were meeting with him.

A half-hour passed, then another. From the conference room came the sounds of heated discussion.

Tirapegui stirred uneasily. He hoped Governor Higgins was not attempting the impossible. He could be stubborn once his mind was set, and sometimes it was better to take fewer gains and be satisfied. After all, three centuries of tradition were behind these

Senores. The Crown never interfered, perhaps because they contributed a large revenue to Spain.

For once, it looked as if Governor Higgins might be checkmated by the Spanish lords. Anxiously, Tirapegui studied the entrance to the conference room.

The door was jerked open, suddenly. The Senores passed Tirapegui, in velvet coats, bright waistcoats, broad hats, shining boots. They looked grim. Even their elegant mustaches stood at attention.

Tirapegui sprang to his feet. He escorted them to where their horses were tethered, snapped his heels, bowed, as they rode away. He watched them race from the patio, going toward the bad roads, toward vast estates where, over maté, wine and many cigars, they would speak hotly with one another against Governor Higgins. Plotting, perhaps, against his life!

Tirapegui hurried across the patio to the conference room. Higgins was pacing the floor, dictating a letter to the Crown to his secretary.

"Contrary to law," he said, angrily, "the workers are held in perpetual service. Their salary is forty yards of flannel, half an arroba of jerked goat meat, one-eighth of a liter of barley for half a month for each family. The slavery has brought on an inertia in the workers that threatens soon to destroy them. These unhappy people know that to attempt to escape their masters would bring them beatings, torture, prison, all the evils that tyranny and abuse can invent."

It was a long letter. Higgins exposed fully the Senores' treatment of the peons.

Tirapegui stared proudly at Higgins. It took great courage to expose evil. But he was afraid for what this action might bring the Governor from the Spanish Senores.

It was fortunate, Tirapegui thought, that it was a letter to the Crown, and not a public proclamation to be read by Higgins in the Plaza of La Serena. He would await the advice of the Crown before proceeding to issue a law.

For some time Higgins paced the floor with restless steps. At last he stopped before his table. He struck it hard with his fist. "I shall now dictate a law that will abolish slave labor, the scourge of Chile," he said, his voice soaring.

"Don Ambrosio Higgins de Vallenar, Governor and Captain-General of the Kingdom of Chile, President of the Royal Audiencia . . ."

His voice rolled on steadily, as if long ago he had written this proclamation and knew it by heart.

Tirapegui was deeply moved.

This was a day to remember, he thought. And he saw again the workers huddled together gripping the mud-soaked cowhides. They would hear of their freedom from slavery. At first they would not believe it. Little by little, the truth would dawn upon their benumbed senses. They would stand in the slop and mire and the truth would seep into their tired minds, bring a little hope and then at last a realization of what had happened. Slowly, their tears would gather, roll over wasted cheeks.

Tonight, Tirapegui told himself, he would triple the guards here. He would not sleep this night, but would watch, both at headquarters and in the Plaza.

He had left Higgins in high spirits, eating his dinner. The Governor promised to retire early and rest.

Now Captain Tirapegui stood in the Plaza where the law had been announced a few hours before. He had come early to be on hand if there was trouble.

Two horsemen stopped near him. "The workers can be intimidated. It has already started," one voice said. "A few dead peons, a few beaten, or perhaps their families taken from them, and the workers will not complain."

"That is not enough," the other said, his voice heavy and angry. "Our enemy is not the peon. We must reach higher, much, much higher. There will be no peace for us until his voice is silenced."

They passed on.

Tirapegui froze in the shadows. At this moment an assassin might be creeping toward the Governor as he lay sleeping.

The Captain turned and ran to Higgins' apartment, and hurried inside.

There at the table was the Governor, dictating to his secretary. "New towns," he said, "will separate the peons and peasants from the influence of mine and hacienda owners. The people will be protected by the police. I will distribute farm land and building lots. The peasants will plant sweet cane, cotton and hemp. And I urge them to cultivate orchards. The people will build a new life for themselves, free from intimidation and threats. One of these towns will be named Vallenar. The patron will be San Ambrosio. Altogether I shall start five towns, thus giving the people a better life."

Tirapegui looked proudly at Governor Higgins. And not a hundred yards away, the Spanish lords were watching the fiesta of La Serena and plotting against Higgins' life.

How great, how courageous a commander!

And now Tirapegui was with Higgins and the party in Quillota where hemp was to be planted as an experiment for this valley. Quillota was the last stop before Santiago.

Tirapegui was happy for this rest of a month in the pleasant village. Standing at his window drinking morning maté, staring east toward the capital and the Andes, he saw far off a horseman riding toward this house, headquarters for the party.

He watched. The rider was in great haste. Clouds of dust swirled as he galloped nearer. It must be a special courier with an important message.

Leaving his room, Tirapegui went into the patio and crossed to the gate. He heard the rider shout to a guard at the entrance, "An urgent message for His Excellency, Governor Higgins." He saw Tirapegui.

Tirapegui entered the Governor's office with its white walls, two grilled windows, an earthen floor. He watched for a moment the fine head bent over his work, the sure hand of Higgins as it moved swiftly across a page. Another letter to the Crown about the successes of the journey to northern Chile, Tirapegui thought. These days Higgins was always in high spirits over the changes he had made to improve conditions for the people. Always working for the Crown, always certain of having the approval of the King.

The Captain laid the letter from Madrid on the table. "It came by special courier," he said, and stood smiling at his chief.

Higgins opened the message and read, then looked up helplessly. His flushed face blanched like a dying man. He spoke. It was a man struggling for breath. "Our beloved King Charles the Third is dead!"

CHAPTER XII

GOVERNOR HIGGINS rode toward the mountains which were as immovable as the grief within him. Wherever he looked there were
giant torch thistles. Everywhere the brittle tufts of starved shrubs,
twisted branches of stunted trees. The unwanted, unwatered land.
Refreshment would never come to this burned-out soil nor to Higgins' black, tired heart. Within him heavy shadows were falling,
and the darkness would increase until there was greater darkness.
And never again the light of hope. Never again anything but deep,
grave-like shadows.

Far off a wolf howled, pouring out the emptiness of a creature
alone in this waste. The sound was Higgins' own heart wailing.
Again the mournful cry echoed across the deserted plain, louder,
longer. Deep in the chasm through which the cavalcade was passing was a thin, sluggish stream dark as death itself, and huddling
above the mountains, the night. There would never be another
dawn.

The burden of breathing, Higgins thought. The burden of thinking painful thoughts. His King was dead! His revered King Carlos
the Third was dead!

Take away his own life, too! For now everything had ended.

Ahead moved the dark line of mules, the shadowy figures of dragoons. Within the sound of his voice were officials, soldiers, servants, mule drivers. Yet he rode in a world apart, an empty world
without friends or hope or comfort. His was a soul in purgatory.

The dreary, flat land. It was like his hopes.

And yet he must go on. He must ride into Santiago and attempt
to comfort the people. There would be a thousand painful duties
to perform although he had not the heart for any duty.

If only he could vanish into some abyss of forgetfulness and never waken! But he must proclaim a period of mourning. He must decide upon the time, whether it should be three months, four, six months.

He must bestow this last service within his power upon a loved monarch. The world had never known and would never know a better King. And now he must be put away, forgotten, after the deep, heavy mourning, the sad rites.

Sorrow seeped into his mind, overflowed into his burdened heart. He seemed to hear the bells tolling, the long fatiguing Masses, the chant of priests. He saw the cathedral filled with grieving mourners, their black garments dimming the candlelight.

The wind was cold. It blew through him.

For miles he slumped in his saddle, feeling only his grief, conscious only of emptiness. Then a river, a swirling, dark sea of water to be forded, dreary cliffs hung with heavy forests.

Let the waters sweep over him, carry him away to the vast sea! He guided his horse into the river.

But the horse swam well. The river did not sweep him toward the sea.

When he arrived at the Palace in Santiago that morning, he announced the death of the King to all the inhabitants. He ordered the rich and titled to wear deep mourning for a period of six months.

The Masses for the beloved Carlos the Third were arranged, were said, the processions of the religious orders passed slowly through the streets, and in Santiago and the provinces the sad and grieving subjects raised their hands and their prayers to heaven.

Now, Governor Higgins must plan for the ceremony of proclaiming Carlos the Fourth, the new monarch.

Higgins thought about it as he sat at his desk facing the portrait of the dead monarch draped in black. Soon the portrait of the son would hang there, beside it the likeness of Queen Luisa Maria, the new monarchs of Spain.

For long years Higgins had thought that Carlos the Fourth was not the strong man that his father had been. His father, the King, had tried to mold him into material for a benevolent and righteous monarch. But the son was indecisive and weak, the reports said.

And weak men are moved by flattery, Higgins told himself. Weak monarchs, like weak men, enjoy applause, and commendation, however small, will give them belief in their own importance. Had Higgins not seen weak men blossom under commendation and approval?

The Governor must have the new monarch behind all the improvements for Chile, or the great Senores would once again become lords of the land, ruling without mercy. The poor would be worse off than before Higgins began his campaign against the evils.

And what of Higgins? What of his future?

The position of Viceroy of Peru had seemed so near until the death of King Carlos the Third.

He stared dully at the portrait of the dead monarch.

If by superior service to the new King he could bring His Majesty to approve of Governor Higgins, the viceroyship might not be lost.

But how? By what method? Where could he begin?

He had already notified the officials of Santiago and the provinces that November third would be the day for proclaiming the august and Catholic monarch, Carlos the Fourth. If he made those ceremonies elaborate and magnificent beyond anything that had been in Santiago, it would be certain to come to the attention of the new monarch. The citizens of Santiago would notify the Crown of the honors. The Madrid papers would give it much attention.

Higgins would have commemorative medals struck to present to important guests. He would make the city brilliant with light and color. He would spare no money. No colony of Spain would excel the honors and attentions which Chile would bestow upon Carlos the Fourth!

For days the preparations. For days the painting of houses, the laying of flagstones in important streets, the cleaning of the city, the planning for parades and floats, for illuminations and entertainment. For days the drilling of troops and inspections, meetings with the City Council and the Audiencia members, arranging details of the ceremonies.

On the morning of November third, the members of the government arrived at the Palace on horseback, in all their regalia, as Higgins had ordered them to ride with him to the Plaza.

In his glittering uniform the Governor mounted the platform accompanied by his officials. He lifted high the standard and cried with a loud and firm voice, "For Spain and the Indies! Long live the King, Don Carlos the Fourth!"

As he had ordered, the bells began to ring.

The crowds filled the Plaza, crying as one voice, until the mountains seemed to echo with the shout, "Long live the King! Long live Don Carlos the Fourth!"

Along the streets Higgins moved with his great company of officials and dragoons, a brilliant company on handsome horses. They marched to the Cañada, to Rey Street, back to the Plaza, to the cathedral where elaborate Masses were said for the new monarch.

At the Palace Governor Higgins had arranged rich refreshments for his guests. That night, the illuminations of the streets and the Plaza made the night like day. Never had Santiago seen anything so fine as the silver and crystal candelabras at each door, or the magnificent fireworks of strange designs.

For several consecutive days Higgins was host to persons of importance until all had been favored. He received them in the audience room which was hung with portraits of King Carlos the Fourth and his Queen Luisa Maria, decorated with the colors of Spain. Sitting in the chair of state, on a raised platform, Higgins had acknowledged the compliments of the proud, ancient Spanish families who were elegant, correct and distant. In laces, brocade, cloth of gold, with diamonds on bodices, at wrists, in their ears, clustered in shining braids, the beautiful, the honored ladies deigned to smile upon him. And the titled Senores bowed stiffly, made polite conversation.

Any stranger watching the guests crowd into the Palace on those occasions would not have believed that the Governor had an enemy in all the land. They smiled, spoke graciously of his achievements.

They had come because it was a duty. They were here to honor their new monarch, Carlos the Fourth and his Queen. The guest list would reach the Court. They all would be recognized as loyal, dutiful subjects. And indeed they were. Many should be living in Spain where their hearts were.

Then the entertainment was over.

On the eleventh day, Higgins forwarded a glowing account of the occasion to Spain.

And others in Santiago sent eloquent and colorful tales of the event, of the dinners provided by the Governor Don Ambrosio Higgins de Vallenar to honor their majesties.

Higgins' next step in winning the approval of the new King was to begin the road to Valparaiso. The government collected taxes on mule and cart loads. Revenues would increase with a good road because cargoes could be moved faster. The new monarch would be delighted with Higgins' business sense and foresight. His Majesty would ally himself firmly with the Governor as his father had.

He was waiting now for his engineers who had already surveyed a route for the road.

Higgins' secretary came into the office. He said, "Good morning, sir. Don Thomas Dolphin has arrived from Concepcion. He seems in a great hurry to see you."

The Governor studied the lean, pale face of his secretary, Reyes. "I was expecting Engineer Rico," he said. "Have him wait when he arrives. Send Dolphin in."

It was strange, he thought, Dolphin in Santiago. He had been here during the proclamation ceremonies. What important matter could bring him on the long ride back to the capital so soon?

Dolphin came quickly into the room. He had not stopped to remove his poncho.

"This is a pleasant surprise," Higgins said, smiling.

His friend closed the door carefully behind him. "Good morning, indeed!" He pulled a black chair nearer to Higgins' desk. Seating himself on the edge of the chair, he leaned forward.

"Bishop Maran and Carvallo are up to something!" he said. "Maran has permission for Carvallo to search the archives of Concepcion. The excuse is that history of Carvallo's. And the surgeon in Concepcion has said that Carvallo must come regularly for treatment."

Higgins studied the lines in Dolphin's poncho, the disturbed eyes of his friend. He knew what Bishop Maran was up to. He wanted Higgins' official records while he was serving on the frontier. He hoped to discover a clew to some incident that could be twisted to look like an irregularity or an indiscretion or a disloyal act against the Crown. For now there was a new King of Spain. Bishop Maran planned to undermine Higgins in the eyes of King Carlos the Fourth, before the Governor had become the favored of the new monarch as he had the old.

But there was nothing incriminating in Higgins' record.

Still, if Carvallo dug deeply into the records from the earliest days of Higgins' service, he might come across some crumb of information that would lead him to Chillan. And by accident he might discover Bernardo at the mission school. There was always that chance as long as the boy was in Chile.

The ticking of Higgins' clock told him there was no time to waste. The shutter at the window rattled like an insistent and curious stranger knocking at a mission gate.

Where could Higgins send the boy for safety? It should be miles from the frontier, far from Maran and Carvallo.

He could send him to Lima. There were good schools there and it was thousands of miles away. "I might ship Bernardo to Lima," he said, thoughtfully. "First to a preparatory school and later to the Colegio of San Carlos." He looked hard at his friend, and then remembered that Ignacio Blake, the Irish merchant, came from Dolphin's home town in Ireland. Blake operated a branch store in Lima and traveled there occasionally from Santiago to look after his interests.

"I will have to take the boy out of Chillan," Higgins said. "I will send him to Callao and have Blake meet him. Will you take Bernardo to Talcahuano and put him aboard a ship?"

Dolphin said, "Yes, I'll put him on a ship for Callao." But then he looked troubled. "Should he go without a companion all that distance? He is young. He has been sheltered."

"And what harm can come to Bernardo after he is aboard the ship?" Higgins said. "Do not children travel alone constantly?" He studied Dolphin's worried eyes. "Well, then, could you not explain to Bernardo that there is nothing to fear, for the Good Lord watches over his own? Could you not explain about how fine it is sailing in the South Sea, how fortunate he is to be attending school in Lima? I would not want the child to be frightened."

"I shall do my best," Dolphin said, as if he still did not approve.

Higgins stirred uneasily. Indeed he was sorry the lad must travel alone, although the voyage took less than a month and any child would be delighted to be traveling on a great ship. Had not he left Dublin unaccompanied when he was little more than Bernardo's age, of his own free will, and happy to be sailing? What you could not help, you could not help. "The boy will be provided with every comfort, Dolphin," he said, "and given excellent schooling. And learn a profession, too. Could a father do more, my friend?"

"It will be arranged then." Dolphin rose. But he sighed heavily. "I shall speak to Blake immediately."

The Governor walked around his desk, took his friend by the hand and shook it warmly. "Whatever the expense, I will pay it," he said. "Only the best of everything for the boy. Everything that the children of the titled families have the lad must have too. Spare no expense."

"I will look after everything, the transportation, his clothes." Dolphin did not smile. "He will be taken from the mission in Chillan at night, so that he will not be seen by curious eyes."

"After the Riquelme family has retired," Higgins said. "There is no reason to disturb the mother and grandfather."

His friend went quickly, taking a short cut through the patio.

Higgins stared at the green baize cover on his desk. He wondered what promotion he could ask of the Crown for Dolphin.

CHAPTER XIII

BERNARDO could see the Southern Cross and quite clearly the Clouds of Magellan, two masses of light made up of clusters of stars. In Chillan, Padre Francisco Javier Ramirez had pointed them out to him. Bernardo watched the night sky, since it told him the direction they were taking.

They were riding southwest.

When they left the mission last night, he hoped that the stranger accompanying him, in black hat and dark red poncho, might take him north to his father.

There was a new King of Spain. With a new monarch you must expect many changes, Padre Ramirez had explained. Perhaps that meant that Bernardo could be near his father. It might even be possible that his mother would join them.

For two nights over a course that followed rivers, steep mountains and forests, seeing neither people nor mules nor houses. And always south.

They were not going to Santiago, to his father.

Disappointed and frightened, he rode, asking no questions, knowing in his heart he would get no information from the silent guide.

If only Padre Ramirez had explained where Bernardo was being taken.

The Padre had come into his bedroom two nights ago and wakened him. He was to dress quickly. He was leaving the mission, and the Padre could tell him nothing more.

Bernardo thought, "My father has sent for me. I am going to him." And shaking with excitement he got into his clothes, pulled

108

poncho over his head, fastened his hat band under his chin. He must say good-by to his mother, he explained.

The Padre shook his head and his eyes were unhappy. The family was sleeping, he said. "They will understand when I explain. Do not forget your prayers, Bernardo."

In the early dawn, Bernardo saw a walled city. It must be Concepcion, he thought. There was no other city in southern Chile the size of the one before him.

His guide stopped in a shaded patio.

Then they went along a covered walk to a door, a small room.

"Now you will eat and sleep," the guide said, and the door closed after him.

Bernardo saw a tray of food. He wanted nothing to eat. He washed his face and hands in the silver bowl. Then sitting on the side of the bed, he stared at the heavy door and waited.

Slowly the day came.

Exhausted, afraid, he slept.

When he wakened, the daylight had gone.

He listened for some sound, his heart pounding fast, and he thought, "I have been forgotten in a strange house, in a strange city."

When he tried the door, it was locked and his terror increased.

He heard a footstep. The lock turned.

A man stood in the doorway holding a lighted candle. He said: "Then you are awake, lad. We will be going."

The face and the voice were familiar. Where had Bernardo heard that voice? And where had he looked upon the face so unlike a Spanish face?

He remembered. It was at Don Juan Albano's. He had called Bernardo in from play to meet this gentleman. "This is Don Thomas Dolphin," he had said.

And now the friendly eyes of Don Thomas were studying him with kindness. Where was he going with the gentleman? Not to the hacienda of Don Juan Albano, surely. Not to his father in Santiago, else why bring him to Concepcion in southern Chile?

Obediently, he followed Don Thomas.

They were nearing the South Sea. Bernardo saw a ship in a bay.

He was going somewhere by ship. Could it be to Valparaiso? Could he be going to his father, after all? The port of Valparaiso was only a little way from Santiago. Or perhaps his father was planning to visit him aboard the ship when it reached the port.

No other person would order him to go aboard a ship. It was his father's wish. And Bernardo was happy again. He would see his father.

The captain of the ship was a Spaniard with a dark face, a beard, black eyes under thick brows. His cabin smelled of tobacco and kelp, of medicine and hides. On a shelf was a row of books on navigation. The lamps cast a yellow light over mahogany walls.

"This is the lad," Don Thomas said. "He will be met in Callao by Don Ignacio Blake, the merchant. You understand."

Frozen, Bernardo stared at Don Thomas.

Callao was a million miles from Chile, his father, his family. It was the port of Lima, and in Lima was the Tribunal of the Inquisition, where you were punished if you misbehaved.

"You are going to school, Bernardo," Don Thomas said. "You are fortunate to be going to such a fine school, and you must be happy. You will not need pesos," he said. "Don Ignacio will give you whatever you need later."

He was gone and Bernardo was filled with an emptiness, a great loneliness.

He would not see his father. Instead, he was being sent far away from all that was dear to him. Don Thomas had acted for his father in having him brought secretly to this ship. It must mean that, for the protection of his father, he was being sent from Chile.

A lump like a stone from the River Itata near Chillan stuck in his throat.

He saw the sailors bring the ship around, saw sails billow like enormous sheets. Overhead, seabirds screamed, gray clouds rolled over the sky, the pelicans cried like lost children. The cliffs of Chile slipped away. When would he see his land again? When would he see his mother, his half-sister Rosa, the good Don Juan Albano? Or his father, if ever?

For several days he was seasick.

Then he was better. The sea air felt good against his cheeks, and except for that constant pain in his heart, he felt better.

He watched the rigging. It swayed like cowhide lassos. The sails were as white as his mother's sheets, which the Indian laundress pounded to whiteness. He could see the green piece of tunia bobbing in the caldron. Her soap was bark of the quillai, and better than fine soap from Mendoza. He could taste the crystals that clung to the bark; like soda it was.

He was comforted thinking of his mother, the laundress, of the mission, the fragrance of mountain air and meadow grass, and fields of white daisies.

Bernardo studied the ropes. The ship smelled of tarred rope and salt air.

The black slave who cleaned his cabin each day walked across the deck, his step heavy and listless.

Like Bernardo, he had been shipped from his homeland and people. He felt the man's loneliness. And once again as in the past his heart went out to all the slaves and poor of Chile.

He stood beside the capstan, staring at the sea. And the sad wind sobbed mournfully through the ropes. Lifting his eyes he saw the Spanish standard whipping in the stiff breeze.

He could not revere and love that flag. It brought misery and unhappiness to the slaves and the poor of Chile. And to his father, his mother, to all his loved ones.

Proudly, the standard waved.

Deep in Bernardo's heart was a hatred for that flag and the Crown!

The saloon of the ship was a black box. Walls, table, massive chairs, serving table—all black, as if even the room mourned the death of King Carlos the Third of Spain. And the dark, questioning eyes of the captain watched Bernardo as if planning something unpleasant. He would take a mouthful of food, then, leaning against the black leather armchair, he would stare.

And the ship lurched and rolled. The timbers creaked, the chains rattled. At night the rushing waves, wailing, lashing the vessel with

great swells that swept across decks as if to swallow anyone who
did not worship the Crown of Spain. For the South Sea, too, was
claimed by Spain.

Bernardo counted the days. There seemed no end to the vast sea.
The vessel reached Callao at last.

He had dressed in his best linen shirt, a new suit which he found
in the box left by Don Thomas.

For hours he had been waiting the arrival of Don Ignacio Blake.

Gazing at him from Callao was the stone face of the dreary castle where men were imprisoned, where they died and were buried.
The cannon were turned toward the bay. To the west was the desolate island of San Lorenzo. The houses of Callao were mean,
squatting in the dust like stray dogs.

Toward the east were white spires. That must be Lima, he
thought. A fresh stab of fear passed through him. It was like a pile
of bleached bones left by the victims of the Inquisition.

He was not going to like Lima.

Don Ignacio Blake came with a hurried step, a tall, active Irish
gentleman with a long face, an anxious brow. He brought a black
servant to fetch Bernardo's box. He said this was Monday, an extremely busy day for him, since there was always a market in
Callao on Monday. Today, there was a slave auction.

More unhappy people snatched from their homeland, to become
slaves in a far country. And Bernardo could do nothing to help.

Sadly, he followed Don Ignacio.

The calesa seated two people, had two wheels and was drawn
by a mule ridden by a postilion. Bernardo and Don Ignacio
climbed into the vehicle, the postilion shouted. They moved off
toward Lima.

A constant stream of people and animals passed, going to and
coming from the market, and many wagons bearing crates of fowl,
skins of wine, hides, firewood, fodder and wheat. About them
clouds of yellow dust. The sun beat down. The breeze was humid
and stifling. Along the way neglected orange and lemon trees.
Everything thirsting for rain. And Bernardo thought of the green-

ness of Chillan, of mountain streams, cascades icy with freshness. He longed for those waters. He longed for Chile!

Bernardo was not prepared for the magnificence of the grand Plaza of Lima, the bronze fountain rising above the paved square with three basins for water. Colored tile lined the basins. A column as thick as an oak was decorated with leaves and flowers and the names of the makers. High above the square at the top of the column was a great figure of Fame looking out over the palace of the Viceroy on the north, the cathedral, an arcade of shops.

He saw the Tribunal of the Inquisition and looked hastily away. He recalled the stories told him by Don Juan Albano, who had been more than once threatened with the Inquisition when he refused to confess that he was a smuggler. He never had been a smuggler, but the authorities would not believe him. They said he had smuggled anti-religious leaflets into Chile. He went to prison. He told Bernardo the Inquisition would have tortured and destroyed him.

The Inquisition was wicked. People were forced to tell lies or be placed on the rack. Bernardo stared at the shops, markets, thinking of Don Juan Albano and the Inquisition.

Don Ignacio was speaking of the preparatory school where Bernardo would earn credits for entering the Colegio of San Carlos.

The school was behind cheerless adobe walls, covered with dry brown moss. The entrance gate was heavily barred and locked. He stared at the gate, feeling like a prisoner entering a jail. Long, sloping eaves and thick, squat trees shut out sunlight. The patio was dark, the earth unpaved.

A priest with a thin, unsmiling face met them.

Don Ignacio was leaving, and Bernardo's heart sank. He could not remain in this dreary prison. He must go with Don Ignacio back to Lima. But he tightened his fists, pushed them into his pockets to keep from crying out. He must not shed tears or make a disturbance. His father had sent him to this school, and here he must remain.

"Study well," Don Ignacio said. "Obey the priests. I will see you occasionally when I return from Chile."

Then Don Ignacio was returning to Chile. Bernardo would be without any friend in this terrible Lima. He stared at Don Ignacio, wanting to cry out, and daring not to speak. Frozen and sick he saw him depart.

The priest looked at him coldly. "Come with me," he ordered.

The corridor was musty and ancient.

His room was like a prison cell. He sat on the hard cot wondering how he could endure the isolation and loneliness. He stared at his trunk, thinking he must write to Padre Ramirez or to his mother to bring him back to Chile.

He opened his chest and removed inkhorn, pen and paper. He saw the guitar his mother had given him. He studied the inlay, but he did not take it from the case, nor touch the strings. His mother seemed a continent away, her voice a distant echo.

How could he remain here, and how could he escape?

That night he could not sleep. He kept seeing that great wall, trying to scale it and failing. And if he succeeded in getting over the wall, he had no friends in Lima. He would be brought back to this school. The strong hand of the jailor-priest seemed to reach out in the darkness and grip him firmly.

Days passed.

Bernardo stared at a page of his Latin book. He understood nothing on the page, but if he asked for instruction from the priest, he would be ridiculed before the class.

The priest would pounce on him, order him to recite.

He could not.

For hours he wrote the exercises by the fading light of the mean schoolroom. Darkness filled the corners, ate into the pale light. By a single flickering candle Bernardo finished the last words.

He would miss supper. He went to bed without any.

One night, lying on his cot, tired, hungry, feeling sad and unloved, he made up his mind. He would escape. And he would escape by studying day and night and getting good marks that would take him over the ugly wall, out of the prison, away from the tyrant priest.

He spoke to the brightest boy in the school. Guillermo was his name, and he agreed to coach Bernardo for money, since he was always borrowing from the other boys. But his price was high. It took almost all of Bernardo's allowance. That meant when he was given a holiday, which was an almost unheard-of treat, Bernardo had no money to spend on pleasures.

Then one of the slaves was accused of smuggling and all the boys were questioned. Bernardo knew nothing. He would not have confessed had he known. But because he defended the servant as an honest man, he had credits taken away.

He worked twice as hard then, to make them up. He had to escape. The way was to work even harder at his studies.

Weeks passed drearily, and months.

He was always tired. He was too thin. Every waking moment he watched lest he offend the priest and sacrifice more credits.

The day arrived for school examinations. If Bernardo passed he would no longer be a prisoner, watched over by a jailor. And if he failed to pass?

He dared not think of failing!

The questions were difficult. He thought he knew the answers, but he was not always certain and the doubt increased his fear. The expression on the face of the priest seemed to promise failure for Bernardo.

Then the tests were over. But that night he dreamed terrifying dreams that he had failed. He wakened and his body was damp with perspiration. And then he could not sleep, thinking it might be an omen of failure.

But he passed and with good grades.

He heard the good news and began shaking as if with chills. His legs refused to hold him.

Not until Don Ignacio Blake arrived, not until the iron gate closed behind him for the last time, did Bernardo breathe freely.

Then he was like an escaped prisoner, his eyes feasting on the heavens as if he were seeing the blueness for the first time, staring at the Andes as if he had never looked upon them. How beautiful the Rimac River. His heart reached out to all he passed.

Don Ignacio took him to a cockfight at the Square of Catalina, near the city wall. They sat in seats that cost four reals and looked down upon the arena where the cocks fought. And Bernardo was happy to be free of the terrible school.

Don Ignacio entered Bernardo in the Colegio of San Carlos. The Colegio was within walking distance of the Plaza and not far from the Rimac. How different from the preparatory school— the spacious patios filled with sunlight and flowers, with fountains and benches, with great, airy rooms. There was a large debating room, a fine library filled with many prohibited books by foreign authors. Bernardo read essays by Voltaire and Montesquieu, but he never mentioned having read them to anyone beyond the walls of the Colegio. The students and professors debated about art and literature.

And Bernardo wore the black uniform of the Colegio, a cocked hat, a dress sword. He was given a horse to ride.

Life moved pleasantly enough, except when the other students went home over the holidays and Bernardo was left to entertain himself. Then it was too lonely. At all times he missed his family and that feeling of belonging, but it was almost unbearable when he was alone.

He would ride into the country, into the hills, along the Rimac, down the valley. One day he went to Callao and followed the coast for miles, watched the balsas far out taking the waves with ease.

He had heard stories of smuggling done by the balsas. They were said to trade with English ships that stood off near some isolated island in the sea. But when he spoke of smuggling to the Indians on the outskirts of Callao, they only looked away. And when he asked about the Indians who worked the Peru mines, they looked at him with unhappy eyes. They thought he was an informer, he supposed, and that if they complained the Inquisition would punish them.

The professors at the Colegio had explained to Bernardo about the system under which the Indians were used in the mines. It was a living death. The Indians seldom left the mines, once they were impressed into service, except when they died.

His father had ended slave labor in Chile. He wished his father was chief of the government of Peru.

On the next holiday he went to a bullfight.

The ring was midway of the Alameda on the bank of the Rimac. The matadors wore satin costumes and scarlet capes. They marched about the arena which was fenced with adobe walls. The Viceroy of Peru and his guests occupied a box above the gate where the bulls were admitted to the arena, and when the Viceroy arrived there was a fanfare and waving of the Spanish colors, and shouts from the spectators.

Bernardo did not like the bullfight any more than he had the cockfight. He preferred a horse race, like those he had witnessed in Chile where the Indians and Chilean peasants rode better, faster than any Peruvian.

The holidays came often: St. John's Day, Church Jubilees, the festival of Lurin, San Pedro de Chorrillo, those of San Christoval, Santiago del Cerade, New Year's Day, Twelfth Day, and all the others.

On the holidays he was always alone. The professors had their personal duties to keep them occupied, and while they were kind, he tried not to trouble them with his presence during holidays.

He was passing the Palace of the Viceroy on one of his holidays. Several times students of the Colegio had attended ceremonies at the Palace, and Bernardo had gone along. There was a guard of halberdiers in blue coats with trimmings of gold lace, crimson waistcoats and breeches adorned with gold, silk stockings and velvet shoes—an impressive sight.

The Palace had many corridors, many tiled balconies, all too ornate. A private passage extended below to a room built by Viceroy Amat for receiving the actress Perricholi, who still lived in Lima near the Alameda. Her life had been a sad one. She was married to an Italian but she loved the Viceroy. How unhappy to love someone one cannot be near, he thought.

A crowd had gathered in the Plaza to watch a man who was being publicly flogged for some offense—gambling, vagrancy, drinking, brawling, profanity. The serious crimes were punished by torture, burnings or hangings.

This prisoner looked like a simple peasant. But his hands and feet were bound and he rode backward on the mule. As the animal was prodded forward by one guard, another applied the thonged whip.

Angrily, Bernardo turned away. If he interfered, he would bring worse punishment upon the unfortunate man.

He entered the church of Our Lady of Montserrat to escape the sight and quiet his anger. But he could only stare with growing fury at the great altar that cascaded from roof to floor, glittering with gold and precious stones, his thoughts disturbed as he recalled the injustices in this land. The riches that adorned this altar and other altars of Lima would buy land for white, brown and black slaves of this colony who lived and died in want because of the evil laws.

Going back toward the Colegio, he continued to think about it. For five years he had lived in Lima, and in that time he had seen too many floggings; and worse. It should be stopped. His heart and mind burned with desire to help end the wrongs. He thought about it constantly. There should be just laws and a government for all, rich and poor.

But speaking openly about the wrongs did no good. Other men had tried. They had suffered terrible deaths for their attempts to change things.

He hurried on, the hatred for Spain rising within him afresh. More and more he despised the Crown.

When he returned to Chile he would work to end inequality for the poor and the slaves. His father was befriending the people in Chile, and Bernardo would find a way to help him. He did not know how it could be accomplished. But he would discover a way.

Don Ignacio Blake came unexpectedly to the Colegio one day. He brought with him servants who carried new clothes, new luggage, the finest of everything. He said that Bernardo was sailing to Cadiz. In Spain, Bernardo would live with Don Nicolas de la Cruz, finish his education and learn a profession.

That was all.

Bernardo was too shocked to reply. Once again he was being uprooted, snatched away. Once again no explanations, only the orders.

When he could think a little, after the first feeling of shock had passed, he remembered that the ship would go by way of Chile. He would notify his mother to come to Talcahuano. The ship would remain several days in Talcahuano. They would have a good visit, a happy reunion before his ship sailed on toward Buenos Aires, then Spain.

But there was no time for letters. They left at once for Callao.

Still, Bernardo thought, in Valparaiso he could send a fast courier by horseback to Chillan. By the time his ship reached Talcahuano his mother would already be there. They still could have the visit.

He reached Callao and went aboard the ship.

With a light heart he heard Don Ignacio wish him Godspeed. He stood watching the ship as the sails filled.

The vessel moved out of the bay.

Then instead of going south, she turned north. They were not sailing by way of Chile. The ship was heading toward Panama.

Black despair swept over Bernardo. Sick at heart, he stared, as the wind filled the sheets, carrying him farther and farther from home.

He clutched the rail, watched the receding coast, looking hard toward the south where his beloved Chile was, asking himself when he would look upon his mother again.

The darkness fell. Still he stood there.

CHAPTER XIV

It still was early. Only the market people were about. Governor Higgins could see them passing along the street beyond his window grille, bringing quarters of beef and mutton, panniers of fruit and vegetables to the market, a constant stream of mules and horses.

Occasionally, a woman dressed sedately in black, a mantilla over her head and followed by her slave, went past, going to the cathedral on the west side of the Plaza. The slave carried a pillow on which the lady knelt to worship, a practice that Higgins disliked.

The gloomy interior of the cathedral in the early morning was depressing, he thought. Why should there be so little sunlight in cathedrals? They were always cold and unpleasant except when lighted by many candles. And why had not the Santiago cathedral been completed, when long ago the money had been donated. More and more he became dissatisfied with this Bishop whom he had recommended. The once simple priest had become the pompous prelate.

He drank hot tea. The breeze blew straight from the snowy Andes into this room. It fluttered the Spanish colors above the portraits of their majesties, Charles the Fourth and Luisa Maria.

The Governor studied the pale eyes of the King.

His Majesty had been pleased with the elaborate ceremonies ordered by Higgins in Chile at the time Carlos the Fourth was proclaimed King. The account had been published in the Madrid papers.

It had given Higgins reason to hope there would be important honors if he could continue to please His Majesty. He had proceeded boldly with his plans for the road from Santiago to Valparaiso, ninety miles away, as if already he had the complete approval of the Crown in all that he did.

Against a storm of protests he had gone ahead with the work.

How many times the rich Spanish had entered this room to berate him and his program. None had come oftener, or spoken with more bitterness against him, than Don Jose Miguel Prado Covarrubias. He could see the titled Spaniard now, his face dark as his velvet suit, sitting erect in the black chair against the wall.

"The road for carts," he said, his voice coldly patronizing, "has been for decades by way of Melipilla. The route of the Cuesta de Mulas for the mules has served since the Conquest. Let those roads serve for the future as well. Everyone is familiar with them. Only the politicans want changes." His eyes were contemptuous.

Higgins had controlled his anger. "The road is no credit to the Conquerors," he said, bluntly. "The Incas without modern knowledge could have built a better. And the people who travel the old road constantly disagree with you, Senor Prado. And so do I. For here in my files are the records. Would you care to know the number of accidents in one year? The number of injured persons, the mules lost and the cargoes destroyed? Have you any idea of the time that will be saved by traveling a well-constructed, direct road? Have you no pride in your country?"

Prado had bristled. "Then lay it another route," he said angrily. "One that does not pass through the heart of my hacienda!"

How these Spanish lords enjoyed giving orders, the Governor thought. Another route! Another course!

Did not Higgins know more about the routes than Prado or any other Spaniard in Chile? Had he not traveled over the cursed bad road many times, and over three routes surveyed by the engineers? And had he not given the subject hours of study, lying awake at night worrying about the matter, when he should have been resting for another tiresome day with the carping Spanish?

Another route! When Prado owned practically every foot of the ninety miles between Santiago and Valparaiso? Any road to Valparaiso would cross his property.

In an effort to be impartial, Higgins had asked an unbiased arbitrator to select the best route. And if that course was not to Prado's liking, could it be helped? Had he not explained to Prado that his claim for damages would be paid.

"Senor Prado," he advised, and his voice was hard, "enter your claims. They will be paid."

"The Crown will hear of this!" Prado walked stiffly from the office and sent long, bitter complaints to His Majesty against Higgins.

The work on the road had continued in spite of the constant hindrances. He saw the long line of angry Spanish residents as they had moved in and out of this room, all haughty, all in rich clothes and each indignant about the new road being built against their wishes. But he had hardened his mind and his heart against them, yielding not an inch to the proud Spanish who gave him neither help nor rest.

Let them write to the Crown!

His own reports went often and fully to His Majesty about the progress of the handsome new road which would increase commerce and revenue for Chile.

One melancholy day when his spirits had been exceptionally downcast, when even the coals in the brasero seemed cheerless, when he was being harassed unduly by the Spanish, he received a notice from the Crown.

He had opened the letter. There on the page were glowing words that warmed his tired heart. At last, he had been noticed by the King! At last a cherished and long-hoped-for honor.

The rank of field marshal was his!

King Carlos the Fourth had approval for his Brigadier, his Governor and loyal subject! Higgins had gone at once to his private chapel and kneeling before the small altar had given thanks. And, still kneeling, he had decided to begin another important work for his King.

There had been a great dinner at the Palace to celebrate his advancement to field marshal. He invited all his officials. There were speeches and toasts. Higgins had spoken with eagerness and affection of His Majesty, the worthy son of good King Carlos the Third.

He had begun construction of the breakwater, and the widening of passes across the Andes. And with his eyes fixed on the Crown, looking toward further honors, Higgins ignored the objections, the criticisms and insults of the Spanish who opposed all of his works here in Chile.

For could any but His Majesty give the Governor the most desirable appointment of all? Could any but the Crown make him Viceroy of Peru? Indeed, and they could not.

How wise he had been. For once again the new monarch recognized Governor Higgins, by confirming that law decreed by Higgins in the north country against slave labor and the great Senores!

With what cheerfulness Higgins had ordered a celebration of the confirmation of the law against enforced labor. Had he not sat here within the Palace that night listening with rising spirits to the singing voices in the Plaza, to the bursting of rockets? His heart had soared like the rockets.

Governor Higgins studied the papers on his desk. The endless work, he thought, and the enemies trying always to besmirch his record, his name, in the eyes of the new monarch. And failing. Even that desperate attempt of Carvallo's, instigated surely by Bishop Maran.

The Governor had attempted to assist the Captain, who deserved no help.

Carvallo, sitting on the carved bench across the room in this office, had said that day with a look of meekness, "I am writing a history of Chile, sir. Could I have your permission to look over the archives of Santiago? It would be of great help. Then if you will give me permission to go to Spain where the book can be published, I will be indebted to you forever."

"I will give you permission to use the archives," Higgins had said. "More, I will ask important residents to give you information contained in old letters about the country. But first, Captain, I must insist upon seeing your manuscript. For what you write must malign no man, living or dead."

Carvallo had turned uneasily upon the bench. "It is not yet in form, sir. Soon it will be presentable. You shall see it the moment it is in shape."

Now the Governor looked hard at the bench as if the Captain sat there.

Higgins had given him access to the archives and for a time Carvallo made a pretense of working. Then he was at his old habits of gambling, spreading malicious gossip and disturbing the peace.

The Governor had ordered him back to the frontier.

Carvallo had not returned to his post. The dragoons searched the city for him. They looked for him in missions, private homes, on the frontier, in the ports of Chile.

With the help of important officials, and Higgins suspected Bishop Maran was one, Carvallo had shipped from Buenos Aires to Spain.

In Spain he had taken his partially written book to the ministers and asked their help in having it published. There was a chapter devoted to Governor Higgins and it was all lies and malice. Never had viler words been written about an honest official. Indeed, Carvallo had written, this Higgins was an Irish pretender of doubtful and obscure birth with no knowledge of government or engineering, who had been a failure on the frontier, who was despised by the Spanish as a Governor, as they hated any leader who was not of noble birth. This Higgins, he wrote, was a vassal of England.

The ministers had not published the book.

It was about this time that a rumor had started in Lima about the parentage of Bernardo, and Higgins had sent the boy to Spain. He was congratulating himself that his son was safely in Cadiz, far from any chance of being discovered, since Carvallo had been ordered out of Spain. Higgins had then learned that Captain Carvallo had not left Spain.

Quickly, Governor Higgins had ordered Bernardo sent to England.

He studied the teapot which a servant left on his desk before he entered his office. Each morning the tray was waiting, the tea brewed as Higgins liked it, for when he was alone at his house he preferred tea to maté.

Would the boy like England? Higgins wanted the lad to be happy. Such a long way, England, he thought. Lima had not seemed far, for he had Don Ignacio Blake to bring reports on Bernardo. And Cadiz had seemed nearer, in a manner of speaking, because Don Nicolas would write often about Bernardo and he could have reports of the lad as he was developing into manhood.

But England? It seemed a million miles. Too many miles to put between him and this son, his only son, whom he loved.

He poured another cup of tea, but he did not drink. Instead, he sat staring at the cup, seeing the tense face of a child, holding an Araucanian kite, whom he could never acknowledge as son.

The picture was disturbing. He was glad when his secretary entered with a letter from the Governor of Valparaiso. "God with you, sir," his secretary said, and laid the letter on his desk.

His secretary departed.

The letter from the Governor reported that two British warships, the *Discovery* and *Chatham*, under the command of Captain George Vancouver, had arrived in the port. The *Discovery* had a broken mainmast. Captain Vancouver requested materials and laborers to help repair her for the trip around Cape Horn and on to England. What were the wishes of Governor Higgins?

Higgins finished reading. This was a fine piece of luck. Here on his doorstep was a Pacific navigator who could give him accurate information on the number and names of islands settled by the English and French in the South Sea. For Vancouver had sailed these seas since the time of Captain Cook. He was aboard Cook's ship at the Sandwich Islands when Cook was murdered by the natives, and since that time he had raised the British flag over more South Sea islands than any other navigator.

If Higgins knew the strength of the British and French in the South Sea, it would be of immense help in defending these coasts.

And if the Spanish ministers had listened to Higgins and long ago sent their navigators to explore and settle the South Sea islands, he would not now be working frantically to keep the coast defended against possible foreign encroachment. Instead they had been foolish enough to sign a treaty which ceded northwest American territory to England and gave the British permission to fish for whale in the waters off Chile and Peru where no foreign ships had been allowed to enter.

Now that he thought of it, this Captain George Vancouver who wanted help with a mainmast in Valparaiso had acted for the British in that northwest America dispute with Spain. He would have a great deal of information both about the islands of the South Sea and the plans of England along the coasts of both Americas.

Vancouver could give him valuable information about the plans of England for invading the South Sea. And Vancouver could also report to his government that Governor Higgins had the defenses of Chile well organized. Higgins wanted them to know about that agreement signed by the Indians at Negrete a short time ago, promising to fight with Spain against all foreign invaders of Chile.

For Vancouver's report would carry great weight with the British government. It would be read carefully. The English would think twice, and seriously, before making an attempt to invade these shores.

Higgins studied the letter from the Governor of Valparaiso.

Without the help of Higgins in repairing his mainmast, Vancouver could not get around Cape Horn, let alone to England.

Then, he would trade with Vancouver. In exchange for help with his mast, Higgins would ask information about English colonization at Botany Bay, in the Friendly Islands, at Otahite, the Sandwich Islands.

And while the mainmast was being repaired, Higgins would invite Captain Vancouver to the Palace for a visit. He would get from Vancouver the information he wanted, and he would give Vancouver the report on the defenses of Chile.

Higgins smiled, anticipating the reception the report on Chile would receive from the British Cabinet members.

He was a match for any British statesman!

Calling his secretary, he said, "Take a letter to Governor Alava at Valparaiso."

"You will please assure Captain George Vancouver that he will be given every assistance it is in my power to bestow in outfitting his vessels and repairing the mainmast of the *Discovery*," he wrote. "Convey to him my congratulations on his having accomplished the great object of his expedition, and having arrived in a country where nothing will be wanting that can contribute to the restoration of his health or future comforts.

"Convey to him as well my invitation to visit the capital if he wishes to come. I will entertain him and his officers at the Palace. See that Captain Vancouver is provided for the trip."

He finished the letter. "Send it by special messenger," he ordered. "And Reyes, bring me a copy of my speech to the Indians at Negrete."

When Reyes brought the papers, Higgins laid them in a drawer of his desk, where they would be handy when he wanted them. He would make an occasion to present the speech to Vancouver. And the Captain would take it with him to England.

Enemies within, he thought, and enemies without.

But he was equal to them all. The enemies would be defeated. The rewards to the Governor would come!

CHAPTER XV

AT THE Palace Governor Higgins was already dressed to receive Captain Vancouver and his men, when Tirapegui brought a message. It announced the arrival of the Britishers at the Country House a mile away. Vancouver requested permission to enter Santiago that evening to pay his respects, and he asked for carriages to accommodate six.

Higgins had planned a spectacle for the crowd. He could hear shouting in the streets as the public gathered to welcome the guests. He could not disappoint them.

Vancouver would be asked to enter Santiago immediately. And on horses unlike the small, slow horses on which the Englishmen had ridden from Valparaiso. Since there were no fine carriages such as those used in England, but only clumsy carts pulled by mules and oxen for traveling over bad roads, the entry would be made on blooded, high-stepping horses caparisoned in crimson velvet and gilt, with carved saddles and bridles decorated with silver, large spiked silver spurs and handsome whips.

He ordered Tirapegui to the Country House to present Higgins' compliments and to see that the guests came immediately.

Tirapegui hurried off.

The Governor entered the anteroom to the Audience Chamber. Among the portraits of the past governors was one Irish face, his own. He studied the figure in knee breeches, white silk hose, black slippers, an embroidered velvet coat, the unadorned table. Behind the figure was an arched window through which blue sky and the Andes peered.

Today, Higgins was wearing the same costume—his finest.

He went on into the public hall. The walls were tiled for ten feet, then plastered in white to the ceiling; on one side doors opened onto a patio. Higgins took his place in the crimson chair of state covered with a red damask canopy that stood on a raised platform at the far end of the room. On each side of his chair were portraits of their Catholic Majesties.

The minutes passed.

He heard shouts from the street and knew that the procession was nearing. He pictured the sight: colorful dresses with bell-shaped skirts, pretty women with shining black braids, black mantillas against white skin, each holding oleander or other gay flowers. And brilliant ponchos; the waving of sombreros. The skies would seem to rain down fragrant flowers. And along the Alameda would come the guests and dragoons in handsome uniforms riding the prancing, glittering horses.

The Governor saw Vancouver, escorted by his guards, glance at the portraits in the anteroom, come into the Audience Chamber. Followed by his officers, he approached Higgins, head erect, shoulders straight.

The company reached the platform where Higgins waited.

Then Higgins saw the shabby, ragged uniforms. And if his eyes did not deceive him, they were wearing their breeches back to front!

No wonder Vancouver had asked for carriages! He wanted to hide the shabbiness of their uniforms, impossible to conceal on horseback. They had turned their breeches hind foremost to present a better appearance. He thought of the years they had spent in the northwest and the Pacific, their garments subjected to salt air and bad weather. How could they be expected to replenish their wardrobe when they were thousands of miles from civilization?

But the eyes of Vancouver smiled as he stopped before Higgins, and he glanced apologetically at his uniform.

The Governor saw an honest, plain English face, fine blue eyes, a broad mouth. Vancouver must be under forty years of age. He had expected him to be older.

Warmly, without pretense or ceremony, Higgins welcomed him and his men. He wanted to put them at ease about their appearance. "It is an honor to welcome brave men who have undergone endless hardships, far from civilization and ordinary comforts," he said.

Vancouver looked at him gratefully. He was indebted to His Excellency for allowing his ship to put in at Valparaiso to be reconditioned and the mainmast repaired. "I regret that I was forced to disregard my orders and enter a Spanish port. But with a useless mainmast I dared not attempt the treacherous Cape Horn. We would never have reached England." His pleasant voice was quiet and deliberate. "I am astonished that Your Excellency speaks English so perfectly after your many years in Chile."

"Indeed it has been twenty-four years now," Higgins said. "During that time there have been few opportunities to speak my native tongue or to mingle with Englishmen. As you know, few foreigners are permitted in Spanish colonies."

Higgins thought of the Irish Don Thomas Dolphin and Don Ignacio Blake, a few others with whom he spoke English.

"I joined the English army early in life," he said. "But promotions did not come. I went to the Continent. My first commission for His Catholic Majesty was in the corps of engineers, then in the Dragoons. I was made lieutenant-colonel. Then I was given the distinguished post of military commander on the frontier of Chile and made intendente of Concepcion. By my attention to the comforts of the Indians, I subdued their fierceness and got them to submit to the Government of Spain. For this service I was promoted to Governor and Captain-General and President of Chile."

He looked around the little group of Britishers. There was admiration in their eyes.

"The Crown of Spain is fortunate," Vancouver said.

"I have no reason to complain," Higgins said. "His Majesty has conferred upon me the order of Charles the Third, and of St. James, the rank of lieutenant-general in the Spanish army, the rank of field marshal." And, he thought, the honors would not end until he had titles and the place of Viceroy. He smiled. After a moment he continued. "A man puts into his labors diligence and sincerity, caring little for the honors. Oddly enough, the honors come. For I have done nothing that any human being would not have done." His voice caressed the words. "I want nothing for myself, only the good of the people of Chile."

Vancouver was looking at Higgins as if he understood that Higgins was underrating his ability and accomplishments.

"Now you must rest," Governor Higgins said. "I have kept you too long. But my heart has been cheered at having near me my own kind. Forgive me if I have been boastful, but to you I feel I can speak freely. At supper I shall have the pleasure of hearing about your travels. Now it is siesta time, when everything stops. Rest well."

The siesta time, Higgins thought as he went to his desk. He never observed this waste of precious time.

But Vancouver would lie on the bed under the netting, and the scent of orange blossoms, the soft music from the Plaza, would drift in upon his senses. He would think himself fortunate to be here, the guest of the lonely Irishman. He would remember that he had been given every assistance with his ships, been received hospitably by Higgins. He would be grateful for this haven after the constant anxiety through which he had passed during the last five years.

He would sleep. And at supper he would discuss eagerly the subjects Higgins asked about.

Supper was an elaborate affair. The dinner plates, goblets, sauce dishes, cutlery and trays were of silver. The candelabras threw brightness over polished dishes and a centerpiece of roses that might have come from England.

There was beef cooked with vegetables, beefsteaks and chicken, roast lamb, quail and woodcock. And meat pastries, small fried puffs filled with fruit and cheese. Then ices, loquats and other fruits that Vancouver and his men had never before eaten. The watermelon was yellow and sweet as sugar.

Music played throughout supper. Now and again bright girlish faces peered through the window grilles, pretty voices called greetings, flowers were tossed into the room.

Vancouver, sitting to the right of Higgins, said, "You cannot know the pleasure all this gives us. The Pacific Northwest and the islands supplied few comforts or time for relaxation."

This was the opening Higgins had been wanting. He said, "Tell me about the islands in the South Pacific."

"There are such a lot of them," Vancouver said. "I scarcely know where to begin about the islands."

Higgins said, "Why not begin with the Sandwich Islands? Or are there islands nearer Chile?"

Of course there were nearer islands, Higgins thought. Pitcairn, for example, settled by mutineers of His Majesty's ship the *Bounty*, and many other isles before the Sandwich group. But he would pretend that he was ignorant of them.

"There is Pitcairn," Vancouver said.

"How near?"

Vancouver said, "Perhaps three thousand miles."

"Indeed? And after Pitcairn the Sandwich Islands?"

The Britisher smiled as if to say how little Higgins knew about the South Pacific. "The Society group lies west of Pitcairn. Then come the Marquesas. There are many islands between here and the Sandwich islands."

"Is it possible?" Higgins managed to sound astonished. "And are the natives friendly to foreigners?" He smiled. "Has the British standard been raised over any of them?"

"Almost without exception the British have been welcome," Vancouver said.

Higgins studied the flame of the candles. How soon before the British tried to raise their standard over Juan Fernandez, off the coast of Valparaiso? Or attempted to seize Chiloe, south of Valdivia? Or, perhaps, one of the islands near Talcahuano? Vancouver had confirmed all his fears about the British.

"I believe," Higgins said, "you helped arbitrate the dispute between the Spanish and English over the Nootka Territory in northwest America."

Vancouver said, "Yes, I acted for my country." He stared at his plate.

Was he thinking, Higgins wondered, that now that piece of land was called Vancouver Island? Was he thinking how stubbornly the Spanish had resisted before giving up the Nootka Territory? Was he afraid Higgins felt bitter about the settlement?

"I have nothing but praise for the manner in which the controversy was arbitrated," Higgins said. "I believe all parties feel the same way. Your conduct, sir, was admirable. It required tact and statesmanship." He studied Vancouver with serious eyes. "Captain," he added, "I have not the slightest doubt that you and the Spanish commissioner, by resolving the matter as you did, averted war between Spain and England. I compliment you!"

Vancouver appeared to be surprised. "You are generous and understanding," he said.

"I would like to read your report on the Northwest controversy." Higgins sat back against his Spanish chair. "News from such far-off places is long in reaching us."

The Britisher stared at the seeds of his melon. They lay on the silver plate—black, shining against the polished moon of the dish. "I would like to oblige Your Excellency. Tucked off in this isolated corner of the world you must be hungry for any scrap of news from outside. But you understand, sir, that since my government has not yet seen the report, I cannot let it be read by anyone."

Higgins said quickly, "Yes, yes, of course. Caution is important. But your exploration of the Pacific Coast is not secret, I hope?"

Vancouver appeared to hesitate. But then he smiled. "No, I think not," he said. "One reason for sailing into the Pacific and along the northwest coast was to make a thorough reconnaissance of the land. And we were looking for a northwest pasage to the Atlantic."

Eagerly, Higgins listened.

For several minutes Vancouver talked about his explorations.

In a nutshell, Vancouver was saying that England wanted colonies, needed colonies, would find colonies. Higgins watched a servant pour coffee from the silver urn. "Here in remote Chile," he said, at last, "I have no relaxation for anything like explorations. I am constantly busy with problems of defense. I ask myself, 'Will the North Americans come? Or will it be the English, or the French to fish for whale, perhaps to smuggle contraband?' Our commerce must be protected, you know." He sighed.

"And Chile has a long coastline," Vancouver said,

Higgins thought he knew what Vancouver was thinking: how could Chile be defended against an enemy, if she were without ships? Spain should keep large supplies of ships and men to protect the colonies. If a foreign power moved against Chile, were the forts well prepared to resist?

"When Sir Edward Hughes sailed with his armada from England to the East Indies," Higgins said, with a burst of spirit, "it was believed he meant to protect British establishments in the South Pacific. As a matter of record, he came to Chile." He paused, glanced about the table. "Word of his plan reached me from Spain."

The guests had ceased their talk about Chile's commerce. All were listening intently.

"Hughes planned to attack Concepcion in South Chile." Governor Higgins stirred his coffee vigorously. "The forts had been neglected. They had quickly to be strengthened. We worked like maniacs to make the repairs. Then, I held a convocation with the Indians." His voice hardened. "Sir Edward Hughes abandoned his plan. I attribute it to his learning that we were prepared."

He smiled. "Tasso," he said, brightly, "fill Captain Vancouver's cup."

"An Indian convocation?" Vancouver said, slowly. "The Indians are your allies? I have heard that you subdued the savages. But to win them over to fight for Spain!" He studied His Excellency with new interest.

"My last Indian conference," Higgins said, leaning forward in his chair, "was the parliament of Negrete. Thousands of Indians gathered on the plains near the Biobio River, coming for many miles. I spoke to them as protector, brother, friend and priest. It was a picture to remember: sunny fields, the blue and red garments, scarcely an ostrich feather moving in their black hair, as they listened. For I have always kept my word with the Indians. They trust me." He glanced toward the windows. He seemed to see the impressive scene, and once again the trusting faces.

He straightened. He said briskly, "The Chiefs of the four nations of Indians signed a compact with me to provide warriors to help defend the Crown should Chile be attacked by a foreign enemy."

He paused, drank coffee. He replaced his cup in the silver saucer and it was the small metallic sound of a flintlock on a musket.

Vancouver said, quietly, "How many Indians?"

"At least ten thousand. But it could be three times that number if I needed them." Higgins did not smile. "These savages are unlike any other Indians. They have never been conquered by the Spanish. I keep peace with them by kindness and firmness, by constructing forts near their borders and feeding them when their harvests fail." He pushed his chair away from the table and prepared to rise.

"Captain Vancouver," he said, emphatically, "I had rather fight fifty thousand English, or French, or Spanish soldiers than ten thousand of the Indians of Chile!" He rose. When he spoke again, his voice was hushed for he recalled the battles, the terror. "I have fought these barbarians! I know!"

The entire company rose.

As Vancouver fell into step with Higgins, the Governor said pleasantly, "If you like, I will present you with a copy of my speech to the Indians at the Parliament of Negrete."

"I would appreciate having it," Vancouver said, eagerly. "I would like to read it. And take it with me to England."

In his office, Higgins picked up the report from his desk. He read aloud to Vancouver the title:

"The Speech of Field Marshal Don Ambrosio Higgins de Vallenar, President-Governor and Captain-General of the Kingdom of Chile to the Araucanian and Other Indian Nations, Met in Convocation in the Camp of Negrete, 4th day of March, 1793."

He handed Vancouver the bulky sheaf of papers. "There it is," he said, "the results of my years of labor for the good of the Indians. I worked to win them with humanity, good sense, patience and perseverance. I have given them the protection of the King. And the tribes have promised to fight with me for Spain against all enemies."

Vancouver stared at the pages. He would read it before he retired, he said earnestly. His eyes were bright. With a quick step he hurried off down the corridor.

For a long time Governor Higgins stood in the doorway to his office that looked onto a patio. Above he saw thousands of brilliant stars, like thousands of polished lance-heads.

Vancouver would pass on Higgins' report to the Admiralty. British statesmen would read it with care.

Let them know that the Irish Higgins could do what he had told Vancouver he would do if Chile was attacked, or her islands invaded! And England should think well before she attempted to invade this colony of Spain.

CHAPTER XVI

BERNARDO had been living at the mansion of Don Nicolas de la Cruz for several weeks. From the window near his table he could see the tops of houses crowded together, the gray waters of the bay, the bare coastline of Andalusia. He longed for the Andes, vineyards and home. He could not forget his disappointment at not coming to Spain by way of Chile.

Little by little he had settled into the new life. He worked hard at his studies.

He went back to his history lesson.

There was a knock at his door. A servant said Don Nicholas wanted to speak with him.

Bernardo hurried along the tiled and marble hall.

"It is a letter from Chile," Don Nicolas said when Bernardo entered his study. "You are leaving Cadiz."

He was going to England. Now another ship, another sea.

He stared at the sea. He was sixteen, soon he would be seventeen. Time after time he had been moved and always in great haste, with secrecy, and without explanation.

He only knew that his destination was London. His agents were Spencer and Perkins, who owned a watchmaking factory. The firm had been forwarded a large amount of money to cover Bernardo's expenses for at least a year. When Bernardo needed money, Don Nicolas had told him, he was to draw on the London firm. More pesos would be furnished as Bernardo needed them.

There had been admonitions from Don Nicolas about reporting frequently. Bernardo was to make no decision, small or great, without the approval of Don Nicolas.

But his friend need not have been so emphatic, Bernardo thought. For he had always been obedient. It was his father who selected the guardians, and Bernardo obeyed them as if the orders came from Don Ambrosio. The command of his father was law. He worshiped the great man. Why should he want to disobey him?

Then the London docks and wharves piled with tar and beeswax, rushes, kegs of spruce beer, barrels of pearl barley, molasses and dried fruits.

Everything strange. He was filled with loneliness.

Senor Perkins was a fat gentleman. His garments billowed as he came toward Bernardo. He stared with disapproving eyes at Bernardo's broadcloth suit and capota. When he saw several boxes lettered "Riquelme," he said, testily, "Then a post chaise will be necessary."

The carriage stopped in a narrow, dark street. Over the door to a bleak-looking house was a sign, "Spencer and Perkins."

The office was filled with ancient iron and junk.

Senor Perkins pushed old locks from a chair. "Sit down," he ordered.

He flipped up the cover to a wooden box. "These are watch parts," he said, without ceremony. "Your job will be to collect the unassembled pieces from workers about London."

There was some misunderstanding, Bernardo thought. This could not be the place Don Nicolas' friend, Senor Romera, had selected.

"I came to England to finish my education," Bernardo said.

Senor Perkins stared. He had agreed to accept Bernardo as an apprentice, to teach him the business. He knew nothing about a school, he said.

By the light of a nubby candle, Bernardo wrote Don Nicolas, explaining the situation. . . .

Don Nicolas answered at once. He was surprised to hear Bernardo's news. He had arranged for him to attend Senor Hill's Academy in Richmond, Surrey, less than five miles from London. Bernardo was to go there at once.

With great displeasure, Senor Perkins put him aboard a coach.

Then along the Thames, past unfamiliar countryside the coach rocked, the driver perched on a box instead of riding an animal as the postilions did at home.

The coach delivered Bernardo at the door of the Academy.

A man servant with a long nose and gimlet eyes opened the door to the frowning house.

He ordered Bernardo to wait.

Bernardo stared at the brown-papered walls, decorated with dull temples and arches, thinking of pleasant white walls and gaily painted ceilings at home. The dark wood floor seemed unfriendly after bright tiles and brick.

On the bulletin board were notices printed in English. From another room he heard a voice speaking in the strange, unfamiliar tongue. He remembered that he had been told how difficult a language English was.

He would never learn it. And unless he did how would he communicate with the masters and students?

And his heart sank.

CHAPTER XVII

AT THE stationers' shop near Richmond Green, Bernardo gazed with pleasure at newspapers and journals, the shelves of books.

His anguished and often hopeless weeks of study had at last eliminated the language barrier. To improve his speech and his reading of English, he came here daily to buy papers and books.

But there was an even greater obstacle that he must surmount.

All his lifetime he had been cautioned about speaking his mind on the evils of the Spanish Crown, the wrongs of government. Because of the wicked laws of Spain, he had never known his father, nor written to him. Now, he must learn to speak freely his opinions on all subjects. He must learn to think and discuss openly his beliefs and convictions, without fear.

It was like learning to walk all over again.

Everyone he met in this country had definite and violent opinions about everything, even the most insignificant matters, and they spoke their views with boldness. They were frank about criticizing even the mildest errors of government. They ridiculed the monarch, the princes and peers and were scathing in their judgment of the actions of Parliament. There were smuggling restrictions, but everyone here in England seemed to think it clever to avoid the tax on tea and other products by using smuggled goods. They thought their recent enemy, the United States, had admirable laws, brilliant leaders and they openly urged English statesmen to emulate the North Americans.

Bernardo listened. He admired their forthrightness, their courage. But his early training controlled him.

Still, in time he would learn. He would improve himself by reading books on politics and government, by keeping abreast of the news, by taking journals and newspapers. He would attend lectures. And he would continue to question his French master about conditions in France, which seemed to be stirring all Britishers.

He counted the journals on the shelf and was freshly amazed. Chile had not one printing press.

And Lima had only a few periodicals, all extremely tiresome and cautious. There was the *Mercurio Peruano*, which printed limited articles on literary and scientific subjects. When the Lima *Gazette* was founded the editors promised to publish important material about current happenings. Once the *Gazette* had mentioned the need of a naval force. It had dared to report that the French nation was being rocked by rebellion. And then the editors ceased to print anything of importance.

The Spanish writers said nothing at all and with great charm. Few articles worth remembering were allowed to be printed. And the need for information was vast. There was a feeling of restlessness in Lima to know what was happening abroad, for the ships that came to smuggle brought hints of what was occurring in North America and in France.

Nothing of social and political changes in the world in any Lima paper, and yet unrest everywhere. It was the same throughout all the colonies.

"The volume that you ordered has arrived," the stationer said.

The man was slender, pale, with intelligent eyes. He handed the book to Bernardo.

Bernardo took it and glanced at the title. "*A Description of Patagonia and the Adjoining Parts of South America. By Thomas Falkner, who resided near forty years in those Parts.*" In the preface was a statement that held Bernardo's attention. He read slowly, for some of the English words still gave him trouble. "When the British Americans become independent," he read, "it will probably induce the inhabitants of the great kingdom in Spanish America to follow their example, which they will be forced to do by their communication with Europe being intercepted; for North America is better provided with timber and all kinds of naval stores than any other country in the world. A great maritime power will be formed there, and the people will have that bold, enterprising spirit with which fine governments generally animate mankind."

The writer was a Jesuit who had been ordered to leave South America. Here, in England, he had written his thoughts boldly. They had been printed in this book which Bernardo could buy for a few pesos.

He thought of the kind priests at the Colegio of San Carlos who would enjoy speaking openly as this writer had. Padre Matias was one. Often he had mentioned to Bernardo the unrest, but always when they were walking alone in the Colegio orchards or riding toward the hacienda owned by the Colegio outside of Lima. And he cautioned Bernardo not to repeat his words, reminding him that the Inquisition was only a short distance away from the Colegio. Padre Matias said he had no desire to leave Guadalupe Street, for a cell in the Tribunal. And while he made jokes about the danger of speaking, actually it was serious.

Bernardo would like Padre Matias to live here in England where his voice could be heard. There must be others like the Padre in the colonies, all afraid to speak out.

And Bernardo wished he dared ship this book to Padre Matias, as well as Mr. Rolt's book that he had ordered and read with interest. *A New and Accurate History of South America*, was the title, and Mr. Rolt's thesis was that Spain's lack of interest in her colonies might lose them for her.

But Bernardo dared not risk the safety of his friend by sending him such books.

For several moments Bernardo read titles of books, wanting them all. He selected *Europe and America*, and *Geography of Plants*. Then he bought a copy of the London *Times*, the London *Gazette*, *Gentleman's Magazine*, and paying his bill, he said, "Good afternoon, Mr. Newton," and departed, delighted with his purchases.

The red brick facade of the Academy looked at him solemnly as he walked up the incline toward the white door with its brass knocker.

Upstairs in his room, he laid aside his beaver hat, hung his capota in his walnut wardrobe and seated himself in a wingchair beside a window.

He opened the *Times* and the first news item to attract his attention was the trade agreement between North America and England.

How calmly the writer remarked on a situation that would have seemed impossible to achieve. For only a few years ago, England had been at war with her American colonies. Her men were dying to keep the colonies for Great Britain. And in America others were fighting and dying to free their people from the rule of King George the Third.

Bernardo folded the newspaper and studied the sheet.

The burden imposed on the Spanish colonists was greater. It was a hundred times worse. And for almost three hundred years the bondage had been in existence.

The North American colonists had defied the English King. They had dared to speak, to act openly against His Majesty. And they were such a few compared to the strength of England. The English had the greatest navy and many soldiers.

He wondered how the American colonists had managed to succeed. A few against many. By what method had they become unified? For they had acted with unity, and together they had won.

If a people were united they could do anything!

Thoughtfully, Bernardo studied the pattern of his bed-hangings. How did one unify a nation?

In Peru and Chile the chains had been lying heavily on the people for centuries. How could they be roused even to desire liberty, let alone be unified? The Jesuits had become too bold and they were exiled by the Crown. Now there were only the fearful men.

And what could he do? He was nothing. He was no one. He had no talent for speaking out boldly against wrongs, for planning or leading. Almost any student here at the Academy had better opinions about almost everything.

They had known free thought and speech from infancy. They had the example of their fathers. And the advice of their fathers.

Slowly, he turned the page of the *Times*.

There was a story about the return of Captain George Vancouver from a voyage to northwest America. He had been entertained in Chile by the Governor Don Ambrosio Higgins de Vallenar.

Bernardo stared with astonished eyes, reading it over again with the greatest delight.

It was as if his father had spoken, reminding him that Bernardo had a father who had been raised a Britisher, with an understanding of what freedom meant. It was as if a voice was speaking across the miles saying he could seek advice from his father.

He glanced at his desk. If he dared write his father!

The newspaper fell to the floor. Minutes passed.

His father had never given Bernardo permission to write, but then he had never ordered him not to write.

And why not write? Why not ask the advice of a wise parent about the problems that troubled him? Had not this great man sent Bernardo to England? And for what reason except that he wanted his son to be educated as a free man with independence of thought and action?

Now that he thought about it, there could be no other reason.

He felt a tingling along his spine. When he picked up his pen, his hands were moist and cold.

In spite of himself, fear made him hesitate.

But he must not listen to fears. He must act with boldness, because what he was doing was right. His father would approve.

And how would he begin?

He would have to compose the letter carefully. It must explain that Bernardo knew his father's secret and yet tell nothing if by chance the letter fell into the hands of strangers. The secret would have to be well protected. His father must not be harmed. And the letter must be general in tone. In another message, Bernardo could ask specific advice.

He began, "Dear Friend and Protector," then tore the sheet up and tossed it into the grate. He tried several times before he had a salutation that seemed appropriate. He wrote in English, since few people in Chile understood English.

"Sir: At last, after great thought, the son of a nobleman who is as great as the Araucanian hero Lautaro is bold enough to write to you. Long ago I learned the reason for my father being taken from me, but it remains locked in my innermost heart. My gratitude for the care and affection given me knows no bounds, and my life patterned after his will be my deep thanks. Lacking the advice of a father, I am sometimes confused about my future course. Given that counsel, I could proceed with sureness. The image of my loved father is always with me. As nearly as possible I shall try to be worthy of him who has sacrificed himself for the good of others. One day I shall learn to be as boldly fearless. If only I knew boldness."

Bernardo wrote on. He spoke of the arrival in England of Captain Vancouver, of Richmond and his studies. He ended the letter with, "God keep you always—Bernardo."

Now there must be a method of sending the letter secretly to his father, some trusted friend to whom it could be sent. He went over the names. There was the Captain of Dragoons, Tirapegui, whose address he was not certain about. And Don Thomas Dolphin had placed Bernardo aboard the ship at Talcahuano the time he had departed for Lima. He was an Irishman. A letter from England to an Irish merchant in Chile would not be questioned. Since Don Thomas was a merchant, he would go occasionally to Santiago and it would be natural for him to visit with Bernardo's father.

On a fresh sheet of paper Bernardo wrote, "Please hand the enclosed to my father. Bernardo Riquelme."

The envelope containing his letter to his father, he left unaddressed, but placing it and the message for Don Thomas in another envelope he wrote on the cover, "Senor Thomas Dolphin, Merchant, Concepcion, Chile." He added the word, "Personal."

Now, as quickly as the mail ship could bring a reply, Bernardo would have a letter and advice from his father.

The supper gong sounded.

He sat staring exultantly at the letter.

It was only a letter, but it was his boldest act and he felt stronger. And happier. Never in all his life had he been happier!

CHAPTER XVIII

By DECREE of His Majesty, Carlos the Fourth of Spain, Governor Higgins was now Baron of Ballenary. And Higgins, standing at his desk, thought the morning sunnier than usual. To have a title at last!

For the King, having reviewed the facts presented in the Governor's application, had acted wisely. He had found that Higgins was a legitimate descendant in direct line of Juan Duff O'Higgins, Baron of Ballenary of the county of Sligo, Ireland, of the old and illustrious house of O'Neil.

What more could His Majesty ask than all those important witnesses to the facts: Chichester Fortescue, a genealogist, Lord Lieutenant-General, Governor and Viceroy of Ireland, the Catholic Archbishop of Dublin and the Spanish Ambassador to the Court of London? If the parish records were missing, as the application plainly stated, was it not because the Protestant government had not allowed records to be kept at the time Higgins was born? So His Majesty had conferred upon Higgins the title of Baron.

The worthy King!

The Governor thought it a pity this news had not come before Vancouver left, for he would have had the added delight of having the Captain report to the British government how he was appreciated by a really great nation, by the Spanish monarch himself.

Already O'Higgins had shown his gratitude. He had promised to contribute two thousand pesos a year to the Crown to help defray expenses of the war with France in the name of his nephews who were serving with the Spanish army. He had been confident the Crown would be pleased. The payment would assure the advancement of his relatives.

He meant to bring the nephews to South America, for a lonely man wants his family about him. More and more the Governor longed for a family. The years crept by, the distance to his homeland made it seem far away. The child of whom O'Higgins was proud he could never acknowledge, could never make known.

But when he glanced at the decree again and recalled that he was a titled man like the Irish and Spanish lords, he brightened. Calling his secretary, he dictated a notice of this honor to the Santiago authorities. He straightened, looked at his secretary, "I am now Don Ambrosio O'Higgins Vallenar, Baron of Ballenary!" he said.

The pale face of Reyes flushed with pleasure, as if he had received the honor himself. He said, "Congratulations, sir."

When his secretary had written the notice, O'Higgins signed the new and imposing title for the first time. With a great flourish of his pen he wrote, "Baron of Ballenary."

How fine it looked!

Then, O'Higgins went outside and walked in the patio, thinking about his services to the Crown, and what additional duties he could perform to bring that highest honor. He must continue to be diligent, to keep himself constantly before His Majesty. For now the coveted position of Viceroy of Peru seemed very near.

He must increase his patrol of the coast to watch for smugglers. Although he had decreed severe punishments for those who traded illicitly, he would enforce the death penalty for smuggling. There would be no leniency. For literature which had been prohibited still slipped in from foreign ships in the form of pamphlets on American and French ideas of government. And occasionally religious medals, snuff boxes, jewelry of various designs and bolts of cotton goods bearing emblems of North American liberty crept into the country by illegal means.

Whenever he heard of such violations he reported them to Madrid. And along the coast he maintained strict vigilance to intercept the entry of unauthorized goods.

Today, he would issue a notice that the death penalty would be strictly enforced if natives or foreigners were caught trading in contraband.

An hour later, while O'Higgins was receiving the congratulations from members of the City Council, a shocking and frightening letter arrived.

Don Clemente, chief clergyman of La Serena, had committed treason! He favored the revolution in France. He openly urged his parishioners to follow their example in Chile!

The Governor moved swiftly to his desk. He said, "Gentlemen, a matter of gravest importance. You will excuse me."

His visitors departed.

O'Higgins sent for his attorney general.

Impatiently, he waited for his officer, thinking of the scandalous affair, of Don Clemente who had been a trouble maker for years, injecting himself into court cases because he fancied himself a lawyer, and giving the authorities no peace. O'Higgins had insisted that the priest be curbed by the ecclesiastical powers in Santiago, but Don Clemente had not been silenced and the Governor never interfered with church matters.

But this was treason that Don Clemente had spoken! Boldly, he had sympathized with the French revolutionists, urging Chileans to resist the government of Spain.

This was an act against the state. And the Governor would proceed legally to punish the priest.

The attorney general arrived and O'Higgins explained the outrageous affair. He gave his orders. "Advise the ecclesiastical authorities at once," he said, "of this astounding matter. Do it secretly. And begin proceedings at once. Have Don Clemente arrested and brought to Santiago. He will be tried for treason!"

His officer hurried off.

That same afternoon a message came for O'Higgins from His Excellency, Don Blas Sobrino y Minayo, Bishop of Santiago, who lived only a few steps from the Palace. It was an impudent memorandum.

He wrote that it was beyond the power of Governor O'Higgins as head of the government to take over the case of Don Clemente, much less write the sentence of the accused. This, he wrote, was a matter for the ecclesiastical powers of Santiago. Don Blas, as Bishop, would handle the matter.

In a word, the Governor told himself hotly, Don Blas ordered him to mind his own business.

But O'Higgins had not asked the opinion of Don Blas. And he had better make that clear to the Bishop at once.

Taking his black hat, his ebony cane with the ivory knob, O'Higgins left the palace and walked briskly the short distance to the west side of the Plaza and the Bishop's residence. Behind him he could hear his guards trying to keep up with him.

Inside the residence he was announced at once.

He entered the study hung with yellow brocade, where Bishop Don Blas sat behind an ornate gilded desk, and stood looking with annoyance at the smug countenance above the rich purple robe.

"It is about the priest, Don Clemente," Higgins said, shortly. "I did not ask your permission in his case. I informed you merely as a matter of courtesy that I intend to proceed against him because he has committed a crime against the Crown!"

Don Blas half rose from the cushioned chair. "You cannot!"

"He will be tried and punished like any secular who has spoken treason against His Majesty's government." O'Higgins' voice was adamant.

"It is a matter for the ecclesiastical authorities. We shall decide about Don Clemente," Don Blas said, angrily.

Higgins stared, trying to calm himself. His course against the priest of La Serena was already decided. "Your Excellency," he said, "when I need the opinion of the Bishop I will ask. No one, priest or layman, is above the King's law when he speaks treason. I shall act at once."

Behind his glasses the eyes of the Bishop glared. His thin, shrill voice said, "Have you forgotten the ecclesiastical law?"

"Look you," the Governor said, interrupting the flow of anger, "you have been recently appointed to this See. I would indeed regret to have to contradict myself by complaining of a Bishop of whom I have said much good!"

Back in his office, O'Higgins ordered Don Clemente brought to Santiago at once under heavy guard.

Then he continued with his arrangements for a trip to southern Chile which had been interrupted by the shocking news about Don Clemente. He planned to rebuild the ancient city of Osorno which many years ago had been destroyed by the Indians. Already, he had ordered settlers to be shipped to Osorno by the brigantine on which O'Higgins would travel south.

A few days before his departure, the priest Don Clemente reached Santiago under armed escort. The Governor ordered him imprisoned in the convent of San Domingo, where he could make no more trouble and where his unwise tongue would have only the walls of a cell for company.

He advised the Crown of his action. Now that the ringleader, Don Clemente had been removed from his parish, he expected no more treasonable utterances.

O'Higgins wanted the King to know that he acted firmly against priest or layman who dared speak against the rule of His Majesty.

The King would be pleased with his Governor!

Jubilantly, O'Higgins rode toward Valparaiso and the ship that would take him to southern Chile. The light over the Mapocho River was the same shade as some apricots in panniers loaded on a passing mule. The light covered the river and the new breakwater, completed in spite of the storm raised by angry Spaniards. Shade trees bordered the walk at the top of the dyke.

His heart swelled with pride.

He rode forward across the new road now completed. And commerce had improved.

When he reached Valparaiso, the ship *Limeno* was in the harbor. Already new settlers for Osorno were aboard, their few belongings stowed in the hold, going unwillingly to Osorno at the insistence of O'Higgins.

But it was for their own good. They would prosper. Soon their gloom would change to joy and they would thank O'Higgins for his goodness. Now they were afraid of the Indians near Osorno.

They were sad at leaving friends and relatives in the villages where they had existed miserably on a pittance.

The ship sailed out of the harbor.

He gathered the settlers about him. He spoke of the beautiful Osorno.

"Friends," he said, lingering long on the word, hanging on it, wanting the Chileans before him to drink in its meaning. "This land to which you are being taken is a paradise of rolling uplands and virgin forests, whose soil is fertile and richer than any other land in Chile. Soon your wheat fields will be sweeping banners of yellow and your fruit trees heavy with magnificent fruit. Strong houses will be built for you on land which I shall distribute to you."

He paused, his hands upturned, his face beaming with good will and affection.

"Each family will be given twenty-five cuadras of land, a strong, fine house. You will be provisioned until your harvests are sufficient." His voice was beguiling. "You will have a governor, city officials, a fort and soldiers to protect you. You must not fear the Indians. They are our friends." And his voice mellowed and became serene, like the peace he had brought to the frontier, for he spoke to them as to frightened children. "I signed a treaty with the Indians, and they will keep their word. They have given us this land at Osorno. They have promised faithfully not to molest our people in this beautiful country or anywhere in Chile. They have never broken their promises to me, and they never will."

The strained expression in the eyes of the solemn-faced peasants lessened a little.

But O'Higgins wanted the faces to smile. They must be joyous!

"From my hacienda in Los Angeles," he said, "I have shipped to you oxen which I present to you freely. Each family will have a pair of fine animals to help plow the fields and bring in the harvests." He heard his voice, sweetly persuasive, roll across the sun-swept deck and he thought how grateful he would have been in his youth had someone offered him these rich gifts. "But I make the sacrifice gladly," he said, "for you, my people."

He studied the earnest faces of the peasants. They would plant and work the rich soil of Osorno, free from the Spanish lords. They would be their own masters. No mines would be developed and there would be no great haciendas, but only modest farms yielding abundant harvests. They would join militias to help defend the south from invasion and supply Valdivia with meat and grain.

A few peasants near him were smiling.

This was what he wanted, he told himself, cheerful, happy people, going joyously toward a land of milk and honey like the people of ancient times when another leader guided them.

He talked on, and soon each face was wreathed with brightness, until laughter filled the air. Then he knew he had succeeded, and that this mission would not be in vain. He looked over the happy company, feeling inspired and refreshed.

The King must hear of the happiness with which the people looked forward to Osorno and a larger life, and of how O'Higgins labored to bring the better life.

Twenty-one days later the ship reached Valdivia, nine miles up the Valdivia River, a protected and ample harbor.

He entered Osorno in high spirits. But his first view of the ancient ruins was depressing. The Plaza and streets were overgrown with forests, the heavy growth of vines shutting out sunlight, the earth giving forth a dank, unhealthy odor, as if the slaughtered Spanish lay where the attacking Indians had left them, their decaying bodies unburied and unsanctified.

First, he ordered the forests cleared away. Then began the building of temporary homes and the restoration of destroyed buildings.

When the city was partially restored, O'Higgins returned to Valdivia, pleased with the progress he had made. Soon, Osorno would provide the Plaza of Valdivia with its needs. Soon the annual allowance paid Valdivia by the Crown would be abolished.

And His Majesty would look favorably upon O'Higgins' work at Osorno and Valdivia.

He reached the courtyard of his Valdivia headquarters, elated in spirit but physically weary. The dampness of the ancient Osorno had settled deep into his lungs. With slow steps, he entered his apartment. He was glad of the comfort of the black chair. He sat quietly, too weary to lift even one letter from the mail awaiting him.

For minutes he studied the walls of the room, the long table, a small altar. He stared again at his mail, began sorting it.

He broke the seal of a letter from the Crown, and read: "Don Carlos, by the grace of God, King of Castile, of Leon, of Aragon, etc., for attention to duty, ability, merit and services of Don Ambrosio Higgins, Lieutenant-General of my Royal Forces, has been chosen and named Viceroy, Governor and Captain-General of the Kingdom of Peru and the President of the Royal Audiencia, at a salary of sixty thousand and five hundred pesos annually. . . ."

He leaned weakly against the table. His hands trembled.

He was Viceroy of Peru!

He tried to read the document over again, but the paper shook hard and his fingers were icy cold. He wiped the moisture from his eyes. His brain was numb. He kept saying the words over, trying to grasp their full meaning.

Then a sudden glow replaced the coldness. He could think again.

The gracious and noble King! The righteous son of a righteous father! God keep the gracious ruler now and always! Into O'Higgins' hands had been placed the brightest, the richest jewel. To him had been given power greater than that of lord or enemy.

He struggled to his feet. The weariness had gone. He felt strong, young, powerful. A great light seemed to surround him, and his spirits soared. The hand of God himself had touched his servant. Bountifully, O'Higgins' thanks spilled from his lips.

Almost immediately, O'Higgins left Valdivia.

He had been in Santiago only a few days when Don Thomas Dolphin arrived. This was surprising, for when they parted in Concepcion recently, Dolphin advised he would not see O'Higgins until he was sailing for Lima. That was weeks away.

His friend entered in great haste. With an air of mystery he placed a chair next to that of the Viceroy. He glanced anxiously toward a closed door, the windows across the room. Obviously disturbed, he opened a paper and laid it before O'Higgins, together with an envelope. "The sealed envelope and this note reached me at Concepcion." His voice was unsteady.

O'Higgins read the message written in a formal English script, "Please hand the enclosed to my father. Bernardo."

For a moment the floor seemed to heave under him.

His son knew about his father!

He stared at the message. In an alarmed voice he said, "How could he have discovered it?"

"I do not know." Dolphin sounded deeply concerned.

The blank envelope stared up palely. It would tell him how Bernardo had learned the secret. How lacking in judgment the boy had been to forward the letter.

Angrily, he opened it.

It was written in English. O'Higgins was glad for that slight comfort. He began to read:

"Sir: At last, after great thought, the son of a nobleman who is as great as the Araucanian hero Lautaro is bold enough to write to you. Long ago I learned the reason for my father being taken from me, but it remains locked in my innermost heart."

As the Viceroy read on, his face brightened. He smiled. This letter divulged nothing of O'Higgins' relationship to the boy. To all appearances it was a note of gratitude to a friend of a child's father.

How cleverly Bernardo had disguised the truth. With what thoughtfulness he had composed this letter and with what feeling he spoke of his father. Not a word of criticism, only complete understanding of O'Higgins' sacrifices and gratitude for his labors, for his goodness to his son. The letter was filled with admiration and affection for his father.

The Viceroy's heart filled with pride and delight in Bernardo, an even greater pride than he had felt when he had seen the boy for the first and only time.

But how, he wondered, had the boy discovered the secret?

Another proof of his cleverness. He had never divulged the truth. And he never would. He was a true son of O'Higgins. Had not kind Don Juan Albano, now dead and God rest his soul, insisted that Bernardo was trustworthy? And he had been right!

To Dolphin he said, "Read. He is a smart, fine lad, my son!"

And as Dolphin read, O'Higgins thought of what Bernardo had written. He was observant, like his father. He gave clear details of what he saw: the distance from London to Richmond; the dimensions of the Academy of Mr. Hill, overlooking a pretty village; the look of Richmond Palace where George the Third lived, of Margate, a seaside resort near London. He was lonely for his father. He wanted counsel and advice.

Indeed, with what fine sentiment he wrote! And how pleased O'Higgins was to have this letter!

But there could be no reply and no advice. For sharp, cunning eyes watched the letters that went from O'Higgins to Spain and other countries. The Viceroy of Peru stood on the highest pinnacle, above all others in South America. In Lima, light would shine brightly on his every act. His life must be blameless.

By not one deed, however harmless, would he mar his blameless record with the Crown.

He would always be a good father to Bernardo, providing him an education and all comforts. And with fatherly solicitude he would continue to protect the people of his kingdom from Spanish tyrants here at home. For as Viceroy his opportunities would be greater and his benevolence would reach further.

Behind him he would leave a happier Chile. He would do as much for Lima and Peru.

On May sixteenth, he embarked on the war frigate *Nuestra Senora del Pilar* for Callao, and Lima.

In Lima the homage, the elaborate entrance into the city headed by militia companies, officials of schools, colleges, universities, tribunals, the Cabildo and the Audiencia, the parade ending in the Plaza where at the cathedral he was received by the Arch-

bishop and the ecclesiastics in their regalia. The cathedral blazed
with light, the jeweled altar had suns within suns.

His private apartment in the Palace was hung with rose brocade,
with gold and ivory brocade. There were sofas of crimson, crystal
and gold chandeliers that multiplied in the gold mirrors.

He knelt in the oratory decorated in crimson with an altar table
on a dais and a painting of San Geronimo and San Camillo. There
was a crucifix, a chalice, a paten of silver.

The honors, the praises. He had two carriages and six horses
for his private use. There was nothing that would not be granted.
One gift from the Crown stirred him more deeply than all the
others. He was given the title of Marquis of Osorno, for his work
in restoring the southern city in Chile.

With pride he wrote his first proclamation: " . . . Don Ambrosio
O'Higgins, Marquis of Osorno, Baron of Ballenary, Lieutenant-
General of the Royal Forces, Viceroy, Governor and Captain-
General of Peru and Chile, President of the Royal Audiencia of
Lima, and Superintendent-General of the Royal Treasury . . . "

At last he had been able to insert O'Higgins into a proclamation.
Madrid had included only Higgins in the decree appointing him
Viceroy, probably because the promotion had been ordered prior
to His Majesty's naming him Baron, which gave him the right to
use the prefix "O," denoting dignity of forebears. . . .

He answered the thousands of letters of congratulation, those
from loyal subjects whom O'Higgins did not know, those from
the titled who had once opposed him, others from old friends.

But there would be no answer to the letter from Bernardo.

That was one letter he must never answer.

CHAPTER XIX

THERE had been no word from Bernardo's father. Now it was time for summer vacations and the students of Mr. Hill's Academy were leaving. They were full of exciting plans about the holidays.

Bernardo had heard about Margate. He supposed it was as good a place as any to spend the summer.

He traveled by coach to London, then by boat down the Thames to the sea and a short run south to the village of Margate.

But he was lonely before he stepped from the boat. He missed the Academy, the familiar routine of classes which gave him less time to remember his aloneness.

The long beach stretched on and on. There were sweeping gulls, a tireless surf, fishing boats. The first day Bernardo walked for miles staring at nothing, his thoughts flowing toward Chile, to his mother carding bright wool, or making lace, singing as she worked, or telling another Araucanian legend: the Milky Way was where old Indians who had died hunted ostrich for feathers to adorn their headbands. He thought of his little sister Rosa at his mother's feet, playing with her doll.

And he saw the picture of his grandfather Don Simon, sitting at the head of the great table, recounting his experiences on the frontier of Chile, telling of ancestors who fought with Pizarro, of Inca sun worship, of Inca builders who understood how to construct stone on stone, balanced to withstand the centuries. They had made irrigation canals still in use by the Spanish. He spoke of Inca gold and emeralds. Most terrifying had been the tales about Sir Francis Drake and the devastation he brought to Chile. Don Simon Riquelme believed Chile should have many swift vessels larger than those brought by Drake, so that Chile could be protected from enemy ships.

Bernardo thought of Drake. South of Margate was Plymouth from where Sir Francis had sailed against the Spanish and defeated them.

If Drake had taken Chile from Spain, instead of leaving only destruction, Bernardo's country might now be an English colony. Chile would have had a better life under England than she had from Spain. But Bernardo wanted his country to belong to the Chileans!

How Bernardo despised the Spanish Crown. And how helpless he was to change things.

He walked on, his sketch pad under an arm, staring at the bleak sea, at headlands of sand.

Eventide in a tamed England was not like home. He yearned for tangled and deep forests, for the wildness of the Itata and the Biobio, for the nearness of his family.

He was sick for home with an almost incurable longing!

That night in his room the wind tugged at mull curtains, ran along rafters speaking to him of Chile. The fog crept slyly through small windows, the cry of lost seagulls searching for an opening in the mists which hid the sea.

When would he see the familiar, loved places again? How could people leave and live in foreign lands?

His heart went out to his father in Chile, far from his native Ireland.

Had he been homesick for Dublin, for the tongue of his people, for familiar sights? Had he dreamed of small cottages and inns with ceilings little higher than his head, of narrow, black stairs crawling mysteriously into another level where small, paneled rooms waited with planked floors instead of tiles, where tiny panes instead of wide openings and iron grilles gave a view of the wide, swinging sky? Or hungered for the scent of smoke and seaweed, for the strong odor of kelp and the cry of gulls hidden by mists that covered the channel and all the earth; hungry for ships of all nations standing in a home harbor?

He had built good roads for Chile. Was it because he remembered smoothly laid roads from London to all the English ports?

Had this land, and Ireland, meant home to him as Chile was home to Bernardo?

His father lived in his work. Was it because he was lonely? Whatever it was, Governor Don Ambrosio Higgins was the best defender Chile had ever had. Or ever would have. No one would ever do more for Bernardo's homeland.

He wished he could do even a little. But he had no gift for winning or leading others. If he was called on during class he stood trying to gather together his scattered thoughts. And only by taking his time, by making himself stand until he had made an attempt to answer the question, was he able to recite.

If only his tongue would say what his heart felt! But it would not. And the need for caution both in speaking against Spain and in protecting his father's secret, had not helped. . . .

The days dragged lonesomely.

At last, the holidays were over. Bernardo returned to Richmond and the Academy, glad that he would have noise, the excited chatter of other students even if they thought him a little stupid because of his slowness at understanding their customs.

He had hoped for a letter from his father.

There was no letter. Only a word from Don Thomas Dolphin, "Letter received. Delivered."

Walking toward the village and the stationers', Bernardo told himself that his father was busy. He would write soon. It was good to know that his father had received his letter. He felt it was an invitation to write Don Ambrosio often. He was glad that he had written him again from Margate.

At the stationers', Bernardo went at once to the shelf which held the history books. He wanted a book on Sir Francis Drake. Now that he had seen the harbor from where Drake sailed, he was interested in reviewing the explorer's life. The schools in Chile and Lima were biased about Drake.

A girl was blocking the space where Bernardo had seen the book. She was looking at a large volume on ships which she had rested on the wide shelf where the histories were displayed, and until she moved he could not get the book.

Twice before Bernardo had seen the girl. Once, she sat ahead of him in church. She was accompanied by a pleasant-looking gentleman with reddish hair, and a woman, and he had assumed they were her parents.

The second time he had noticed the girl was one day when he passed the brick houses near the Green. She had stepped from a carriage with yellow wheels. The feather in her hat had been yellow, too. She glanced at him briefly that time, and then looked hastily away. He had walked on with the feeling that she was looking after him. But perhaps it had been only a pretty fancy.

Today, her bonnet was small and untrimmed except for a ribbon tied beneath her chin. Her hair was fair, touched with red, or perhaps the sun falling through the many-paned window gave it that gilded look. He had seen white floripondi blossoms lighted by the evening sun. That was the look of her creamy-white skin.

He picked up the London *Times* and pretended to read the news. He kept sketching the girl's profile in his mind. If he had drawing paper and crayon he would catch in this light her eyes fringed with thick, downcast lashes, her mouth caught in an expression of deep concentration.

Whatever would this girl want with a book on navigation?

Slowly, she turned the heavy leaves of the expensive book, pausing to study the details of each illustration as if she understood about ships.

And yet, he had a curious feeling that her mind was not entirely on the engravings, as Bernardo's was not on the London *Times*. He had an idea she wanted his attention.

He studied the slender line of her close-fitting coat with a small cape that reached just below her shoulders.

"I will take the book," she said at last. "My father makes small ship models, while I play and sing to him." Her smile was gay, and the quiet face of the stationer smiled, too.

"Indeed my father is completely spoiled," she said and, from the gentle way she spoke, Bernardo knew she adored her father. "As for myself," she said, closing the book, "I would like to travel on ships. How fine to touch at all ports of the world in fast ships! But for that one needs wealth and languages."

Bernardo listened. Her voice was musical, like a low-pitched flute. But how mistaken she was about the pleasures of traveling to far countries. Those he had seen were unattractive and lonely. He preferred remaining in one place, perhaps on a farm in Chillan. His own life had been a succession of travels to strange places.

The stationer said, "I will send the book within the hour, Miss Eeles."

"There is no hurry." Again she smiled. "My father's birthday is not for another fortnight."

She was gone. The echo of her voice seemed to remain, singing among the books, maps and globes, the porcelain figurines. Bernardo paid for his purchases.

Walking back to the Academy he thought of Miss Eeles. Somehow he must arrange a meeting. Perhaps Mr. Hill knew the Eeles family.

But Mr. Hill would make a ceremony of the meeting and Bernardo would feel conspicuous.

And why should she be interested in a nobody? He might as well try to forget Miss Eeles. He began going over in his mind a phrase in the Mozart number with which he had been having difficulty. Tomorrow his music teacher would expect him to have it memorized and would order him to play the number through without stumbling.

Miss Eeles said she played and sang. He wondered if she liked Mozart?

And then he had a fine idea.

The Eeles family liked music. The daughter played. Perhaps his music teacher was acquainted with them. Tomorrow Bernardo would speak with this French refugee who came regularly to the Academy to coach the students in music. And he would practice his Mozart number until it flowed from the keys of the pianoforte without one error.

He practiced the music, going without afternoon tea, working at it until he was called to supper, and after supper going over it again and again. And even after he was in bed he played the notes over in his mind, pushing aside thoughts of Miss Eeles that kept slipping in with the music.

If he was as certain of remembering the piece as he was of the picture of her, then his teacher would indeed praise him.

"You have done it perfectly," his music teacher said, and his mild, plain face looked pleased, "with fine style."

He was preparing to leave and Bernardo had not asked the important question. The words somehow seemed difficult. And already his teacher was going through the door, and down the long hallway toward the entrance.

The front door closed behind the Frenchman.

Bernardo dashed through the hall, pulled open the entrance door and raced after his teacher. "I am going to the village," he said. "I will walk with you."

"Then get your hat, young man," his teacher said.

"Sir," Bernardo said, "do you know a family in Richmond named Eeles? If you do, could you please introduce me?" The words sprang from his lips almost too eagerly, too anxiously.

"I know the family." The Frenchman smiled.

Bernardo flushed. "Could you introduce me, sir?"

"Well," and his teacher's voice was quietly amused, "perhaps it is not impossible. If your lesson is well done next time, we shall see."

Two weeks later Bernardo and his teacher were invited to the Eeles residence for dinner.

In his room Bernardo dressed carefully. He had changed suits twice, and then all his waistcoats looked wrong, and the one he selected was missing a button. He kept going to the small grate fire to warm his hands. He wished his hair was less curly, and he never before had noticed that his nose was too large. If only he had known about this engagement in time to let his sideburns grow longer! Suppose Miss Eeles preferred dark eyes to blue and a very tall gentleman to one of medium height?

At last he was ready and polished, his long capota tossed back across one shoulder, beaver hat tilted smartly, cane in his gloved hand.

Walking with his music teacher to the Eeles house he asked Miss Eeles' first name.

"Clara," his teacher said.

Carlota. That was how it was called in Spanish. Bernardo repeated it to himself. It was a beautiful name.

When he was introduced to her, his face flushed hotly. But he remembered to keep his heels together, to bow formally and to kiss the hands of both Miss Eeles and her mother.

At dinner he ate almost nothing although there was roast duck, roast pork, plum tarts and wine such as he had not tasted since he had come to England. He answered questions about Chile and Peru. He watched Carlota Eeles whose eyes were golden and smiling. For the first time in his life his heart was entrapped by a girl.

Then, following dinner, more talk of places, books. There was music. He listened eagerly to descriptions of Ireland where the Eeles came from. Bernardo gathered in each word about his father's homeland. The longing for home was in all Mr. Eeles' words. No other land or continent could boast the velvet green of hills and valleys of Ireland, Mr. Eeles said. The sea rushed in to embrace the bright coastline. Small was the island, he said, and yet as large as all the great hearts that ever came from there.

Mrs. Eeles laughed softly, as if she enjoyed the sound of his extravagant words.

But Bernardo thought that for a man who loved home, there were no superlatives. The finest words elude him. The best words to describe a loved homeland had never been invented, for the true meaning of home was not in any combination of letters.

Carlota said she would sing of Ireland to Mr. Riquelme. She would play her father's favorite ballad about their land. And she glanced up at Bernardo standing beside her at the pianoforte. Her golden eyes filled with pleasant mockery.

She sang, and it was of Scotland.

Her parents enjoyed her prank, as he did. These merry people, he thought. This pleasant Richmond. This perfect Carlota!

Carlota. He said it over constantly during the days that followed.

He was invited to Mr. Eeles' birthday party. He sent a gift of Spanish decanters; Spanish wine. For Carlota he took with him to the party a sandalwood fan.

And, because she had insisted, he brought along Spanish songs. He sang them for the guests. Chillan, his mother and all that he loved seemed close. The dances of Chile, Carlota liked. She learned them quickly. There should be castanets, he said. He would bring them another time.

During the following weeks he went often to the Eeles' home. He met people from Richmond, London, from the Continent. Among them were many French refugees whose conversation was filled with anxiety about the political agitation in France.

One Sunday, Bernardo and other guests of the Eeles' were gathered around the fire in the sitting room. The conversation shifted to North America.

"In Philadelphia," one of the Frenchmen said, "a number of North American statesmen are interested in helping to free South America."

Bernardo straightened. This was the first he had heard of Americans being leagued for freeing Spanish American colonies.

"The London group must be aligned with the Americans," another said.

Bernardo had heard of the London group. No one could tell him anything more about it than they read in the papers. "We only know what we see in the newspapers," they always said.

Now he said, "What is the name of the American group interested in freedom for Spanish colonies?"

Mr. Eeles said, "I doubt if there is any such group, Bernardo. The British Cabinet would be concerned if that happened. They want South American trade for the English."

"But I hear rumors of an English group working with Spanish colonists to free their homeland," Bernardo said.

"In the newspapers only." Mr. Eeles smiled. He glanced around the circle. "We all read about it," he said. "It has been talked about in the papers for years. But nothing happens. It is probably a planned campaign on the part of our British statesmen to frighten the Spanish into signing a favorable trade pact with England."

Bernardo recalled that the English ships entered the Pacific to bring smuggled goods and thought Mr. Eeles might be right. But he also felt a trace of sadness that his people could not have the same freedom the North Americans had.

Carlota said there had been too much talk of politics. They would have music now.

The following Sunday he walked with her near the Thames. They crossed to Twickenham to wander along the other bank. He told her of Chile, of its bondage. If only he could help, he said.

For the first time he spoke openly of his hatred of the Spanish Crown!

She listened, twining her soft arm in his, looking up with gentle eyes. It was almost too good to believe that she liked him.

For a time he was silent. He watched her, thinking how beautiful were her golden eyebrows, the heavy lashes, her white skin. He studied her proud nose, her eyelids cool and smooth looking, the thoughtful softness of her mouth.

They walked on. The roadside was scattered with bluebells as bright as her dress. She picked a cluster and tucked them into her coat, stood looking at them and his heart filled suddenly with her sweetness, and a rush of happiness. The air was fragrant—rich flower scents, the odor of crushed grass under their feet.

She glanced at him, discovered the longing in his eyes. Her face flushed and her eyes warmed with a brighter glow. Almost imperceptibly she moved toward him, the swaying of a young branch in a slight breeze.

Impulsively, he kissed her. He felt the scarlet young lips. He took her in his arms, held her close, feeling completely happy. He released her, feasted on her face, his heart pounding hard with joy.

would have her sweetness. He would see her tomorrow.

The world was too beautiful. His heart was too jubilant.

In his room that night, staring into the darkness he lived again the moments with her. The night had her softness, tomorrow

They were going on an excursion to London. Carlota sat beside Bernardo in a coach that could accommodate six comfortably but was overcrowded with six adults and two children, with hatboxes tied with gay ribbons and many parcels.

He was sorry he had not hired a private coach, but there was none to be rented in Richmond. Another time he would try to manage it. Everything of the best for Carlota, he thought.

She pushed back her sunny hair, framed by her bonnet. Her eyes clung to him. "Tell me about Chile," she said, suddenly. "About the carriages and houses and people. Would I like it there?"

Would she like it? He looked away, saw tidy thatched houses, clean streets, winding lanes.

He looked down at her bright face. "If you like Indians," he said, and smiled. He told her of great mountains and rushing rivers, wide spaces, warm sun pouring over acacia and fields of orange poppies. But she would not enjoy the heavy carts with wheels six feet across, hauled by slow-paced oxen whose only harness was a yoke attached to the wagon tongue. Even on steep hills the only brake was a lasso tied to a wheel. She would be terrified going down steep mountain grades in the wagons.

He thought of the homes, the singing, the music, the people. She would like them.

If he could keep her with him forever, then he could ask no better future. With her to believe in him, he might perform some service for Chile.

She was singing, softly and for him, an Irish ballad.

He thought of nothing but her during the journey. And while

they were at the theater in London watching Mrs. Jordan, he heard the pleasant voice of the famous actress, but the words escaped him, for he was thinking only of Carlota.

Carlota! He said the name over to himself. How he loved her!

And he would marry her. He could not live without her!

The voices from the stage went on speaking the lines. Bernardo heard only his own thoughts, heard only that important question that he kept asking himself.

How could he marry Carlota? There were obstacles. There were many obstacles. For he had no money, he had no profession.

Worst of all, he had no name!

And suddenly his heart felt joyless and cold.

Then, she moved toward him and laid her warm hand on his, and the blood surged into his desolate heart.

He must find a way to marry her. He must find a way.

And he would think of a way! He would get money. He would give her his name, his true name.

For he would marry Carlota!

CHAPTER XX

THE DAYS passed and weeks. Bernardo tried to straighten out his turbulent thoughts about himself and Carlota. Now the Academy seemed too noisy. He walked often into the hills and along the river, needing to think out the problems.

Today, he had come to Richmond Hill. He stared at the hurrying sky, listened to the stirring of trees that whispered the name he loved.

There was only one way out.

His father must consent to his telling Carlota everything about himself. His rightful name should be her name. Carlota Higgins, he said aloud.

Without that permission he could not divulge his father's secret. His father must understand.

That night he struggled to write a letter. For half an hour he stared at the open fire in his room trying to word a letter in his mind.

At last he went to his desk. But he wrote nothing. He kept telling himself that he must write, for without his father's consent to speak to Carlota about his irregular birth, and his permission to use the name Higgins, he could not marry. He would not. For he wanted Carlota to have his true name. He would keep nothing from his beloved; he wanted to be completely open and honest with her.

If writing the letter was only as easy as choosing a profession. Days ago he had decided to enlist in the Royal Navy. England wanted recruits, to train as officers. He had a good education, an aptness for the sea. Soon he could become an officer. It was a noble profession and he could support a wife. There would be no carriages or fine houses for years, but he and Carlota could live simply and happily.

He would ask her to wait for him until he finished his training.

Now he had only to win his father's consent to using the name of Higgins, and his approval of a naval profession.

His head cleared. He began the letter. He said he was considering a naval career, for which he had some talent. He would like his father's approval. Without it he would do nothing, for the wish of his father would be Bernardo's wish.

He spoke of the Richmond families he had met. One was an Irish family from Dublin, a mother, father and daughter. The young lady was beautiful, agreeable and accomplished. He liked her very much. If his father knew Carlota he would approve of her thoroughly.

There he left the matter. His father would be able to read between the lines. It was better than asking outright for permission to marry, to mention the use of his own name.

Within a few days, he added, the Christmas holidays would be here. He wished his father happiness, and he prayed daily that God would guard and keep him.

Then the waiting. His father had not answered the other letters. But this one was important. It required an answer both about the name and a career. It would take months to hear, but his father would reply to this one.

Then December. The parties, the dancing, the theater in Richmond Green. England, at Christmas with Carlota near, was a beautiful world.

He was at the Eeles' home often.

Today, Mrs. Eeles was serving tea at the table piled high with a handsome tea service that she explained had been handed down from her mother. She spoke time and again of family. Of her own and the Riquelme line. She thought his family must be ancient and honorable people, and proud like the Irish. Her own family could be traced back to the Irish kings! And her eyes shone, her head lifted as she said it. "Tell me about your father," she said. "And your mother. You never have mentioned them, you know."

The copper-tinted liquid flowed smoothly from the arched neck of the teapot into a delicate porcelain cup.

Bernardo flushed. He could tell her of Don Simon Riquelme's noble family and an ancestor who had been secretary to Pizarro. He could speak of heroic deeds of the Riquelme family over centuries, both in Spain and in Chile, and of proud Don Simon who lived nobly like the gentleman he was. He could speak of the acres that rolled over Chillan mountains and valleys, of cattle, and sheep, servants and houses.

But his father he could not mention. And even if he could, she would never understand. Why should she, never having lived in constant danger on an Indian frontier where life was more important than a certificate of marriage?

This he could not explain to Mrs. Eeles.

He studied her plump face, her rounded figure. She wanted a proper background, a family line that conformed to custom.

Bernardo stared into his teacup, feeling depressed and cold.

Rising, he excused himself and crossed to the Academy.

There was a letter from his mother. It was filled with expressions of love, of her sadness at having him far away. Letters took such a long time. He glanced quickly down the pages written in his mother's usual charming style. One paragraph stood out.

"Chile has a new governor and president, since Don Ambrosio O'Higgins, Baron of Ballenary and Marquis of Osorno, has been named Viceroy of Peru."

The words thundered into Bernardo's head. His eyes fastened on the miraculous words.

His father Viceroy of Peru!

That position was next to the King in importance. In the colonies a viceroy acted for the King. Bernardo read the titles over: Baron of Ballenary, Marquis of Osorno, Viceroy of Peru!

His hand tightened on his mother's letter.

Now, more than ever, his father would refuse Bernardo his name. He would never openly acknowledge his son!

All the titles, the honors, the background. The O'Higgins, old and honorable. Irish titles and Spanish honors and titles. And names, names, names.

He stood motionless, his hand clutching the letter.

He could claim none of them. He could not even use his rightful name. He had no name. He had neither roots nor place, he was unwanted, unloved. And all was blackness. Blackness, blackness, blackness, ahead nothing but darkness. He wondered he did not die?

The days passed. The heaviness grew deeper within his heart.

Twice he saw Carlota. There had been long silences between them.

Tonight, Dr. David Dundas, a friend of Bernardo's, and surgeon to King George the Third, was giving a party for French refugees. Bernardo had promised weeks ago to entertain the guests with Spanish songs.

He would go.

Carlota would be there. He would explain to her that his future was hopeless, that he was nothing and possessed nothing of his own except his love for her.

He began dressing for the evening, choosing his finest white shirt, the handsome black suit, wanting to look his best for Carlota. He brushed his clothes twice.

Slowly, he walked to the Dundas residence which faced the Green. He tried to think how he would explain to Carlota that he was without a name, without fortune or profession.

He reached the house, passed the ancient yew tree in the garden. At the door a servant took his hat and capota. He said, "Miss Eeles would like you to come to the study, Mr. Riquelme."

Carlota was sitting in a wingchair beside the lighted grate. She saw him, sprang to her feet. Running to him she clasped his arm with her pretty hands. "Bernardo!" she said, tears in her eyes. "We are leaving for Dublin! My father has been called back suddenly. We leave at once!"

"Carlota!" Feeling desperate, he looked at her dear face. He could not let her leave him, he must cry aloud that he adored her, would love her forever, that she belonged with him. For if his love was taken from him, there was no living, no need for living without Carlota.

With despairing eyes he gazed at her. But his lips remained mute.

She looked at her hands on his arm, waiting for his protests, for words of love, of marriage, for words he could not, must not say. But he would explain. She must understand. His distracted mind tried to form words. "Carlota," he said, the words spilling forth, "I shall never marry!"

Her face turned pale as death. "Bernardo!" she cried. She darted from the room, her dress fluttering like a flame in the wind. Then the light was gone.

The music of pianoforte, flute, viol coming from the music room was a dirge and in his heart was the sharp, blinding pain and in his mind utter desolation and anguish.

He leaned hard against the mantelpiece, hearing the dirge, the sorrowful lament.

Then there was silence and the slow, painful beating of his heart.

Dr. Dundas called to him from the doorway: "Mr. Riquelme, will you play for us now?"

Bernardo looked at him dully, unable to answer.

"That Spanish song." the doctor said gaily, "Carlota's favorite."

No! Not the fiesta song, Bernardo told himself. Not that one. He could not. He must excuse himself. For he never would sing again. He would tell Dr. Dundas that he was ill.

But the friendly blue eyes of the doctor watched him. And Bernardo had promised. You kept a promise. It was your word. Small or great, you kept your word, for your word was what you were.

He said, "Yes, Doctor, I will play."

After a moment he was steady enough to cross the room.

At the pianoforte he rubbed warmth into his cold hands. He struck a chord. Then another chord, and still a third. At last he was able to speak the words. Slowly, at first, and softly. The fiesta song was supposed to be sung with great gusto and to come from the heart.

He began to shout the song. The shouting helped.

CHAPTER XXI

RICHMOND without Carlota was unbearable. The school year would never end, it seemed to Bernardo.

But somehow the weeks passed. Instead of going to Margate, Bernardo went to London for the summer. He had written Don Nicolas asking permission to continue his education in London. With good tutors, he wrote, he could finish his schooling in six months. After that, he explained, he planned to join the Royal Navy, for it was an honorable profession and to his liking. He gave Don Nicolas the address in York Street where he had rented rooms.

In the small parlor on York Street, Bernardo wrote an advertisement for tutors in mathematics and languages. He had spoken to a Frenchman whom he met in Richmond and the gentleman suggested a man named Don Francisco Miranda. Born in Venezuela, he had been an officer in the Spanish army and because of his sympathy with revolutionary French ideas, he was unable to return to Spain. His income had been stopped by the Spanish. This gentleman, Bernardo had been told, was extremely well educated and an expert mathematician.

Today, he was going to meet the man.

He left the small brick house on York Street, walked toward the river. For a little while he watched the ships. Soon he hoped a ship would be his home.

He walked on, going toward Great Putney Street, feeling depressed and sad in spite of the sunshine. He kept telling himself that another six months and he would begin a profession. Then he would have something to work for, something of his own that belonged to him; there would be a goal, a little light.

But his unhappiness was heavy upon him, because without Carlota there was no meaning to his existence. Drably the time passed now she was gone from him forever.

He climbed the steps to Number 33 Great Putney Street, where Miranda resided. He knocked. A servant ushered him into a plainly furnished sitting room and asked him to wait.

Bernardo sat on a rush-bottomed chair near a plain table, which held a bust of Apollo, a silver candlestick, books, writing paper, glass inkwell, gloves, a snuff box of silver engraved with the initial M.

Slowly, his eyes traveled about the room, to the windows hung with deep crimson, shutters pushed back to let in sun, the mantelpiece, dark somber eye of the unlighted grate. Above the white shelf was a large map of North and South America.

He studied the map, located the slender country of Chile. A little warmth went through him. He searched for Peru. Found it and quickly, glanced away.

Then the door opened. A gentleman of medium height entered with a brisk step. His brown hair was unpowdered and he carried himself like a soldier. He might be fifty. He did not look like a tutor of mathematics.

"Mr. Riquelme?" His voice was quick and cultured. His gray eyes smiled.

Bernardo rose. "Mr. Miranda," he said.

The gentleman stretched a hand, clasped Bernardo's in a hearty grip. He swung around the table and dropped into a chair.

Bernardo sat down again. "As I explained in my letter," he said, "I need a tutor for several months, chiefly in mathematics."

"Why?" Miranda looked at him, earnestly.

"I hope to join the British navy."

"It is a difficult life," Miranda said. "Mathematics will not make a sailor."

Bernardo felt annoyed. Apparently this gentleman had judged from his hands, his good clothes, that he had no capacity for hard work. "I know ships," he said. "I have skill at arms and particularly the sword. The profession appeals to me."

"You want to fight, then? You wish to be a hero? For some girl, I suppose?" he said, sharply.

Bernardo stiffened. "No, sir," he said, stoutly. "It is not glory

I seek. It is a place I want, where I can serve within my limitations. Let others lead," he said. "Let them have glory. I am happy to follow. I want no honors."

Thoughtfully, Miranda studied him. "You are extremely modest, young man," he said. "Your choice is commendable. I know important officers in the British navy. I can help you."

A stranger offering him help, and unsought? Bernardo was astonished. After a moment he said, "Thank you, sir."

"Well, then." Miranda pulled his chair nearer the table. "Shall we begin? Where did you leave off in mathematics?"

"I had not expected a lesson today," Bernardo said. "I thought you would only want to question me. I brought no textbook."

"Question you? But I already know about you, young man. You are Bernardo Riquelme from Chile. You are about twenty. Four years ago you entered the Academy of Mr. Hill in Richmond." He gazed steadily as Bernardo, a twinkle in his lively eyes. "It surprises you that I know all this? Well, Mr. Riquelme, I make it my business to learn about every South American who comes to England. There are not so many."

Bernardo was startled. That he had been watched had never occurred to him. And why had he been spied upon? Who had been the spy? He thought over the people he knew in Richmond. Was it one of the refugee Frenchmen? Perhaps the one who had recommended Miranda as a tutor.

In that case, Miranda was more than a tutor.

"At the social gatherings in Richmond," Miranda said, "you discussed politics. You were informed of what was happening in North America and in England. You were aware of a group that was working to free South America and you asked repeatedly where the leaders could be located. But you were disappointed." His voice was kind. "If you had not come to me, soon I would have invited you here, to explain that there is such a group."

With a feeling of intense excitement, Bernardo studied the serious face of Miranda.

Then there was a group working to unify South Americans! A

group working for the freedom of all the Spanish colonies! Bernardo had been asking all these years about the group. He had given up asking, for none could answer. And now he had his answer. There was such a group. He asked eagerly, "Where can I find the leader? I must join him! I must help!"

The room was quiet.

Miranda broke the silence. "Young man," he said. "You are looking at him!"

When he was able to speak, Bernardo said. "Sir, how can I help? I will do anything."

"The young make promises with eagerness," Miranda said. "I have had you watched, and I believe you have qualities needed by this cause. But you must be certain. The work I am doing has been my life since I fought in the North American Revolution. At that time my imagination was fired by General George Washington. Later, I saw him enter Philadelphia, the hero, almost the saint of the people." His voice was reverent. "An acclamation such as I never expect to see again."

Miranda studied the tall candlestick on his table. "There will never be another Washington!" he said.

For a moment Bernardo stood in Philadelphia beside Miranda, gazing upon the erect figure, the patient face, of the incomparable General Washington.

"In all the world, Mr. Riquelme, there are only two countries that have free governments. They are England and North America." He gazed soberly at Bernardo.

Bernardo said, "I have given the freedom of South America great thought."

"This cause will demand of you your fortune, your entire interest, perhaps your life," Miranda said. "Every moment there will be risks. The Spanish will hound you as they have hounded me. By every ruse they have attempted to trap me into entering Spanish territory. They have promised me amnesty, a haven, the return of my fortune in Caracas, advancement in military rank."

Rising, he went to a window.

"Often I think of my father's spacious home in Caracas, with sun on vast groves, of tufted royal palms, of great walls, tiled roofs, long valleys of blue mist and the green of sugar cane." He sighed and stood quietly as if seeing his homeland beyond the window.

Bernardo thought of Chile, its beauty, the hacienda of his grandfather. How often he wanted to be there. How he longed for Chile.

"I wish to return to my country," Miranda said. "But when I do, it will be to free my countrymen. And who can predict when that will come? There have been many disappointments."

He turned and faced Bernardo. "These are the things you must weigh before you decide. For you will be required to take an oath. And once the pledge is given, there can be no turning back."

Bernardo thought of the risks, as he had in times past. The spies of Spain were everywhere. Even in England and North America were the informers, searching out the rebels. But what did life offer comparable to an opportunity to help free his country and all South America? The risks? Had he not been under shadows all his lifetime because of them? Had he not always been on guard to keep his father's secret?

"My life is my own," he said. "I have thought long on the need to free South America from the yoke of Spain. I will take the oath now, and gladly!"

Don Francisco Miranda looked at him sternly, "Are you very sure?"

"I will take the oath! Today, tomorrow, whenever you say." Bernardo got to his feet, feeling strong and confident. "I shall never be more certain than now. But if you prefer, sir, I will wait."

"Then today," Miranda said. "Wait here for me."

He left the room.

The sunlight danced along the candlestick, lighted the corners, even the black eye of the grate. Bernardo waited impatiently, feeling himself on the threshold of a great and thrilling experience. The risks seemed close and the dangers. He felt superior to them.

Miranda returned and handed Bernardo a paper to read.

He took it, his hands as steady as those of a helmsman's on a wheel. If his heart beat fast, it was the anticipation of learning more about the great cause. And if his spine tightened it was because he realized the importance of this moment.

He glanced at the paper. At the head was the name of the organization, *Gran Americana Reunion*, and below were the articles which each member pledged himself to abide by. He read them all carefully. There were thirty-five.

They were to: give fortune and life to work for South American independence, profess the democratic faith, influence colonial administrations to favor the cause, attempt to win over public officials who could aid in a successful revolt, call members brothers.

They were not to: put messages in writing, hold a meeting of more than seven members, reveal the existence of the Lodge by word or sign on penalty of death.

The motto of the Lodge was, "Union, Strength and Virtue."

Bernardo finished reading the articles and handed the pages to Miranda. His heart beat fast and his lips were dry. When he tried to breathe there seemed no breath.

"I am ready to take the oath," he said, firmly.

Standing before him Miranda said, "Raise your right hand, and repeat after me these words."

Bernardo lifted his right hand. He spoke the words of the oath after the leader Miranda.

As he spoke, the room vanished. Around him were his oppressed countrymen, their eyes pleading for his help. Their distress was his, and their sorrows, the bonds that shackled them would be his to shatter, and until they were free Bernardo would never rest. With his heart he would labor to unite them. A great tenderness for his people surged up to fill his being, and as he repeated the words after Miranda, he felt dedicated and inspired. Like a great condor, his spirits soared higher. This moment made him one with all the enslaved, until all were free.

"So help me God!" Bernardo said, earnestly, ending the pledge.

And the forces of good would be with him, because he had sworn to fulfill a righteous cause. As the North Americans had forged the first link in the chain of liberty, so he would help to forge another, and yet another, until all people of all nations were at liberty. The fetters that burdened his countrymen would drop away. He had dedicated his life to that purpose. It was all he had.

Miranda clasped Bernardo's hand. "This day is decreed in the book of destiny," he said, solemnly. "Wisdom, valor and constancy will protect you from the blows of the tyrants."

The blows? He did not fear them. Bernardo felt at that moment strong enough to resist anything.

There would be a meeting with other Lodge members on the coming Friday, Miranda said. He gave Bernardo the address and directions about reaching the place.

"Sir," Bernardo said, gratefully, "I feel as if my life had only begun. You have given me a reason for my being." Tears rushed to his eyes.

Walking toward his rooms, Bernardo thought how beautiful London was. He had always liked the city. But he had never before realized its perfection of setting. The light over the river, the beauty of bridges, the tidiness of houses and the attractive plantings of trees and gardens. He was akin to every person that passed. Each face was friendly, all seemed stamped with nobility and greatness.

A great sense of belonging possessed him. Existence had meaning. He had a place. His career was decided for him. The restlessness and doubt had vanished.

He crossed Pall Mall and went toward St. James Park. He thought, how wonderful to be linked with his countrymen who were dedicated to bringing liberty to the Spanish colonies.

He understood how his father felt about his sacrifice to bring happiness to Chile. His father would delight in his course.

How Bernardo hated the Spanish tyranny. His father must despise it too, and he would be first to approve the enlightened change in the colonies, for he had worked to bring reforms against great odds. How thankful his father would be to learn that thousands in both North America and England were joined with him in his efforts.

With what pleasure Bernardo would follow in the footsteps of his father to bring even greater happiness to the people of Chile. For the freedom of the individual was the only true happiness.

And then, he reached his residence in York Street. He began to sing as lightly he ran up the steps.

Friday evening came at last.

Eagerly, Bernardo hurried to the address given him by Miranda. He passed through the door of the handsome building as he had been directed, crossed a carpeted hall and reached for the bronze handle of an oak door.

He was standing in a room with windows at one end, the other three walls filled with books to the ceiling. At a round table in the center of the room sat Don Francisco Miranda and three other Lodge members.

One was dark skinned, an older man with tired, unhappy eyes. He stared disapprovingly at Bernardo as he was introduced.

"Pedro Jose Caro," Miranda said. "Bernardo Riquelme."

Caro said shortly, "He looks very young."

"Would that we all were as young," Miranda said.

The man named Caro watched Bernardo suspiciously, as if he distrusted him.

And the feeling was mutual. Caro seemed entirely too much the fictional revolutionist to Bernardo. His fantastic disguise, which he had brought from France for the approval of fellow Lodge members, was too theatrical. The black wig was almost a perfect imitation of the hair of a negro. With a little darkening of Caro's skin, he might pass for one. He had a stain for his body that was almost impossible to remove, Caro said, and it was not affected by perspiration or water. With this disguise he planned to enter the Kingdom of Santa Fé in South America and spread the gospel of liberty secretly among the negroes.

The disguise was clever. He had taken great pains to have his appearance a complete deception. But he appeared more concerned with the disguise than his mission. He seemed to want personal glory and rewards. He kept speaking of finances. He wanted more money, he said. Where was the money to come from?

At last Caro was quiet.

"The immediate duty of the Lodge brothers is to unite the people in the colonies," Miranda said. "This we are doing by sending our members into the various colonies to preach the word quietly. Already we have contact with residents, in almost every country in South America and in the islands owned by Spain, who are willing to work with brothers of the Lodge. They are not members. Later some of them may be. The work demands patience. It will take much time. It will require years. Each member will have his work carefully planned for him." He glanced at Bernardo. "For the present," he said, "Mr. Riquelme will remain here in London. He plans to join the British navy where he will learn navigation. We shall need naval officers in our work."

The great candles in the bronze candelabras burned steadily, lighting each face around the table.

For Bernardo the place was hallowed, and the leader Miranda a prophet, a seer, one of the great who would live throughout history along with General Washington. As he listened to the voice of Miranda, he felt again the inspiration of that first day of their meeting when Bernardo had dedicated himself to this cause. He listened, hanging eagerly on each word.

"In the beginning the government of the colonies will be modeled after the English plan, a liberal monarchy," Miranda said. "Benefits will be equalized. Both native and Spanish will share in government. There will be no privileged class. Excessive taxation will be abolished. The terrible *meta* and *encomendium* systems will be abolished. There will be equitable distribution of land and freedom of commerce with the world will bring prosperity. The Church will no longer control government. Free public schools and libraries will be established."

"We know all this," Caro said, impatiently. "How is the money to be provided?"

Miranda said, "But Mr. Riquelme is a new member. He does not know."

Bernardo thought, how painstakingly this great man worked. Everything was important. With such a leader the cause would not fail! He felt rededicated here in this room, listening to the golden words that foretold emancipation for his country.

"Backed by North America and England," Miranda said, "the Spanish colonists will have strength. With the example of how England lost her American colonies as a pattern, the Spanish Crown will consent to the plan offered by colonial patriots. No blood will be shed. For the colonists hold the power. It is they who provide Spain with her revenue and products. See, how already North America and England under their pact of amity have prospered as never before. They have renewed their ancient friendship. That is how it will be between South America and Spain."

A bloodless revolution! That was how all revolts should be conducted. Bernardo stared at the brightly burning candle near him. No more would the people of his country fear the Crown or the Inquisition. He seemed to see the happiness on the faces of the people in the plazas as they heard, and to hear bells ringing from each church until the glad sound was ringing the length of South America. That happy day!—he thought. That happy moment when there were free courts and unbiased judges. And no beatings in the marketplaces. Every child would have a school reader, tablet, pencil and be able to read a Chilean paper, just as he had the London *Times*.

"Even the whist table is a place to spread the word of freedom," Miranda said, glancing up from the paper before him. "Make everything an opportunity to publish the gospel of freedom." And he related some of his experiences in Russia to illustrate his point.

It was over the whist table that he had first interested Catherine the Great of Russia in the cause. He had met in South Russia the princes Potemkin, Viasemsky and Nassansiegen, during a journey of Catherine to her provinces. It was seventeen degrees below zero. The traveling coach of Her Masjesty was an apartment de luxe on wheels. In the salon were a whist table and a library, and daily the Austrian ambassador, the British Minister Fitzherbert and the French Minister the Comte de Ségur, came to solve puzzles, play charades, to recite poetry and to play bridge. It did not require any great intelligence to realize they were there for something more than games. One did not travel into below-zero weather for parlor games.

Miranda smiled at his friends about the table. The great clock against the wall ticked loudly. And the tall candles burned lower.

Through the Prince Potemkin, Miranda had met the Empress. He was introduced to Catherine's lover, General Mamonow. A game of whist was arranged. At the card table Her Majesty asked Miranda about America and Spain, and if the Inquisition still existed. She wanted to know about Arab architecture at Granada and the gardens and baths and literature of Spain. And what about his native country? She did not know where Venezuela was located. But she wanted to know about the natives, the Jesuits, Charles the Third of Spain. He remembered how she looked in her gown of gauze and how expertly she played whist, yet conversing all the time about many subjects.

Miranda glanced about the table as if it were the whist table in the palace of Catherine and he was deciding how to play a card.

It was at the whist table on another occasion, Miranda related, that the Empress again asked, most earnestly, about the Inquisition. She thought he should remain in Russia. He would be burnt by the Inquisition if he returned to Spain. She thought that would be a pity.

How gay Miranda's face was when he laughed!

And yet, how right Empress Catherine had been about the Inquisition!

She had given Miranda ten thousand rubles to prosecute the rebellion; in her private apartment there was enough lapis lazuli and mother-of-pearl to finance an army. And she was in favor of independence for the natives of all countries except her own. She would not lend her open support.

The Spanish government had attempted to take Miranda from Russia. But he escaped them. He went to Stockholm and then to England.

Years ago, Miranda went on, when he was in Boston, Samuel Adams had given him valuable information about the origin, principles and events of the recent revolution in North America. He had spoken with James Bowdoin on the same subject. And General Knox had helped formulate a plan for co-operation in liberating the Spanish colonies.

"And everywhere," Miranda said, "I made friends for the independence of South America. Now William Pitt, Prime Minister of England, and other cabinet officers are considering a plan which has been worked out by men more competent at that sort of thing than myself."

He paused and glanced around the table. "Several years ago," he continued, "I visited Prime Minister Pitt at his country place in Kent. I presented to him a plan for freeing the colonies. That plan was prepared with the assistance of Thomas Pownall who was British governor of the North American Colonies prior to the Revolution."

Miranda stared at the sheets before him. "Mr. Pitt looked with favor upon the plan," he said. "There have been delays. Now another plan is ready and it will be presented to him. There are only minor differences from the first plan. We can only wait. These matters take years to materialize.

"Our plan asks for men, ships and money," he went on. "And in return we are asking to have a canal cut across the Isthmus of Panama. It will facilitate commerce with the west coast of South America and the Orient. As you know Spain has always guarded the Isthmus like a dog in a manger, forbidding any official even to speak of a canal. The Crown believes that a waterway at the Isthmus makes her colonies more vulnerable, less easy to protect from foreign conquest."

Bernardo remembered that hot, tiresome ride he made across the Isthmus when he journeyed to Spain. It was obvious, he thought, that a canal would be a boon to navigation. And it was certain to come. It would come with the freedom of the colonies.

Miranda glanced at Bernardo. "All this I have reviewed for Mr.

Riquelme," he said, "our new member. Now, let us speak of current business. Caro," he said, "what about Santa Fé?"

The clock ticked off the hours.

For Bernardo the new horizon broadened. He listened to each word, laid it away carefully in his mind. He must listen and learn. One day he would require all the information that was being given him in this library, on a quiet street of London.

The hours were rich and full now he was working with his countrymen for the freedom of their homeland. They had a common interest. No longer the loneliness, the feeling of being unwanted.

He could think of Carlota without that sharp almost unbearable sensation of pain.

Each morning he went to Great Putney Street for coaching in mathematics and government, for instructions about working for the cause. At Miranda's house he met English business men and officials who were interested in the freeing of the Spanish colonies.

With each day, he arose hoping there would be a letter from Don Nicolas de la Cruz, giving him permission to remain in London for the coming school year, and continue his studies with his tutor.

And each day he was disappointed. The letter from Don Nicolas had not come when summer was over. It was almost time to return to the Academy in Richmond.

Bernardo thought about it that morning in his sitting room on York Street. The prim Academy, the proper Mr. Hill and the students seemed now to belong to another world, a distant and uninteresting world where there was talk of tennis, holidays and social affairs. He had outgrown the Academy. He seemed a thousand years older than when he left Richmond a few months ago.

And then, there would be no Carlota.

He studied the pattern of his draperies.

But Don Nicolas represented Bernardo's father. Until he sent instructions from Cadiz, Bernardo must remain at the Academy.

He must go now to his agents, Spencer and Perkins, for tuition and expense money for the coming year, since his funds were running low. And he may as well go immediately.

With a heavy heart, he left his rooms and crossed London to the office of Spencer and Perkins.

The same piles of rusty iron, broken shutters, the same pale-faced clerk.

Mr. Perkins was discussing scrap iron with three men. When he saw Bernardo enter, he did not speak.

"Good morning, Mr. Perkins," Bernardo said, trying to appear cheerful. "When you have time, may I speak with you?"

"What you have to say, can be said now." Mr. Perkins' face hardened.

He supposed Mr. Perkins was still annoyed because Bernardo had not left the Academy in Richmond. He had offered the Israelite College of London if Bernardo would come with him as an apprentice, but he had refused.

He objected to discussing his business before strangers; still if Mr. Perkins insisted, he would have to. "I want to draw on my account," he said.

Mr. Perkins turned on him. He said angrily: "There is no more money! I owe you nothing!"

But of course there was money. Mr. Perkins was trying to embarrass Bernardo, and before strangers. "I will wait. When you have finished with your customers, we can talk," Bernardo said.

"Get out!"

Bernardo could not believe his ears. He stared at Mr. Perkins. The man could not be serious. "Look, Mr. Perkins," he said as calmly as he could, "if you are disturbed because I would not come as an apprentice, that is your business. But I will not go until you turn over my money to me."

"The Israelite College is not fine enough," Mr. Perkins said.

"I was ordered by my guardian to attend school at Richmond," Bernardo answered, and his face flushed.

The customers and clerk stopped what they were doing to watch. They were enjoying Bernardo's embarrassment.

"You get no money." Mr. Perkins struck his hand against the

desk. "Mr. Romera owes me much money. That is reason enough for me not to advance you cash."

Bernardo said indignantly, "I am not responsible for Mr. Romera's debts to you. You have my money, you are my agent, and I must have funds for tuition and living for a year."

"Get out!" ordered Mr. Perkins. His voice was scornful.

Bernardo controlled his anger. He let the insult pass a second time. He would not stoop to a brawl with Mr. Perkins. Fighting would get him nothing. Although he was confident Mr. Perkins was withholding money due him, he was in no position to demand restitution until he had an accounting from Don Nicolas de la Cruz.

He walked out. Rude laughter followed him.

Disturbed, he went along the street that was cluttered with debris and ash cans. It had never occurred to him that there would be trouble with the agents over money. And now he must get a letter off to Don Nicolas, immediately.

A gust of wind sent dirt and papers whirling about him.

Don Nicolas had not answered his letter about returning to the Academy in Richmond. But that was still three weeks away and any day there would be a letter. It was one thing to delay a letter about another school term in Richmond. But Don Nicolas would be greatly disturbed if he thought Bernardo was without funds. And he would remit the money immediately.

At home he wrote the letter to Don Nicolas. He posted it at once.

Then a week passed and there was no reply from his friend in Cadiz. Two weeks passed and then a third. Still no letter.

It was too late now to return to the Academy in Richmond.

Bernardo was troubled at not having heard from Don Nicolas but he was not downcast. Life now had purpose and meaning. He was rooted in a great cause and it steadied him. He kept telling himself that a letter would come. And he was delighted not to be attending the Academy in Richmond.

He wrote another letter to Cadiz. He conserved his dwindling funds.

The weeks passed.

Bernardo allowed himself one meal, daily. For lunch he ate an orange or an apple instead. He spent hours at the library reading books on government, suggested by Miranda. Regularly, he went to Great Putney Street for lessons and to the meetings of the Lodge brothers. Sometimes he was invited to dinner with Miranda by some important Englishman who was interested in the cause of freedom for South America.

At a dinner at the house of John Turnbull, one evening long after Bernardo's last letter to Don Nicolas, Miranda and their host discussed finances. The firm, Turnbull, Forbes and Company, had been advancing money for the cause. And with an eye on trade with the Spanish colonies.

Mr. Turnbull looked at Bernardo across the handsome damask cloth, the choice dinner service. Perhaps he noticed the pallor of Bernardo's face, the loose manner in which his coat fell about his shoulders since he had lost weight. Or, he may only have spoken out of kindness. "Mr. Riquelme," he said, "if you need financial help for living expenses, call on me."

"Thank you, sir, I need nothing," Bernardo said, proudly. He was grateful, but he could not accept charity.

And then his last money was gone and he had eaten nothing all day.

In desperation, he went to Mr. Perkins.

"If there is no money, Mr. Perkins," he said, "let me have enough to travel to Cadiz. I will straighten the matter out and return. You will be given suitable interest for the loan."

But Mr. Perkins only said again, "Get out!"

Against his will, Bernardo was forced to accept Mr. Turnbull's charity.

It was a brisk morning in March when he reached Miranda's residence for a lesson. Before he had been five minutes in the sitting room, he forgot about the lesson.

"Momentarily," Miranda said, "I am expecting word that England will help in freeing the Spanish colonies. The British will provide money and ships, and America will give troops. The moment the message arrives, I must send word at once to our compatriots in Trinidad and in Philadelphia!"

Bernardo sat transfixed, gazing at his teacher.

If only he would be given the boon of carrying word to the friends! His heart was beating fast. His lips felt dry as if chill winds of the lomas had blown across him.

He wanted to be the one to deliver that wonderful message!

"Sir," he said, and his heart was praying, "let me carry the message to Philadelphia!"

Miranda said kindly, "If all our colonials had your devotion to this purpose, how easy the victory would be!" He was thoughtful. After a moment he said: "We will arrange for you to carry the news. We will go now and discuss it with Turnbull."

In the street they hailed a carriage.

A shipment of goods was going to North America within a fortnight, Mr. Turnbull said, and Bernardo could travel on the ship at Mr. Turnbull's expense.

"And in Philadelphia," Miranda said, briskly, "you can join the army that General Washington is training for the liberation of our countries. Or you can continue on to Chile and work for the freedom of your country."

To train under General Washington!

The floor of the office seemed to heave like a ship at sea. Bernardo steadied himself by gripping the desk.

He stood watching Miranda writing at the desk. After a few minutes, and still holding the quill in a hand, he read aloud what he had written in a vigorous, clear voice:

"The Honorable William Pitt,

"Sir: A young Chilean who is actually in London would voluntarily undertake to transmit this decision . . . "

Bernardo studied Miranda. He was speaking of Bernardo Riquelme in the letter to the Prime Minister of England. It sounded important. And Bernardo was not important. He was only a messenger willing to carry the wonderful news.

He felt too weak to continue standing. Slowly he dropped into the wingchair beside him. He felt as if he were going to suffer an attack of chills. But he was also deeply proud.

Somehow, he got back to York Street, walking unsteadily as if he had taken too much wine. He wanted to sing, his feet were eager to dance the fandango, except that on the London Street he must not dance. The clouds piled up above bare branches like sails of a great armada going to free his people. He was as light in spirit as the clouds.

At home he began packing. Pulling his trunks into the small parlor with the worn Turkey carpet, he got in all his belongings, except the clothes he would wear. He was sorry his suits were so worn. The most presentable one looked shabby in places.

He was packed and ready. For although Mr. Turnbull said it would be a fortnight before Bernardo sailed, Mr. Pitt might want the message delivered sooner. Bernardo might have to sail immediately.

He began a letter to Don Nicolas de la Cruz, in Cadiz, for he must let Don Nicolas know that he was leaving England. He wrote rapidly. He said that in two and a half years he had received only one letter from Don Nicolas, although he had written repeatedly asking for advice and money. He had been forced to accept loans from London business men for his bare necessities. The agents, Spencer and Perkins, had refused to advance money. He was waiting no longer, feeling he had been abandoned by his friend, and he was leaving London.

"My intention is to go from here direct to America," he said in closing. "I have some business friends who have agreed to give me free passage to Trinidad or Philadelphia and from there I can go on to make my living in Spanish America where no matter how bad, it could never be worse than here."

Then he mailed the letter.

There would be no answer. And now, Bernardo did not care. For he was going to North America where men were entirely free of the bondage of domination! He would learn from the magnificent and heroic General Washington how to help free his countrymen. He would have a share in breaking the shackles placed on his people by the Spanish Crown. Republics soon would be born in

South America. They would be an example for nations of the old world. North America had shown the way. He would be linked to the struggle.

Ahead his future stretched, certain and clear. The cool March wind tugged at his worn hat, penetrated his worn suit, for long ago he had sold his capota with the wide skirt, the handsome collar, thinking soon money would come from Don Nicolas and he could replace the cape with a greatcoat. But he did not mind the cold tonight, for his happiness was too great.

As he walked back to York Street he repeated those words of Alexander Hamilton, written to Miranda, which Bernardo had memorized because he wanted them with him always.

"The plan, in my opinion, ought to be a fleet of Great Britain and an army of the United States—a government for the liberated territories agreeable to both the co-operators about which there will be no difficulty. To arrange the plan, a competent authority from Great Britain to some person here is the best expedient. Your presence here will, in this case, be extremely expedient. We are raising an army of about 12,000 men. General Washington has resumed his station at the head of our armies; I am appointed second in command. With esteem and regard, I remain, Dear Sir, Your very obedient servant. A. Hamilton."

Bernardo quickened his step.

Only a few days and he would be sailing on his great mission. How close and friendly the stars. How good to have a purpose. How wonderful to belong!

The days passed. A letter came from Don Nicolas. He ordered Bernardo to leave London immediately, for Cadiz.

CHAPTER XXII

In his rooms on York Street, Bernardo read the letter from Don
Nicolas de la Cruz ordering him to Cadiz at once. A few steps away
from where he stood were his trunks packed for his trip to North
America, carrying a message from the British Prime Minister to his
compatriots about freeing the Spanish colonies. He stared at the
trunks. He would not go to Cadiz! He would not give up this experience, this opportunity to help the cause. He would not!

For years he had obeyed his guardians without question. For
months upon months Don Nicolas had neglected him, and now
suddenly almost on the eve of Bernardo's great adventure, this
cruel letter commanding him to return to Cadiz. No reason was
given. Like a puppet he was expected to obey. Well, he would not!
For now he had another who commanded him. The cause demanded his allegiance. He had given his word. His duty was to the
cause of freedom.

He went that afternoon to show Miranda the letter. "I am not
going to Cadiz," he said. "My mind is made up. I am going to
North America."

Miranda read Don Nicolas' letter. He looked up and his eyes
were disturbed. "Don Nicolas will notify the Spanish," he said. "In
America the Spanish Ambassador will question you. His secret
service men will hound you, watching your every act. You do not
know the evil Spanish police. They will read wrong into your innocent answers. I have suffered at their hands." His voice was anxious. "You must return to Don Nicolas," Miranda said, "for the
good of the cause."

Standing at the open grate trying to warm his hands, Bernardo heard the advice and his heart went dead. He stared at the flames. His hopes had been bright too. Now they were ashes. He would never train with General Washington.

For the good of the cause, then, he must not refuse to return to Cadiz. He must not take risks if it endangered the hope of freedom for his country. Reluctantly, he let the happy dream go. "I will write Don Nicolas that I am coming at once," Bernardo said.

"You can take messages to the Lodge brothers in Cadiz." Miranda tried to make it sound cheerful. "And special instructions to the officers of the Lodge. You must memorize them. You must carry nothing about the Lodge in writing."

A little hope crept into Bernardo's heart. At least, he would be serving the cause in Spain. It was all that he lived for.

He learned the messages, repeating them several times until Miranda was satisfied that he knew them perfectly.

That afternoon he arranged for his transportation to Cadiz. He bought only a few shirts, trousers, a pair of shoes for himself. He intended to keep enough money to pay his fare to Chile from Cadiz. For he was going home to Chile to work for freedom. Nothing would stop him.

Once more, for the last time, he visited Great Putney Street to say goodby to Miranda. "It is doubtful if we will meet again," Bernardo said. "I am going to Chile. My life shall be given to the great purpose to which we are dedicated. All my life I shall be grateful to you for your inspiration and your help." He felt close to tears. He turned away, stared at the map of the Americas.

"The cause will succeed in Chile," Miranda said, "because your heart is single in its devotion. When you reach your country, start a branch of the Lodge. Don Juan Martinez Rozas of Concepcion will join with you, I believe. He may know of others who are interested."

Rozas! He had visited Don Juan Albano's hacienda that time. It was through him Bernardo had learned that Don Ambrosio Higgins de Vallenar was his father.

His father's friend Rozas, one with the cause of freedom. Then, perhaps his father, too, was already working for that same free-dom. The thought gave him great happiness.

"I have written some words of advice for you, Bernardo." Miranda gave him a packet of papers. "They may give you comfort when the way is dark. For the tyrants may find you, the way will be rough at times."

Then a long firm handclasp. For the last time Bernardo walked quickly along Great Putney Street.

The coach rolled between fields already pale green with April. Primrose, white violets and bluebells under the hedges. Farmers were turning the earth in their fields, using modern ploughs. Bernardo remembered the rude piece of metal attached to a stick that provided a plough for Chileans.

He was going to Falmouth in the south of England. Since England and Spain were at war, Bernardo would board a ship going to Portugal. In Lisbon, he would go by small coastal steamer to Cadiz.

With an aching heart he slackened his hold on the fields, the hedges of England. At small and comfortable inns, he tasted new bread, currant jam, delicious tea. The small fires on the hearths reached out to warm him, the polished wainscoating danced with brightness. Sturdy tables, strong chairs, rows of burnished pewter plates and mugs spoke of this country he had learned to love. Here in England, he had discovered himself and a career that would continue to his grave. Here he had learned what it meant to belong and be needed.

Then, small lanes peering at him. He thought of Friar Lane in Richmond where he and Carlota had walked, spoken of love, kissed. He stared at oak, hickory, elm, thinking of the times he and Carlota had walked beneath them on Richmond Hill. He heard her voice again, that low musical voice asking, "Dear Bernardo. Dear, quiet lad. Cannot you speak your thoughts?"

He could not speak. He dare not. How was she to know the reason?

Her enchantment was with him in this inn where he rested, on the highway going to Falmouth.

He watched the fire blazing brightly, thought of her hair, of sunlight on her beautiful face, of her lilting voice and dancing feet, of her love for him and his adoration of her. And soon he would be more miles from her.

If only she could go with him, remain beside him throughout his lifetime. He would love her forever. There would be for him one love, and that Carlota, and he would remember her always with longing to be near her.

Carlota! My dearest Carlota! He rose and went hurriedly toward the door, feeling again the grief at being separated from his love, wanting to be alone with his sorrow.

Then Falmouth, the River Fal and a busy harbor, sheer cliffs and a windblown coast, bare and rugged. Bernardo went immediately aboard the ship. He stood looking back at England, drinking in the view, saying good-by. When would he see this happy, civilized land again? When would he travel to Ireland and to Carlota?

The wind was brisk, an eager, impatient wind that filled the sails and carried the ship toward Portugal, heedless of his heart that clung to England. In his cabin he opened the letter that Miranda had written for him, needing consolation at this unhappy time.

"Upon leaving England," he read, "you should not forget for a single instant that outside of this country there is in all the world only one other nation in which you can discuss politics outside of the tried heart of a friend. That country is the United States. Choose therefore a friend, but choose him with the greatest care; for if you blunder you are lost. Upon different occasions I have suggested to you the names of various South Americans whom you can trust if you meet them in your journeys.

"Youth is the age for ardent and generous sentiments. Among the young men of your age you will encounter many ready to listen to you who are easily convinced. But, on the other hand, youth is the age of indiscretion and temerarious acts; therefore, you should beware of those defects of the young men as well as of the timidity and the prejudices of the old."

Bernardo read on. There was much good advice. He would abide by it. And Miranda. He would be grateful to him, forever.

Nine miles up the river Tagus was the port of Lisbon, its wharves holding cork, olive oil, wines, fish, salt, delicious grapes and figs. The city was like a Moorish citadel. It climbed the hill, along narrow streets the mean houses, the marble palaces, endless convents, churches and cathedrals. The odor of the poorer streets was ancient and offensive. Faces of Moor, Jew, Dutch, Russian, Spanish, Negro. And beggars everywhere. And always another rich jewel, or silks, or lace in another shop, asking to be purchased for Bernardo's mother and sister. But he had no money for gifts. He was hoarding his pesos for that journey to Chile.

From Lisbon he traveled by coastal steamer to Cadiz.

Once again, he entered the massive door, above it the carved cross symbolic of the name of Cruz.

There was little warmth in Don Nicolas' face as he greeted Bernardo in the library, which was crowded with rare books and paintings. "God with you," he said, and a sigh escaped his lips. A shadow lay across his face.

"God with you, Don Nicolas." Bernardo tried not to sound stiffly formal, but he did not succeed. "I trust you and Dona Maria are in good health."

Don Nicolas said irritably, "What bargain did you make with the stranger for free passage to North America?"

"He was not a stranger," Bernardo said, quietly. "He was my friend. I was penniless."

He studied Don Nicolas' annoyed eyes. This arrogant man had never been without friends in a strange land, nor hungry and destitute.

"Penniless?" Don Nicolas said, indignantly. "You should not have been. Before I traveled to Italy two years ago, I remitted your annual payment to the agents in London. A year ago I wrote Romera to forward to the agents another three thousand pesos. How could you possibly have been in need?"

Bernardo looked at Don Nicolas in astonishment. He did not understand.

"The agents, Spencer and Perkins, advise Romera that they advanced you every peso sent to them for you," Don Nicolas said, angrily.

Again Bernardo saw the insolent Perkins, heard his coarse voice, saw the piles of scrap iron, smiles of amused customers as Bernardo was ordered out. "For more than a year," he said, hotly, "I have had not one single peso from the agents!"

"Romera forwarded the pesos." Don Nicolas actually sounded as if he did not believe Bernardo.

There was nothing Bernardo despised more than lies. "Did you ask Mr. Romera to show the receipts?" he demanded. "For every peso advanced me by the agents, I signed a receipt."

Don Nicolas bristled. "Romera would not stoop to dishonesty," he said.

"Mr. Perkins said Romera owed him money. That was reason enough to withhold money from me." Bernardo gazed steadily at Don Nicolas. "I have been without funds for more than a year. My letters to you asking for money went unanswered. I received no explanations from anyone. This suit I am wearing is four years old. I have been living on the charity of London business men."

"I have been traveling." Don Nicolas moved uneasily in his chair. "Some of my mail was never forwarded. I have only just returned from abroad."

Someone had acted dishonestly, Bernardo thought. But badly as he needed money, he would not quarrel over pesos. Friendship was more important than money. Let Don Nicolas straighten out the finances with Romera and the London agents. He was happy to know that his father had not forgotten his son.

"I will get to the bottom of the matter," Don Nicolas promised. "And now," he said, "about your future. My idea was to purchase a commission for you in the Spanish army. But that avenue, I realize, is closed."

And while Don Nicolas did not explain further, Bernardo knew the answer. The Spanish army officials would demand the name of Bernardo's father, for if you were colonial-born, Spain sifted out your background. Don Nicolas should have known that. Or had he actually thought money would make the Spanish officials overlook the background?

"Don Nicolas," Bernardo said, "as quickly as possible, I am returning to Chile, to my grandfather's hacienda."

How good it sounded, he thought. Going home to the beautiful land, to his grandfather and mother and half-sister. He would work quietly to rouse his countrymen to rebel against Spanish domination.

Don Nicolas said, "Spain and England are at war. Few ships are sailing. In any case, the risk is too great." Gloomily, he stared at Bernardo. "You can help me here." He did not appear to relish the idea.

Bernardo told himself that somehow he would find a ship that was going to Chile.

At the dinner table that day the same formality in the gilded and oak dining hall, the noiseless service by servants, impeccably uniformed, who moved like automatons.

Don Nicolas' lady, the Dona Maria Joaquina, beautiful, each hair in place, her brows perfectly arched as if painted, correctness in the regally erect figure, glanced at Bernardo's frayed sleeve.

He moved his hand, trying to hide the worn place. It would be better, he thought, if hereafter he took few dinners at this table, particularly if there were guests. For here the elite dined. And Bernardo's clothes were not suitable for Dona Maria Joaquina's smart affairs. He did not want to embarrass her.

That evening he left the mansion to meet with the Lodge brothers. The air was cool. Bernardo enjoyed the long walk from the center of Cadiz to the Columns of Hercules a good distance away and near the salt pits. Across the bay was the dark hulking coast of Andalusia. The Columns came in sight. He walked on across the deserted land.

The remoteness of the Columns of Hercules made them a good

meeting place for the Lodge brothers of Cadiz. The great rocks had been standing here for centuries. One myth was that they were the ruins of a temple built by Hercules when the Greek hero traveled west.

The Lodge brothers arrived, singly.

Bernardo delivered his oral messages. He outlined the plan by which South America would be freed. And although he had never before met any of these men, he felt akin and brother to them. They were linked by a common purpose and a useful and unselfish one.

Then, one by one, they returned to Cadiz, careful to watch for enemies. For the danger, Miranda had warned, was always present, beside you, behind you; it waited at your door, inside your home. In Spain, the secret eyes were everywhere.

There were no ships going to Chile. Each day Bernardo inquired. Each day the same disappointing answer. Slowly, the time passed. He helped Don Nicolas. He wrote long letters home and he met regularly with the Lodge brothers at the Columns of Hercules.

A shocking letter came from his mother. Don Simon Riquelme was dead. His mother and his Aunt Lucia were with their father at the last. He had spoken with great affection of his grandson, Bernardo, longing to see him once again.

Bernardo thought sadly of his grandfather lying against the white pillows in his simple bedroom, his handsome face quiet, his gentle voice silenced, and the grief he felt seemed unbearable. Now he could think no longer of a time when the family united about that cheerful board, would hear again the fantastic and remarkable tales, see the smile, the love in his grandfather's eyes as he looked upon his grandson.

He longed to be with his mother. And here he was trapped, a captive in Cadiz, unable to go to her. And kept from beginning his important labor for the freedom of Chile!

Jealously, Bernardo hoarded his little fund of money, buying nothing for himself. And Don Nicolas offered not one peso.

Nor had the agents, Spencer and Perkins, replied to the letters written both by Bernardo and Don Nicolas, and, he assumed, by Mr. Romera.

Trapped, frustrated, imprisoned, Bernardo made himself hope, reminding himself when he became discouraged that the war could not last forever, that any day there would be a ship.

His hope was finally fulfilled. A convoy was leaving Cadiz for the Spanish colonies. Bernardo booked passage on the merchant frigate *La Confianza*.

For an entire year, he had been in Spain. He said farewell to Don Nicolas with a happy heart. He never wanted to look upon Cadiz again. From the ship he stared at the city walls, thinking how ugly they were. They were prison walls, the houses peering above the barrier were prison cells. And he had escaped! His spirits rose like those of a condemned man whose sentence has been commuted.

Then for five beautiful days the frigate flew through the sea like a bird, speeding toward Chile. Five days nearer the moment he could begin working for the cause. The sea was a friend for this journey, he told himself, recalling the times when it had been an enemy, taking him away from his homeland.

The night of the fifth day at sea, Bernardo was wakened by a loud banging on his cabin door. "Enemy sails!" shouted a voice.

Leaping from bed, Bernardo found his shirt in the darkness. With cold fingers he buttoned it. He pulled on his trousers. His shoes had vanished, but at last he found them. Then his coat had disappeared.

He would go without a coat.

He jerked at his door, dashed onto deck.

A cannon ball thundered across the main sail.

From the quarter deck came confused shouting. He saw shadowy figures of crewmen scattering. Above Bernardo were ghostly sails, blackness of sky and below the shifting sea. Standing off a little distance was the outline of an enemy warship.

The Spanish captain bellowed an order to crowd sails, and Bernardo saw crewmen swarm over a jungle of spars and crossarms like wild monkeys.

Then, he felt the frigate leap ahead, and he shouted. "Let a fast wind fill the sails! Let us outrun the enemy!" And his heart tightened like a clenched fist as the frigate, loaded heavily with cargo, strained, groaned, slowly picked up a little speed. Like a great whale she ploughed ahead. "Let her move faster!" he prayed.

She had escaped. A shout went up from the crew.

Then, without warning, other vessels began firing on the frigate. A cannon ball roared across the bow. Once again, confusion, a frightened crew scattering for safety, the sound of other cannon blasting the darkness. It was a grim nightmare.

Beside Bernardo, the captain of the frigate gripped the trumpet and ordered the men to lower sails.

"They may be French ships," he said.

Bernardo thought it might be better if the captain tried again to outrun them, whether they were French or English.

Then the crewmen ran for the spars and down came the sails.

Like a sea monster emerging from the depths, a warship appeared to windward. Two vessels slipped out of the blackness to the leeward side, at pistol-shot distant. It was impossible to make out the standard on the vessels.

But Bernardo heard English voices, and he thought how he would welcome that familiar tongue at another time, in a more friendly situation. Hearing them now, they were voices of doom. "They are English!" Bernardo shouted, trying to make himself heard above the firing and the howling of the wind. "They order you to surrender! Your ship will be sunk if you refuse!"

The captain pushed the trumpet into Bernardo's hand. "Tell them we surrender!" he shouted.

Bernardo repeated the order in English. "We surrender!" he roared, the order filling him with unhappiness for now they were prisoners of the English.

Prisoners of the English! And the British government was planning at this moment to fight with South Americans for liberty! But that would do Bernardo no good here. These English were warring against Spain and Bernardo was a Spanish subject. He would be treated as a prisoner.

Back and forth across the deck of the frigate, the tramp of conquering English!

The English admiral ordered Bernardo to serve as interpreter since no one else on *La Confianza* spoke English. Then, up and down ladders, answering questions, interpreting orders until his throat was strained and swollen. At last rest in the gray morning of another desolate day, his bed hard boards of the deck.

All Spanish prisoners were put aboard one of the English ships.

Bernardo's belongings were stolen by the English. He was eight days on the prison ship. Then he was put ashore at Gibraltar, after having been three days without food. He was ordered to leave Gibraltar at once.

Four miles across the bay was the Spanish port of Algeciras. He would have to circle the bay and walk to the port in the intense heat, and without food. He glanced behind him, saw the frowning face of the rock Gibraltar, and began to walk.

Half dead from hunger and fatigue he reached Algeciras. A coastal boat was preparing to sail for Cadiz. He staggered onto the boat and asked to be taken along. "In Cadiz I have friends. My passage will be paid by them," he promised.

The captain looked at his tattered clothing. "I take my pay in advance," he said, harshly.

"I will scrub decks, anything you ask." Bernardo, too weak to stand, grasped the railing. "I have been a prisoner of the English for days," he said.

"The English!" the man said, gruffly. "Then I will take you to Cadiz. But if there is no money, you work until the amount is paid."

Bernardo moved his head in assent. He was too tired to speak.

Algeciras was behind them. It was another day. Soon they would reach Cadiz. Bernardo admitted the thought reluctantly.

He glanced up. Bearing down on them was an English warship. With all the strength he could muster, he helped with the lines and sails. But he did not pray. He listened to the blasting of cannon, heard the angry wind whistle in the sheets, the rattle of rigging, saw the waves sweep across the deck. Soon he would again be a prisoner of the English!

Then, ahead loomed Saint Peter Castle. And safety!

Inside him a voice that seemed not his own said Saint Peter himself had saved them. Bernardo was safe, and for a good reason, the voice said.

In the darkness they entered the bay of Cadiz.

How he hated having to accept the charity of Don Nicolas. His friend did not say it, but he implied that Bernardo had been an idiot for attempting to sail for Chile in war time.

A greater feeling of desperation engulfed Bernardo. He left the house and walked to the Columns of Hercules.

There were no brothers of the Lodge here at this hour. But standing beside the ancient landmarks, he thought of them and how their hearts were with him. They all were one in spirit and purpose. He repeated the pledge, the oath he had taken in Miranda's sitting room that day.

He must accomplish the duty he had sworn to perform. And that meant he must surmount desperate moments like this, and disappointments. They must not be allowed to embitter him.

But he felt trapped and imprisoned again. He was back where he had started a year ago and the outlook was bleak. Still, he must not yield to discouragement. He must learn more patience. He must continue loyal to his purpose through darkness and doubt. For he had pledged his life to freeing his country. Somehow, he must find a way to make good that oath.

And he would find a way!

Bernardo stood looking at the dark Columns of Hercules.

CHAPTER XXIII

FOUR YEARS Don Ambrosio O'Higgins had been Viceroy of Peru and Marquis of Osorno. From his carriage he looked out at the massive bronze fountain in the Plaza of Lima where at the top, high above colorful flowers, rose the figure of Fame. Once he had stood in this Plaza envious of those names etched on that bronze column of the fountain. Now his name was written, more securely than any of them, in the records of Spain.

No official of Spain had greater power. The word of O'Higgins was respected in the Council of the Indies and it was almost law to His Majesty. He had won the affection of the King by his devotion to duty and his often-tested loyalty to the Crown. To the day of his death, he would remain powerful and beloved in Madrid and in these kingdoms. And after his death his name would be honored in a manner usually bestowed upon kings.

Proudly he rode, bowing with great dignity to those who passed.

Four years. When he first came to Lima as Viceroy he had ridden from the port of Callao in clouds of dust. The road had been a disgrace to His Majesty. One of the Viceroy's first acts had been to order a new road. Now, a broad paved avenue with ample walks for pedestrians and shaded by many trees made a fitting approach to this beautiful city of Lima, the pearl of all His Majesty's colonial cities.

This morning the Viceroy had inspected the placing of additional artillery at the castle of Callao. Without ships or sailors, he had succeeded in keeping foreign ships from these ports. The death ban against smugglers was enforced here as it had been in Chile.

All that, and more, he had accomplished. He would give his life, if necessary, to His Majesty!

And the King in turn was faithful to his Viceroy. His least wish had been granted. His trust of O'Higgins was so great that against precedent the King had asked the Viceroy to continue to supervise the settling of Osorno from Lima, although the work rightly belonged under the direction of the Governor of Chile.

His Majesty realized that the Indians near Osorno respected Viceroy O'Higgins even more than they did forts and dragoons of the Spanish, and so long as the Viceroy managed Osorno there would be peace with the Indians. Then, too, the King had seen Osorno prosper under O'Higgins. The rapacious Spanish had been kept out in resettling that beautiful land.

O'Higgins had sent Captain Juan Mackenna to manage the colony at Osorno. Mackenna had served loyally as an officer in the Spanish army. Trained as an engineer, the young Irishman had energy, he was honest, accurate and spirited. The Governor of Chile, Aviles, could not intimidate Mackenna, who would mete out justice to both peasant settlers and the Indians, even at the risk of displeasing the Spanish subjects.

And Mackenna had fulfilled the hopes of O'Higgins. Osorno was prospering. The skilled Irish and English workmen, who had been made prisoners on ships captured during the late war with England, were introducing new industries. The land was giving richly of grain and fruits.

Indeed, there was no blemish in O'Higgins' service to His Majesty. In all the kingdom tranquillity and loyalty. From these subjects His Majesty had only increased devotion.

This the Viceroy had done. O'Higgins, who had begun as Higgins the peddler, without help from anyone except his King!

At the palace door facing the Plaza of Lima the Viceroy left the carriage.

To his right was the guardroom, to his left a short flight of steps to the salon of the Viceroy. He passed his guard of halberdiers in blue coats, crimson waistcoats and knee breeches. It always amused him, the amount of gold lace on these uniforms. But in a parade his twenty-five halberdiers made a colorful sight.

His apartment was along a corridor looking into a small garden.

In a sitting room which was furnished with two tables, five settees covered in crimson damask, a bust of His Majesty and oil paintings of their Majesties, O'Higgins paused to study the face of King Carlos the Fourth.

Once, before he learned better, he had thought the features of the gracious monarch weak. But what he had taken for lack of character, he now considered only gentleness. How unlike his father and yet like his father, how generous and understanding! How much O'Higgins owed to the royal father and his royal son!

He hurried on to a larger sitting room, fitted with rich sofas, rather too many, he thought. His desk was too ornate for his taste. And flowers! He never got accustomed to them.

From his private file, which he kept locked in a carved cabinet, he took a letter from Madrid about the conspiracy to liberate the South American colonies. He reread it to be certain he had overlooked nothing he had been ordered to do.

The Ambassador in Paris, the letter stated, had documents that confirmed the plan of Don Francisco Miranda to make the South American possessions independent. It spoke of the perfidy of England. Here were the complete plans, including the roles to be played by England and North America, which had been prepared by Miranda, the Venezuelan, the traitor, the rascal. No punishment could be devised that would be suitable for his crime against the Crown!

This upstart Miranda! This would-be hero! He had known of rebels like him. They ended on the gallows.

Viceroy Don Ambrosio O'Higgins was to be vigilant, the letter said. He should watch for and imprison suspects among families and friends of the conspirators. If any were found guilty, the traitors were to pay the penalty of death.

Death was too good for such traitors!

O'Higgins laid the document on his gilded table. He would continue to be vigilant, as he always had been. For the Crown he would leave no stone unturned to root out the traitors, if there were any in this kingdom. He would prosecute without mercy anyone suspected of spreading the views of Miranda. He had already warned his officers to be zealous against foreigners and their papers of naturalization, to be watchful for dangerous conversations in taverns, among students at schools and colleges, at the theater, the bullfights and baths. He had increased his spies to search for suspects.

Already, he had written Madrid advising that in Peru there had never been greater vigilance of his officials, nor greater loyalty.

He replaced the file, locked the cabinet. Going to his bedroom, he lay down and tried to rest. After a moment he rose, removed the satin cushions and lay down again. He could not become accustomed to softness, not even on his bed. Too long he had been a soldier on the barren frontier where even bedsteads were scarce. Sheepskins, bullock hides, the earth had been his resting place. He lay thinking of the frontier, the kind, sun-wrinkled faces of the chiefs.

An hour later he went back to his desk, since it was time for the mail. He liked to be on hand for any important mail.

There was a letter from Bernardo. It had been forwarded from Concepcion with one from Don Thomas Dolphin, the letter from the boy placed in an unaddressed envelope.

What scrupulous care Bernardo observed in protecting his letters to his father. There was never the slightest clew that would lead unfriendly eyes to O'Higgins.

And this one was no exception.

The boy had sailed for Chile. His ship and almost the entire convoy had been taken by the British. His son had been a prisoner of the British. He read on eagerly:

"Because of the darkness we could not distinguish any flag, nor could we hoist ours. The English frigate of war called to us in their tongue. I, understanding the language, took the trumpet to answer. They ordered us to give ourselves up or we would be sunk. At the same time they kept firing upon us. Already, of our sailors not one man remained on the quarter deck, all having hidden in the magazine room. The Captain and I were alone on deck. Being near to being boarded by the frigate and two warships, we surrendered. The English admiral sent his well-armed boat to take possession of the ship and to transfer all prisoners to his ship. I, as interpreter, was taken up and down for hours."

The rascally British, O'Higgins thought angrily.

But he was delighted with the manner in which Bernardo had handled himself when he was forced to act as interpreter. He had performed his part manfully. Again O'Higgins returned to the letter:

"They stole everything from me, although little, leaving only what I was wearing. They took us to Gibraltar. I was three days without food, sleeping on the floor for eight days. From Gibraltar I went on foot to Algeciras. . . . I have come to stay in the house of Senor Don Nicolas de la Cruz whom I hate in my soul to bother in the slightest. . . . Farewell, until heaven shall be pleased to give me the opportunity of embracing you."

The English had treated him shamefully. They had stolen his few belongings!

O'Higgins studied the gold brocade on his wall. He was relieved that Bernardo was back in Cadiz. He did not want him in Chile. The enemies were in Chile.

And how had the boy got money to travel? Don Nicolas had been asked by O'Higgins to advance Bernardo no funds. For the lad had used up three thousand pesos within an incredibly short time, and he must learn the value of money by going without for a while.

It must be that Carlota he had written about. Previously, Bernardo had never wasted money. But he realized that every youth was supposed to sow wild oats, and pretty girls could always ensnare a susceptible boy.

Let this be a lesson to Bernardo. Living with Don Nicolas he had shelter, a good home, plenty to eat and people watching over him. He would not suffer too much, even if he disliked accepting Don Nicolas' hospitality.

That young pride! O'Higgins had always had pride.

Young love comes alike to all, he thought. This affair with the Irish girl had been nothing more. It had been a moment of extravagance with words and money, a squandering for gifts and entertainment for the young lady. It would teach him a useful lesson in finances. He would be all right, for he had a good sensible head on his shoulders.

Weeks passed. Another letter came from Bernardo.

As O'Higgins rode to Callao to inspect the completed repairs to the Castle, he read the short, unhappy note.

The lad was without proper clothes. He kept to himself and seldom left his room lest he offend his host and hostess. He felt imprisoned in Spain and wanted to be home in Chile.

The Viceroy studied silvery-green poplar leaves along the boulevard to Callao.

When he returned to Lima, he would write Don Nicolas to outfit Bernardo with clothes. And he would suggest a weekly allowance, enough to give him a little freedom, but not sufficient to leave Cadiz. Don Nicolas should have ordered clothes for the lad and forwarded the bill to O'Higgins. He did not want Bernardo looking shabby, walking in and out of Don Nicolas' fine residence as if he did not belong among the guests.

He would write Don Nicolas a polite but a stiff letter. Use your head, he would say. Cannot you understand that the lad needs clothes? Give him some handsome suits, fine hose, good shoes, a winter coat and hat. After all, Bernardo is the son of a gentleman, the son of the Viceroy of Peru, the Marquis of Osorno!

Upon O'Higgins' return from Callao, he wrote the letter.

Then, a few days later, the Viceroy was going through the foreign mail before seeing important visitors who were waiting in his audience chamber. In these days of stress there were always urgent letters and edicts from the Crown. The business of His Majesty always came first with O'Higgins.

His secretary had placed the letters on his desk and departed quietly. The whisper of the Viceroy's paper knife along the parchment was the only sound.

Standing at his desk, the Viceroy looked through the stack of mail, the sun touching rich velvet of his coat, adding gold to the gilt braid, to medals, ribbons, his badge of office. One of the envelopes seemed bulkier than the others. It was one from the Crown.

This Royal Order from Madrid was dated June 29, 1800. He glanced at the contents.

The rebel Pedro Jose Caro had turned himself over to the Minister of Spain in Hamburg. He had asked His Majesty of Spain for clemency for the crime of treason which he had committed in promoting and obtaining means for the general insurrection of South America. And he had turned over documents of intrigue and plans. They included the names of the conspirators.

Indeed, the Viceroy thought, this was good news. He read down the list of revolutionist-conspirators. He would not be familiar with any names other than Miranda, but he should know them in case some had relatives in Peru, for then the relatives would have to be questioned by his officials.

Halfway down the page one name stood out like a black streamer: "Bernardo Riquelme, son of the Viceroy of Peru!"

O'Higgins read, and the name seemed to dance. His hands shook and he could not hold the sheet. It fell to the table, looked up like an evil thing. Then, his body began to tremble and he gripped his table, stood with head bowed, eyes closed, while a hard pain pressed against his heart. Too weak to stand, he tottered to his chair. He sat thinking of all that he had worked for and built up destroyed by his own flesh and blood. And raising his ancient hands to his eyes, he moaned softly, letting hot, angry tears stream unheeded onto velvet coat, over medals and ribbons.

After a long time he straightened. With hurried movements he whipped some paper from his desk. He thrust his pen into the massive gold inkwell, and began a letter to Don Nicolas.

"Order Bernardo from your house!" he demanded of Don Nicolas de la Cruz. A viper, a monster, a treacherous and false man deserved no consideration from decent people. Give him neither shelter, money, pity nor mercy. He deserved none. Shun him as something loathsome. Bernardo was no longer his son!

All this he wrote and the minutes passed. Still his pen raced on, pouring his agonized fury onto the pages: his hatred of traitors, his detestation of liars, the double hearted and the ungrateful, his savage denunciation against a son whose father had sacrificed endlessly to give him everything that was good. He had repaid the generosity with wickedness. He had dishonored his father!

The Viceroy finished the letter. Hastily, he addressed an envelope, and calling his secretary, he ordered the letter taken at once to Callao. A mail ship would be sailing early in the morning from the port.

His secretary returned. He said the messenger was already riding toward Callao. He reminded O'Higgins that visitors were waiting.

"I cannot see any of them, today," O'Higgins said. "Dismiss them all."

He saw the shocked expression on his secretary's face, for O'Higgins had never refused to keep an appointment, either official or personal.

The secretary departed, distress in his eyes.

Then the Viceroy was alone. He leaned against his chair, eyes closed, anger spent. Now only the disgrace, the shame, to torment him. He slumped lower in his chair, thinking of it, of the vileness of the informer Caro. For certainly he must be a Spanish spy, planted to uncover the revolutionists.

But how had Caro discovered that Bernardo Riquelme was the son of Viceroy O'Higgins? How, his tortured mind asked, had Caro learned the secret that had been so watchfully guarded over the years, both in Chile and in Peru? Time after time Bernardo had been moved to protect that secret, and at last an ocean had been placed between these colonies and the lad.

Painfully, he thought about the matter.

A fresh wave of anguish went through the Viceroy as he recalled that he had not taken the same endless precautions to guard the secret in Spain. That was where he had erred. He had not warned Don Nicolas over and over again to use the greatest care in matters relating to Bernardo's background.

And while Don Nicolas would not wittingly betray him, that desire for prestige and honors might have tripped his friend into boasting that the son of Viceroy O'Higgins of Peru was a house guest. For the de la Cruz family were eager for social distinction.

Could Don Nicolas have told? Or, perhaps while his friend was traveling in Italy that time, some business associate looking after his affairs in Cadiz had stumbled upon one of O'Higgins' letters to Don Nicolas about the boy. The secret might have been discovered in that manner.

Somewhere there had been a slip. And Caro had learned of the secret. And now the news had reached the ears of His Majesty in Madrid. When the King heard the news, he would be stunned, and refuse to believe. "It cannot be true," he would storm. "This informer Caro may be in league with the enemies of my Viceroy. For O'Higgins served my father honorably and he has never failed me. Before I believe this, let us speak with the Viceroy. For he is a righteous servant, a loyal servant. He would have no part in treachery. Let us deal with him justly."

The Viceroy straightened, sat forward in the chair.

Perhaps if he wrote to His Majesty fully about this matter, explaining his sacrifices of love and family for the Crown, if he plead his case honestly, with humility, he might retain the favor of His Majesty. Write, he told himself, before enemies have a chance to influence the King!

He studied the gold inkwell.

Better still, why not go to Spain? Travel to Madrid and confer privately with His Majesty. Speak as one man to another of duties well performed, of sacrifices, of justice. The Viceroy had moved others with his tongue. Could he not reach His Majesty with his earnestness?

A little warmth came into his hands.

He would arrange the voyage to Spain. He would ride to Callao and when the mail boat sailed from Callao tomorrow, the Viceroy would be aboard it.

Then he saw the mail which he had not finished reading. He had not read the Royal Order that accompanied the news of Caro's confession.

He reached for the document.

The pale light fell between rose window-hangings, across rich carpet, his chair, over the ornate table. The Viceroy read the familiar prelude with which all such documents began. One line, two, three lines. The formal openings always took too much space, too much time to read. Then he came to the heart of the matter.

It was of himself it spoke. Of the Lieutenant-General of the Royal Armies, Marquis of Osorno, Viceroy, Governor and Captain-General of Peru and President of the Royal Audiencia in Lima, who had served the Crown for fifty years.

His Majesty removed O'Higgins as Viceroy of Peru!

O'Higgins' enemy, the Marquis of Aviles, had been named the new Viceroy to succeed him!

Then he could no longer see the official document, the table, the room. He staggered, fell into his chair, feeling lifeless. When he tried to move, his limbs were dead. He attempted to call out. No sound came. There was a sick, broken sensation in his head. Blood gushed from his nostrils.

It is death, he thought. A feeble prayer fluttered in his anguished mind. "God the Father!" he began.

And he remembered nothing more.

Lying on his great bed in the palace bedroom where he had been carried after the artery ruptured, O'Higgins looked at papers Don Ramon Rozas had brought for his signature. He insisted upon signing everything although the doctor urged him to rest. And

Don Ramon, brother of Juan Rozas of Concepcion, both brothers his old friends, begged him to rest.

But how could he find repose when thoughts would not give him peace, when they burned deep into his mind? How could he sleep when he remembered that His Majesty had sentenced his Viceroy, his faithful officer, without giving him a chance to defend himself?

That was the most bitter thought!

He signed the papers and leaned back exhausted against the great square pillows.

Don Ramon said, kindly, "There is another letter from Bernardo."

The Viceroy's anger flared. But it passed. He turned his head on the pillow, wanting to hear of his son. "Let me have it," he said, his voice weak.

This would be a plea of forgiveness from Bernardo. It would be a letter from the prison in Madrid, a last letter perhaps. And his heart went cold and he thought, "God forbid that the boy should be punished for his indiscretion! Let them punish the older men, the evil instigators like Miranda who trapped the young and innocent and foolish, the untried and trusting who had no parents to advise them." For Bernardo's crime belonged elsewhere.

He clutched the letter. At last, he opened it.

The same affectionate salutation. He spoke of his wish to be near O'Higgins, of his love for him, of the sacrifices made for him. He spoke of wanting to embrace a father. He mentioned that he had been ill for many days and near death with the black vomit. Great numbers had died of the epidemic which had raged in Cadiz. Don Nicolas removed him to San Lucar de Barrameda, but there the contagion spread and many died daily. They had expected Bernardo to die, but he pulled through. And in his rational moments he had wondered if ever he would see O'Higgins, whom he longed to know.

The sick man stared at the brief note from Dolphin which accompanied Bernardo's letter, and he thought of the constant precaution the lad had always taken in writing to him. And then he

thought of him sick, far from his people. He might have died! And
O'Higgins closed his eyes, for the light seemed too strong, his eyes
too ancient.

By now, O'Higgins' last letter to Don Nicolas had reached Cadiz.
And Don Nicolas had ordered Bernardo from his house. The boy
was wandering, God knew where, without friends or money, if the
police had not already arrested him. God spare him the Spanish
police!

But wherever Bernardo went, Spain's secret police would find
him. He would certainly end in prison.

And who had sent the lad to England, to Miranda?

In letter after letter the boy had pleaded for the advice of his
father. Had he not written always that he would do whatever his
father advised? And his father had given him nothing but money
and silence.

O'Higgins had condemned his son. He had sentenced him without hearing or mercy, as His Majesty had judged O'Higgins, and
never a trial of any kind. Prison! The Inquisition! Would his son
stand before the Tribunal? Would he be tortured if he refused
to speak out?

O'Higgins stared at his old hands on the smooth sheet.

He did not believe Bernardo had wantonly betrayed him. Knowing that O'Higgins believed in greater good for all, he must have
supposed his father would approve of his revolutionary ideas.
With an effort he lifted himself higher on the pillow, for the anguish was almost too great to be borne.

How could he help Bernardo now? By what method could he
speak to him, tell him his father cared, regretted his action, loved
him?

He lay back feeling drained of strength, drained of thought and
feeling the coldness of death itself.

Don Ramon leaned forward. He said, "I shall call the doctor."
Faithful Don Ramon.

"No," the Viceroy said. "Bring me pen and paper. I must do what
should have been done years ago. I must make my will."

Part II

THE SON

CHAPTER XXIV

His father, Viceroy Don Ambrosio O'Higgins, Marquis of Osorno and Baron of Ballenary, was dead. And the son, Bernardo Riquelme, was going home to Chile. With great kindness Don Nicolas de la Cruz had provided everything needed for the journey. Now that the Viceroy was dead, the reason for that last bitter letter would never be known. The father had died hating his son!

For weeks the heavy mist, then the turgid sea of Cape Horn. Day and night the wailing of a storm running across the mountainous waves, moaning of a father gone and no last comforting message for a son who worshiped him.

He had not gone peacefully as he deserved. Even in death, no peace for the great man. Why had he been dismissed? What had killed his honorable father?

Dully, Bernardo watched the coast, the timbered hills and crags, the slopes that climbed forever with not even a wild creature to give them life. The land dead, mourning his father who had loved and protected Chile against all enemies.

And at last Valparaiso. A sailor, pointing to one of the forts, said, "El Baron, after Don Ambrosio O'Higgins."

At the customs house, Bernardo hired a muleteer to take him and his trunks to Santiago. Along the one main street that faced the bay, then through a suburb and up endless cliffs to a plain and a highway.

"This road," the muleteer volunteered, "was built by the great Don Ambrosio O'Higgins before he became Viceroy of Peru. Chile never had a better friend." The man glanced toward the Andes. "A father to everyone, his heart big enough for all, his spirit beyond malice or injustice."

Bernardo stared hard at giant torch thistles. What misunderstanding could have turned a father against his only son?

The road went east, southeast, a skillful engineering feat. His father must have been proud of this highway. Would that he had died feeling as proud of his son!

Casa Blanca. More stories of Don Ambrosio O'Higgins and his zeal for Chile. Here he had set aside a building for an inn. Captain George Vancouver had spent the night in the building on his way to Santiago to visit O'Higgins. Tonight, there would be entertainment for the guest, Bernardo Riquelme.

Then the highway again. He followed the muleteer past a great dyke. On a pedestal he paused to read an inscription: "D.O.M. in the reign of Charles the Fourth and during the Government of this Kingdom by Don Ambrosio Higgins de Vallenar; who ordered these dams to be constructed in the year 1792."

Bernardo studied the words. How magnificent a person his father had been. How great his anger against Bernardo, to have written Don Nicolas as he had!

The muleteer said that he would take Bernardo to the residence of Captain Thomas O'Higgins, here in Santiago.

It was Don Nicolas who had suggested that Bernardo stop in the capital to visit with Captain O'Higgins, a nephew of Bernardo's father. Perhaps he would know the reason for Viceroy O'Higgins' dismissal, about his death.

And so Bernardo came to Santiago hoping for news.

Inside, the patio was shaded by magnolia trees. A servant went to call the Captain.

Thomas O'Higgins appeared at an archway. His blue eyes looked friendly.

"I am Bernardo, son of Don Ambrosio O'Higgins," Bernardo said, walking toward the Captain.

A look of surprise and astonishment went over the face of Captain O'Higgins, and he stared, his eyes looking stunned.

"You did not know that my father had a son?" Bernardo said quietly. "But almost no one knew."

The Captain came forward, stretched out a hand. "I'm sorry," he said. He pulled forward a chair. "Sit here," he said, hospitably, and he half turned and shouted for a servant to bring maté.

"I came about my father," Bernardo said. "Can you tell me why he was dismissed? Or how he died? In Cadiz we heard only that he was no longer Viceroy, and that he died."

Slowly, Captain O'Higgins moved his head. "It was his enemies. The Viceroy had enemies who worked secretly to remove him, to turn the Crown against him, to destroy him. What else could it have been? Don Ambrosio O'Higgins was an honorable man, a loyal subject, an ardent exponent of righteousness. He served His Majesty well. It was wicked, his being dismissed."

He stared at Bernardo unhappily, and his eyes darkened.

"The Viceroy was good to me," he said. "And to my brother Demetrio. Because of his good offices, Demetrio became governor of a province in Peru."

Bernardo said, feeling grief deeply, "I never knew my father. I shall always regret that. Even in death I was not present to look upon his face."

"It was a magnificent funeral, I am told," the Captain said. "He was buried with honors in the church of San Pedro. Up to his death he handled state affairs as loyally as if there had been no dismissal by the Crown. The last paper he signed was his will. He remembered everything."

He was quiet for a moment, still looking searchingly at Bernardo. "Bernardo Riquelme?" he said, thoughtfully.

"It is the name I have used all my lifetime," Bernardo said.

"Then you know about the will, of course?"

Bernardo said he knew nothing about a will.

Excusing himself, the Captain disappeared inside the house. He returned shortly. "Here is a copy," he said, and he pointed to a line. "Read this."

Bernardo looked at the paragraph. "I bequeath to Don Bernardo Riquelme, when he shall return from Europe, the hacienda of Las Canteras with 3,000 head of cattle."

Like one in a trance he reread the words trying to understand.

Then his shocked mind saw the name of his beloved father and the date: March 14, 1801.

With rising excitement he realized that this paper had been prepared weeks after his father's bitter letter to Don Nicolas in which he denounced his son!

His heart leaped with happiness. This was the message he had prayed for. These were his father's last words to his son. They told him that Don Ambrosio had not died hating him. Whatever had happened, Bernardo had been forgiven. This paper told of his love!

The closeness of that love warmed Bernardo. Once again the nearness, the inseparability that would never again be challenged; once again he was his father's son. And gratitude filled his heart!

Before he left Santiago for Chillan, Bernardo wrote to the executors of his father's estate:

> "Executors of deceased the Most Excellent Marquis of Osorno, Don Jose de Gorbea y Badillo and Reverend Padre Augustin Doria.

> "Dear Sirs: After having arrived here in the merchant frigate *Aurora,* I have seen a copy of the will of my loved and dead father, sent by Senor Don Jose to my cousin Don Tomas de O'Higgins; and acquainted with the disposition which it contains and being satisfied and certain of the integrity and goodness and other excellent qualities which characterize the upright hearts of you gentlemen, I do not delay in giving you some idea of my situation."

He wrote on, giving information needed in settling the estate. He closed the letter:

> "In consequence of all that I have outlined, I hope that soon an order will be given to Senor Don Pedro Nolasco del Rio, who is in charge of the administration of the farms belonging to the said will, to turn over to me the said farm."

Then he signed his name for the first time, "Bernardo O'Higgins de Riquelme."

CHAPTER XXV

Bernardo hurried toward his mother in Chillan. He crossed the Maipú River which raced foaming from the blue Andes that seemed to soar to the roof of the heavens.

The land was more endless than he remembered, the hills greener, the rivers more turbulent. The vast spaces, the silence, and the warm, bright sun.

He loved it, this Chile!

His heart sprang to meet the pleasant tiles, the great walls of his grandfather's house. Dismounting, he left the muleteer to follow with the luggage, while he walked toward the house.

A parrot squawked. Through the arched door leading to the first patio Bernardo saw gardens, linnets in reed cages, and a fountain dripping coolness.

His mother's voice came from a distance. Something about Bernardo's room. Her voice was low and musical. "It must be dusted again," she said.

Joyfully, he walked down the corridor.

In his room the counterpane was spotless. An Inca vase with a jaguar handle was filled with lime blossoms and purple lupine. A bronze candlestick as thick as his forearm held a tall candle. On the Spanish chest was the polished box trimmed with metal made for him by his grandfather that birthday long ago.

His heart stirred with love for that grandfather.

Back in the corridor and on toward his mother's room. She was at a window pinning a gold ornament in her black braids. She was as beautiful as he remembered her.

Turning, she saw him at the door. For a moment she stood, surprise and affection in her eyes. Then she opened her arms toward him. Her arms went around him and his about her. Kind eyes looked him over with a mother's appraisal. Too thin, she thought. His eyes, too sad. But he was handsome, although he looked older than his twenty-two years.

Rosa came, pretty, shy and bright-eyed. Her hands clasped his arm. "You are to have my bay horse," she said, her voice pitched high with excitement, with wanting him to know he was welcome. "Now you will never leave us!"

"Dear Rosa." Bernardo smiled down at her. "I could not take your fine horse. But I shall borrow him occasionally."

Until late into the night came more people, the familiar faces and the unfamiliar, all friends and each with a warm welcome. It made Bernardo rich with happiness.

His mother's eyes followed him proudly. He thought how lightly the years had touched her. He was home for good she explained and he would manage this hacienda.

Indeed he told himself he would never again leave Chile, but would farm both this hacienda of his grandfather's and the one inherited by him from his father. And while he managed the farms, he would spread the gospel of independence for Chile and all of South America.

He glanced around the sala, wondering which of these kind people would be first to embrace that cause. There would surely be many converts from the beginning. He pictured them filling this room to listen with eagerness to the plan for making Chile free without bloodshed. It would be a better land, a richer, and the people would be free. The Crown would profit, too, once Chileans were independent with the ports open to foreign trade and the monopolies ended.

The following week, he applied for permission to use the name O'Higgins. He was told to present an affidavit giving the complete facts about his mother and his father.

He could not subject his mother to the indignity of having the facts of his birth entered in the public records!

Slowly, he walked back to the house.

His mother greeted him. "It is all settled, then, about the name?" she said, gaily.

"There is no haste," he said.

"And why not?" she said.

He changed the subject. Chillan had not altered, he said, and he wondered if he remembered any Araucanian words. How fine to see the Indians again!

Later, his mother went to a desk and began writing. Twice Bernardo left the sala and returned to discuss business about the hacienda and each time she was engrossed in writing.

Then she called to him. "These are the facts that you need, Bernardo."

He read:

"Bernardo O'Higgins y Riquelme is a native of the city of San Bartolome de Chillan, province of Concepcion, the kingdom of Chile, and a resident. He was raised here. He is the natural son of His Excellency, Senor Don Ambrosio O'Higgins, Baron of Ballenary and Marquis of Osorno, Lieutenant-General of the Royal Forces of His Majesty, Viceroy, Governor and Captain-General of the kingdom of Peru and Chile, and President of the Aquella Royal Audiencia, now deceased, and of Dona Isabel Riquelme y Mesa, resident, and one of the principal families of Chillan, born and bred in a state of celibacy. Isabel Riquelme, a child in years, sheltered by her parents and with the modesty and decorum corresponding to her rank and good breeding, was betrothed to Don Ambrosio Higgins at his repeated solicitation. He gave his word of honor."

There was a strange quietness in the room. But there was no quietness in Bernardo's heart, only a sudden angry stirring. There had been a pledge, and it had been broken!

"The parents accepted him. The girl trusted and loved him. There had been great affection between them. Dona Isabel accepted the repeated promises of marriage in good faith. But the marriage vows were not fulfilled.

"He, Bernardo the son, was born on the 20th day of August, in the year 1778."

That trusting young girl, Bernardo thought, and this wonderful mother. "I will not accept this sacrifice, Mother!" His voice sounded choked.

"You made the sacrifice, Bernardo." Her voice was calm. "As for myself, I have no regrets. A son like you repays me a hundredfold. And I loved your father. He was my country, my honor, everything. You must not feel angry or hurt."

But Bernardo said, "I will not let you do this." He tossed the paper onto the desk and started across the room toward the garden, feeling stifled.

"Then I shall sign the paper and have it notarized," she said. "I shall enter it in the public records. As you love your mother, my son, please sign your name. You will cause me great unhappiness if you do not."

He looked at his mother standing proudly beside the desk, her fine eyes filled with affection. If he refused, she might think that he condemned her. And he did not. How could he?

With slow steps he returned, stood beside the desk. Reluctantly he took the quill and signed his name.

Don Juan Martinez de Rozas and Don Thomas Dolphin of Concepcion contributed their affidavits of the facts relative to Bernardo's being the son of Don Ambrosio O'Higgins. The good Don Ignacio Blake, who had befriended Bernardo in Lima, had died, as had Captain Domingo Tirapegui and Don Juan Albano, and their statements could not be included.

The official notice authorizing Bernardo to use the name O'Higgins arrived just after the siesta hour one Wednesday.

Rosa, weaving a poncho for Bernardo, sprang up from a bench at the loom beside the sunny window. She said in excitement: "My name, too, is O'Higgins. I shall be Rosa O'Higgins and then people will understand that I am your sister!"

How valiantly Rosa attempted to make amends for what she considered unfairness to him.

The settlement of his father's estate dragged on. His cousin, Captain Thomas O'Higgins, wrote from Santiago that he doubted if ever the inheritance would be paid, and he suggested that Bernardo marry a wealthy girl before she discovered that he was penniless. Then Don Pedro Nolasco del Rio, in whose care the hacienda of Las Canteras had been placed by the Lima executors, began talking of Bernardo's going to Lima to check into the inheritance. Don Pedro feared that if Bernardo did not go he might lose the hacienda.

Bernardo had faith in the executors. Had not his father selected them? And one was a priest. Then, Bernardo did not want to travel to Lima. He had no desire to be any nearer the Inquisition and the new Viceroy. All followers of Miranda were being sought by the Spanish police.

For days he thought about it.

Then he remembered that Don Thomas Dolphin was acquainted with important residents of Lima. If Dolphin would accompany him, there would be less danger of being apprehended and questioned.

He and Dolphin sailed from Talcahuano on a Friday. Bernardo saw from the ship the massive fortresses, the intricate fortifications built on both sides of the bay by his father.

Dolphin said, "Your father believed the British would attempt to take Talcahuano, and then all of Chile. He built forts to withstand British cannon. He increased the artillery and the force. Day and night he set a watch from the towers. And yet his enemies called him the English Viceroy, the vassal of England!"

For the first time, a lifetime friend of Don Ambrosio was speaking freely of this parent whom he had never known except in his heart, and whom he worshiped. Eagerly, Bernardo asked why his father was dismissed as Viceroy, the cause of his death?

There was little Dolphin could tell him, except that Don Ambrosio had dearly loved his son.

In Callao, and in Lima, eyes scrutinized his passport, his face. But with Dolphin beside him there were few questions. Still, as they approached Lima, Bernardo felt the insecurity. How changed the road to Lima! Once, he had traveled it in clouds of dust. Now

the avenue was handsomely paved and shaded with trees. The
work of his father, Dolphin explained.

They reached Lima. In the Plaza Dolphin showed Bernardo the
name of Viceroy O'Higgins embedded in the paving, and the date.
Together they went to his father's tomb.

The church of San Pedro. Long ago Bernardo had visited this
place when he was alone and trying not to be lonely. Now he
stared at the elaborate inscription on his father's tomb, the flowery
Spanish praise. "They killed my father," he told himself, "and on
his tomb are words they should have spoken before he died."

Here lay a soldier whose spirit would never die. He felt overflowing love and grief as he embraced the memory of his father.

"For two days he lay in state, like a king! People came for miles
to look once again upon his kind face. He was greatly revered
and beloved, and he was greatly hated," Dolphin said, "because he
wanted progress for these colonies."

As they stepped into the street, a figure moved quickly into an
archway, then into the darkness of a corridor.

Bernardo felt his heart skip a beat. He hurried on.

Dolphin had not seen the man.

Now and again Bernardo glanced behind him as he walked.
Each arched doorway seemed to hold an enemy: the vendor of
lottery tickets in the name of the Holy Virgin; the lace and fringe
maker, the fresco merchant that turned suddenly away, the tinker,
the flower women peering up slyly from their tables.

The executors of the will were taking too long. Bernardo urged
Dolphin to try to hurry them. Day after day the questions. Day
after day the priest Doria, one of the executors, would want something more about London, about Richmond: when did Bernardo
leave England, and Cadiz?

And always he slipped in information about the conditions in
Lima. "Here in Lima," he said that last day, just before Bernardo
was to leave for Callao and a ship to Chile, "everyone wonders
who will be the next to be imprisoned and questioned about se-

dition, for there are traitors among the people of Peru. But which are they? That is what the Crown would like to know." His twisted mouth smiled. "The young from abroad are doubted. It is not an easy time. We all must be careful." There seemed in his thin voice a warning, and his eyes shone coldly, like ice.

Did the priest suspect that he was a follower of Miranda? He was filled with dread, until he stood with Dolphin on the ship.

Looking at the coast of Peru, he said hotly, "It is inhuman how the Crown and the Inquisition terrorize the inhabitants. It is evil! One day it will change!"

The violence with which he spoke alarmed Dolphin. Hastily, he glanced around. "Bernardo! Keep such talk to yourself. The informers are everywhere!"

Bernardo said earnestly, "Dolphin, do you not agree? Should there not be here the same freedom as in North America and England?"

"In the colonies such opinions lead only to the Inquisition chambers," Dolphin said, his voice cold and unfriendly. "I came to Chile a poor man, Bernardo. I have acquired riches. Here the officials are my friends. I purchase patronage, and the taxes are fantastic, and the tithes to the Church. But they leave me in complete peace to enjoy my fortune and my life. With money I can do much good."

He faced Bernardo. "Never speak this way again. The executors have agreed to turn over your inheritance to you immediately. Take it and forget the restless talk. Enjoy yourself and take no foolish risks. Let your future be happier, more secure, than your past. Be content, I beg of you!"

Be content? Secure? It was sound advice. But what gave contentment to Dolphin might bring only restlessness to Bernardo. Each man had his own prescription for contentment. There was no pattern. Except that deep within each human being was a driving need to be free and master of himself. No man wanted to be a slave.

He had hoped that Dolphin, being an Irishman with an understanding of liberal government, would welcome a plan to make

Chile independent. He realized now he had been mistaken. Dolphin's wealth was another form of bondage, and would clamor more loudly than freedom for Chile.

But other men, and particularly younger men without riches, would gladly embrace the cause. And in Concepcion Bernardo would speak about the matter to Juan Tirapegui, the son of his father's old aide.

The young men like Juan Tirapegui, they would listen to words about freeing Chileans!

CHAPTER XXVI

For THREE days Bernardo was in Concepcion visiting with the Tirapegui family.

In the sitting room was a sword which he had been told was carried by Captain Domingo Tirapegui when he was serving under Don Ambrosio O'Higgins.

He thought of himself and Captain Tirapegui. Of a child displaced, frightened because of a wicked and ancient law of Spain.

"They were faithful friends, your father and Don Domingo," Juan said. "They despised injustice."

Bernardo thought, Juan despises the evils, too. And he will join in this fight for an independent Chile.

That morning when Bernardo started for Chillan young Tirapegui would ride with him to keep him company for an hour or two. On the forsaken highway there were no watchful eyes, no listening ears. They could talk freely of the great work that lay ahead and of the Lodge which must be started in Chile.

He glanced at Juan, riding with the careless ease of all Chileans, features handsome like those of the kind Captain Tirapegui. The Captain had wanted justice, and Juan wanted it. One word from Bernardo about loosing the Spanish yoke and he would ask how he could help. He would seize the opportunity to serve.

"When you take over the hacienda Las Canteras," Juan said, as eagerly as if it were his own, "you will want to begin a roundup. If you need extra cowhands, let me know. You should allow for deductions when you take the final count of the animals. Taxes to the Crown, those for the Church." His voice was less cheerful when he mentioned taxes.

"Then there will be shares deducted for the workmen," and as Bernardo spoke, he watched Juan Tirapegui.

A look of amazement crossed Juan's face. "The workmen receive only wages and shelter," he said. "Perhaps we can reduce wages this season." He stared thoughtfully at the fields, as if figuring how great a reduction.

But Juan had never know hunger. There had always been a tight roof over his head, plenty of food. His clothes were the best.

"We will not decrease wages, Juan," Bernardo said. "If possible I will increase them. You and I should think of better pay, better homes, more land for the poor of Chile. We should consider how our ports can be opened to ships of other countries. This would bring prosperity to Chile."

He waited, his eyes on Juan's face.

His friend's voice was a harsh whisper as he said, "You could be hanged for such remarks, Bernardo!" He glanced ahead at the muleteer too far away to have heard, and turning in his saddle he glanced behind him.

He said nothing more about the cause. Silently, he and Juan rode ahead, until at last his friend, his voice edged with sadness said, "God with you, Bernardo."

Bernardo rode on alone until he saw the walls of San Javier hacienda where he planned to visit with Don Juan Martinez de Rozas who had married the rich heiress, Dona Maria de las Nieves Urrutia Mendiburn y Manzanos. Her estate was the largest and finest in southern Chile.

But within this splendor was a true friend of the cause. Don Juan Martinez de Rozas had corresponded with Miranda and was eager for freedom of the colonies. And although Juan Tirapegui was frightened, Rozas would not be. This was to be the first time Bernardo would speak to Rozas about the cause and the Lodge which he expected him to join. The last time he met Rozas, there had been lawyers present and there was only a discussion about Bernardo's using the name O'Higgins.

He recalled when he first saw Rozas. It was at Don Juan Albano's hacienda long years ago. Such ages ago, he thought.

Then he was ushered into a garden where Rozas was entertaining Spanish friends.

"This is Bernardo O'Higgins," Rozas said, "the son of Viceroy Don Ambrosio O'Higgins, Marquis of Osorno. He has recently returned from abroad." His eyes, intelligent and keen, smiled.

The guests bowed stiffly; stared.

The conversation was general: mining, commerce, horses, their fine haciendas. Rozas seemed to agree with everything that his guests were saying. Not once did he criticize the Crown or speak of unfairness to Chile and her people.

Bernardo answered questions about Spain and England. When he mentioned the great number of books and periodicals in England, available to anyone by walking to the nearest stationer and buying them, the guests looked as if they thought he must be mistaken.

After dinner there was music and dancing.

Bernardo excused himself at a late hour, as he was leaving early in the morning. In his room he stood looking into the small garden, his mind clouded. He had counted on Rozas' interest in the cause. The young men were frightened and the older men, once eager and daring, had become softened by riches. And poor, neglected Chile waited!

He heard a furtive rap on his door. Rozas, blinking owlishly, entered, looking more the professor than ever. "Now the Royalist guests have gone and we can visit about the matter nearest our hearts!" For an entire evening he had managed to be amiable, interesting, witty, clever about nothing important. And, all the time, wanting to be secreted in some corner speaking with Bernardo about the vital matters that concerned the future of Chile!

"Begin with your meeting of Miranda," he said, eagerly, leaning forward in his chair.

Bernardo spoke of the plan in which England and North America would join. Of the Grand Reunion Americana. Here in Chile, he said, the organization would be called the Lodge Lautaro.

"The Lautaro Lodge will unify us," Rozas said. "And this is right and good!"

British and American ships would enter South American ports with thousands of troops, Bernardo explained. "That will be the time for us to demand of Spain the changes we plan."

Rozas said, "The English and American forces on our shores will give us strength to demand changes. The Spanish Crown cannot refuse!" And his wise eyes brightened, as if already he saw the excitement in the Council Chamber in Madrid as the ministers spoke with distress of foreign troops in colonial harbors.

"A bloodless revolution!" Rozas said with animation. "It has been my dream." He ran a hand quickly across his thick, graying hair.

Bernardo thought, "Rozas is old enough to be my father, yet his enthusiasm is that of a young man."

"Now," Rozas said with spirit, "will you induct me into the Lautaro Lodge as a brother member?" And standing he lifted his right hand.

Slowly, Bernardo recited the provisions. How rightly he had been directed to this hacienda by One who gave freedom to all, he thought, prayerfully.

Rozas repeated the oath. "So help me God!" he said, with great sincerity, the words seeming to come from his heart.

Across the garden the pale morning dawned, pearl-colored.

Bernardo thought, "Now there are two in Chile, united to free our country!"

CHAPTER XXVII

BERNARDO returned to Chillan in high spirits and immediately began a quiet and cautious campaign for the independence of Chile. Always conscious of the risks even in his remote corner of the colony, he selected as a meeting place a location on the Itata River.

Two weeks later, on a fiesta day, when Chillan was filled with merrymakers, he held his first meeting. With him at the cliff on the Itata were Don Pedro Arriagada, corregidor and head of militia of Chillan, a friend of Rozas, the priest Acuna, and a Chilean who operated a parrot circus and acted as spy for the corregidor.

Bernardo spoke of the work in England and North America as he had to Rozas, of the plans for a bloodless revolution.

"We must be cautious," Bernardo said. "We must be fearless. Our greatest enemy is fear, for our people have been shackled for centuries by terror. Never forget the danger."

Month after month the meetings. Bernardo kept them small, as Miranda had taught him. When peasants came he talked of the importance of land.

And slowly, but surely, the work for the cause prospered.

The year he was twenty-four, he at last was given possession of his father's property, Las Canteras, south of Chillan on the inland island of Laja, lying between two great rivers.

He began a roundup the latter part of January. It would be the first count of the herds inherited from his father. The number should be more than the three thousand mentioned in his father's will.

Proudly he thought of his herds, his acres!

Each morning when he stepped into the new day, the wonder of owning this hacienda returned. He never tired of riding over the land, or of walking from patio to patio, from room to room; and now, staring at the great wall, he thought with what care his father had planned it. In this courtyard Don Ambrosio had stood, walked. In this house, his father had deliberated upon matters of importance to Chile, had seen happy and unhappy days, had struggled with problems and overcome them.

And to this hacienda Bernardo would devote all his time once the Revolution was finished. For he was at heart a farmer. He had no talent for statesmanship or for operating a government and he wanted no such post.

His ambition lay within these acres, once Chile was free. And how perfect if Carlota could come and share it with him!

He thought of her constantly.

He mounted his horse and rode toward the hills.

For three weeks the roundup went on. It was the evening of the eighteenth day. Bernardo stared into the embers of a campfire, thinking of the cause. As soon as possible he wanted a meeting with Don Juan Martinez de Rozas to discuss a national congress for the new government when the time came. While they waited they must prepare for the future welfare of the country.

Across the fire a cowhand was playing a guitar. Whenever Bernardo glanced up the black eyes were staring at him. The face of the man was familiar. Perhaps he was one of the men who had attended a meeting about freeing Chile. Bernardo was thoughtful. It was important to remember the faces and the names.

Bernardo listened to the guitar. It was pleasant music and, after a hard day in the saddle, restful.

He dozed.

The voice of the singer seemed much closer.

Quickly he opened his eyes, noticed that the man had moved his sheepskin nearer the fire. The words came softly, blending with the strings, a song about Chile. About the land, the mountains and liberty.

Bernardo did not stir, but words rushed to his lips about a time when they all would be loosed from Spanish tyranny.

He curbed his tongue, looked more carefully at the man. The clothes were those of a cowhand. Except that they were new—trousers, poncho, the sleeve against the guitar all good. No worn or faded patches, no frayed edges.

He recalled Pedro Caro, the studied perfection of his masquerade. And this man was an informer, too. He wanted Bernardo to utter words which would announce him a traitor to Spain. Perhaps yonder in the darkness other Spanish agents were waiting for some signal from this man, telling them that Bernardo had betrayed himself.

He thought, "It is better if I appear to have heard nothing." And he pretended to sleep. With cautious movements he felt for his pistol.

After a long time the man rose and walked into the night.

But Bernardo never rested easily, night or day. He was always conscious that the Spanish were watching him, hoping one of their informers would catch him in some overt act.

One night, weeks later, Arriagada arrived breathless. He shouted, "The English attacked Buenos Aires. They failed to take the city!"

With shocked eyes, Bernardo stared. Why had the British attacked without warning the Chilean patriots? It had been understood that Lodge members in all the colonies would be alerted by the British or the North Americans, or by Miranda, when the first blow was to be struck against Spain. But it was not to be bloodshed. A warning was to be sent to the Crown. Someone had bungled!

Arriagada said, "Bernardo!" He sounded frightened. "Your name is linked with the English in this attack. The Spanish officials in Santiago have been notified that you are mixed up in the affair, and are a traitor. They are coming to take you!"

Bernardo's hand tightened, "But I am hundreds of miles from Buenos Aires. They can prove nothing!"

"A charge will be trumped up. They have been trying to link

you with a plot against the Crown. You will be sent to Lima, to the Inquisition!"

Bernardo struggled for breath.

"I know a smuggler who lives in the hills toward the coast. You can hide there," Arriagada said. "We will contact a British or a North American ship and spirit you to the vessel in his small boat. You must escape, Bernardo! When things have quieted you can return, secretly. The cause needs you."

Bernardo called to a servant to hurry with a horse. He ran for money and poncho.

Along the road the hooves of his horse beat wildly, each step shouting of Spanish police, Lima, the Tribunal.

He was far ahead of Arriagada, going toward the coast, the hills bordering the Biobio, where the smuggler lived.

He could feel his horse shaking with terror. He never used the whip on any animal. Tonight, he had been using the lash freely. He pulled up alongside the road and laid a hand soothingly on the moist neck of the beast. He spoke quietly, telling him there was nothing to fear. "Quiet, fellow," he said. "Quiet."

The words checked his own panic. He thought, "I am asking a dumb animal not to be afraid when I am the untamed beast. I am running like a coward. I am running from my people, my beloved country. The cause I have sworn to defend with my life, and I am deserting it."

Arriagada reached the place where Bernardo waited.

"We will return," Bernardo said, firmly.

There was a painful silence. Arriagada said, as if praying for his own life, "Bernardo!"

Once again the terror reached deep into Bernardo's heart. But he closed his mind against it, refusing to listen. Whatever came would come. But he would not be afraid. He would be greater than the fear. That was the only freedom! "I am grateful to you, Arriagada," Bernardo said. "I shall be grateful to you forever."

Then he turned his horse and together they rode slowly back toward Las Canteras.

CHAPTER XXVIII

EACH MORNING Bernardo rose, wondering if today he would be arrested. When news came of Miranda's attack against Venezuela having failed and that the Spanish held him prisoner, Bernardo despaired.

Soon the police would come for him. For the Spanish watchdogs were alarmed. They would find him.

He waited, trying to be calm as he supervised the building of adobe fences, the picking of grapes, the making of wine after the recipe of Don Juan Albano. And he recalled the peaceful childhood days when he lived with the Portuguese, when the making of wine was a high point in the year. But now watching his workers dig a pit and line it with scrubbed bullock skins and cover the pit with reeds for holding the grapes, he thought of informers and prison. There was no longer peace.

One day he received a letter from Rozas.

"Word has come that Napoleon has imprisoned the Spanish Royal family at Bayonne, France. Minister Don Manuel Godoy, the favorite of the Queen, has influenced His Majesty, Carlos the Fourth, to sell the throne of Spain for a pension of six million francs and the palace in Compiegne.

"Joseph Bonaparte has been made King of Spain. Rozas."

The throne of Spain sold? A Bonaparte, King of Spain? This could not be! No Spaniard, even the weakest rascal, would turn over the kingdom to a foreign nation, and never for money!

Bernardo reread the words. His mind refused to accept them as true. But the Queen was dominated by Prime Minister Godoy and the King by Queen Luisa Maria. And before him rose the picture of Carlos the Fourth, that weak face, the dissolute, evil features of his Queen, the fat and greedy Godoy.

Immovable Bernardo sat, as if chained to his chair by thought of their treachery. This was a day for those who were loyal to the Crown to closet themselves in shame, to pray that the French Joseph be dethroned.

Now, all Spaniards should understand fully that they owed no loyalty to the Crown! Let every Spaniard join with the patriots and, under a united banner, work for independence! And Bernardo felt the shame, even though he despised Carlos the Fourth and all that he represented. Every man touched with even a trace of Spanish blood would feel the disgrace.

He wrote Rozas that he was riding to Chillan. He would speak there with the patriot friends. Bonaparte as King was unthinkable. An independent government must be formed in Chile. The unhappy event had played into their hands.

A letter from Rozas was waiting for Bernardo at his grandfather's hacienda in Chillan. Rozas was in Santiago.

He wrote that the patriots of Santiago were trying to form an independent government ostensibly loyal to the Crown, but hoping ultimately to make Chile a republic by emphasis on the good intentions of the patriots' interim government. Little by little the changes would be made, the Chileans would realize the advantages gained.

And Rozas was right, Bernardo told himself, his heart freer than it had been in years.

He hurried with the good news to Arriagada at the Town House and to Acuna at the hospital. He thought how brilliant was the sun today, how green fig and palm trees. The Andes stood out clearly. He passed Indians from south of the Biobio who had come to Chillan to trade, each gaudy with brightness.

How fortunate the patriots were to have the able lawyer Rozas helping to form a free government. And a man who co-operated intelligently and listened patiently to Bernardo and his plans. With his disarming mildness and his cleverness as a speaker, he could present the advanced ideas as Bernardo could not.

At the Town House a clerk looked at him strangely when he inquired for Arriagada. His face paled. "Senor O'Higgins," he said, softly, as if he feared he might be overheard, "Arriagada and Acuna have been arrested for conspiracy against the government. They have been sent to Lima!"

In the outer corridor, Bernardo dropped weakly onto a bench, his body heavy with grief. Arriagada had feared that Bernardo would be taken. And now, he had been arrested himself.

With a feeling of utter despair Bernardo watched the people in the Plaza, mules, wagons. He was helpless to do anything.

And now he would certainly be arrested.

Back at Las Canteras, the days passed but the police did not come.

Another letter arrived from Rozas. At the demands of the citizens the Spanish governor had resigned! Engineered by Rozas, a Council was formed to govern Chile and Rozas headed the body.

This was greater progress than the patriots anticipated. Already, Rozas, a member of the Lautaro Lodge, was actually the chief officer of the country. Now the reforms could be quickly enacted. Ports would be opened, a newspaper and schools started.

He read on. The Council had already opened the ports to foreign trade!

This was the greatest day Chile had ever known! This was the beginning of freedom for the people! Feeling the importance of the moment, Bernardo thought about it, his excitement mounting.

At his desk, he noted on his calendar, "September 18, 1810, Chilean independence begins!"

The new government would need militia. From his tenants and neighbors, Bernardo organized two regiments. Then, for days he and his mother and his sister Rosa went about the countryside urging men to join the regiments for the protection of Chile.

Finally, Bernardo was able to write a letter to Rozas telling him of the regiments he had formed. He offered his services and the regiments to the government.

Rozas, as head of Chile, accepted Bernardo's offer. But he put the regiments in charge of his relatives, the Mendiburns, brothers of his wife.

For a long moment Bernardo sat in stunned disbelief. He respected Rozas as a father, and believed him beyond smallness.

He looked on the quiet acres and the gentleness and greatness of the land calmed him. Gradually, the anger departed.

Actually, he told himself, he was ignorant about military tactics. The Mendiburn brothers knew little enough, but Bernardo knew even less. Yet he had expected Rozas would make him a colonel of the regiments! To head a fighting group, an officer should be competent to train his men. Bernardo could not even repeat the Manual of Arms.

As for Rozas, he had always been honest and fair. He constantly supported Bernardo, presenting his ideas of government and winning adherents to the cause. If, in this instance, Rozas had appeared to act unjustly, Bernardo told himself, it was with reason. It might be that he had appointed the Mendiburns to appease the Royalist element in Chile who were friendly with the family. For the patriots wanted to bring all Chileans to accept a republican form of government. The cause would succeed. It would be revolution by reason, as he and Rozas planned it.

He looked at the valley, which stretched endlessly. How unimportant his grievances seemed. It was most necessary to the cause of independence that Rozas form that Congress which Bernardo had urged him to start. And, to achieve that, Rozas would be forced to oppose powerful Royalists. All the talent and astuteness he possessed would be required to break down the prejudices of the rich Spanish who feared for their fortunes. It took great moral courage to attack his opponents and sustain the attack. And Rozas would stand firm. How ungrateful Bernardo had been even to question his friend.

He wanted only to free Chile. That alone mattered. If his country demanded it, Bernardo would be satisfied to be a foot soldier. But he would learn how to do well whatever he was called on to do. He would be the finest soldier in Chile. To learn he must have a good instructor. And where would he find one? There were few in Chile.

Colonel Juan Mackenna!

Mackenna was military engineer at Valparaiso. Once he served under Bernardo's father when he was Viceroy O'Higgins in Peru. He was governor of Osorno under the Viceroy, carrying out Don Ambrosio's plans for restoring and settling the old city and making it prosper. Bernardo had met Mackenna several times, and now and again they had corresponded, and always about the cause of independence. For Mackenna was a patriot.

He wrote Mackenna of his needs and a month later Mackenna's reply reached him.

Mackenna wrote of the risks of the last days of Viceroy Don Ambrosio O'Higgins, and of what Bernardo's father had endured from the evil Spanish.

"I am pleased by the civility, the good sense and modesty of your letter," he continued, "and this makes the task pleasanter of becoming your military instructor. You are a pupil who will without doubt do honor to his teacher and therefore I feel a great satisfaction that you will owe me the first lessons, in the science which I unquestionably place first, the science of war.

"The first step in order to make progress is to be convinced of the necessity of progress. I see with pleasure that you understand this perfectly and therefore I expect good results. I wish that all the young officers gaudily dressed who today swarm through the streets like so many butterflies had the same feelings. But unfortunately, they think that the only thing necessary for being a good officer is a rich uniform and a pair of epaulets and that this is enough for commanding a regiment and even an army. Such vanity and presumption is the result of the enormous ignorance in which South America has been sunk during centuries.

"I foresee the most unhappy consequences during the fight for independence. Do not doubt that that fight is going to come and in all parts of Spanish America. I fear, too, that it will be long and bloody."

Long and bloody? And Miranda had believed the revolution would be bloodless.

He stared at the letter, his mind feeling cold.

Mackenna was expert about wars as Bernardo's father had been, and he had been chosen to manage Osorno near the Indian border because he was the best warrior in South America and would keep the peace, and by war if necessary. He was an experienced officer who understood the Spanish mind.

He believed Mackenna. And he would trust his judgment and be prepared. He returned to the letter and continued to read:

"In order to learn any art, especially the art of war, one must begin at the beginning and for this reason a young soldier must make his appearance as cadet with his musket on shoulder and rise, rank by rank, according to his merits and good conduct. As you have reached in one jump almost to the top of the ladder, you must fill in with study what you would have learned in camp.

"With this object in mind, find the sergeant of dragoons who has the best reputation as instructor; get him a permit and take him to your house. With him you will soon learn the use of the carbine, of the sword and the lance and cavalry and infantry exercises in which your father was accustomed to train his regiment. Then use a horse; become expert in the use of the sword and the lance and when you have learned how to use them well, you can then form a company of your regiment for instructed exercises, helping your sergeant in the work for in no way can you learn better yourself than by teaching others.

"When you have mastered action of a company call to your assistance an intelligent officer of dragoons, a squadron, and only when you can command them perfectly will you find yourself in

the position to command a whole regiment without fear of losing
the esteem of soldiers because of some sign of ignorance. Your men
must be convinced that you know more than they do and that can
only be acquired by a complete knowledge of all the details of the
duties of each one from the trumpeter up to sergeant-major. Be certain that this is of enormous importance because nothing contrib-
utes more to the success of war than the unlimited confidence of
soldiers in their chiefs and that can be based only in the conviction
of their superior knowledge. I have seen more than one officer of
considerable ability and knowledge in his profession who has lost
his credit in the army because he was ignorant of small details
which he had disdained to learn."

There was more good advice about selecting officers, about the
Chilean peasant whose ability to manage a horse and the lasso
made him good material for light cavalry. Even the gaucho of the
Plata river could not excel him, Mackenna wrote.

This Bernardo knew well enough. He had been brought up with
them. And he loved the tough peasants who feared nothing.

He sat looking at the letter, thinking of Mackenna's words: the
disciplined could control others; a true patriot gave life and
fortune for his country; Bernardo had made sacrifices from baby-
hood; Mackenna had the greatest confidence in him and Chile
would suffer no disillusionment in trusting Bernardo.

The following morning he went to Los Angeles and bought a
house large enough for himself and his family. For if he was to become a good soldier, he would remain months in Los Angeles. He
would have to be content with occasional visits to Las Canteras.

The military commandant at the fort said he knew exactly the
right sergeant. He would send him to Bernardo tomorrow.

The sergeant stood like a straight ironwood tree, and he looked
harder. His eyes, only, appeared to move. They went over Bernardo, inch by inch.

Bernardo had thought he was in fair condition. Daily, he had
walked about Las Canteras for hours at a time. He worked man-

ually at pruning trees and building walls, and he rode his horse hours at a stretch. His weight was down, his muscles hard.

"Pull in your stomach," the sergeant said. "You got to work off that flesh!" His eyes glinted. "You will work it off."

Bernardo pulled in his stomach. It was amazing, he thought, how much there was to hold in.

"Straighten up!" the sergeant said. "Feet together."

But he had always stood erectly. Bernardo rather prided himself on his posture. But he squared his shoulders and was surprised to find that he felt inches taller. He snapped his heels together, hard.

"Where's your musket?" The sergeant looked at him as if he had broken all the military rules.

His musket was right here, Bernardo said, cheerfully, and he stepped to the table in the patio to pick it up.

There appeared to be no relation between the words Bernardo had memorized from the Manual of Arms forwarded by Mackenna and what the sergeant was saying. He got nothing right.

"I thought you said you had memorized the Manual of Arms!" The sergeant looked at him with cold eyes.

Bernardo grinned, nervously.

"What are you laughing at?"

He does not want an answer, Bernardo told himself. The sergeant only wants action from me.

"I asked you a question?"

Bernardo said, hastily, "I beg your pardon. Sergeant, you'll find me the most inexperienced recruit you ever trained."

For a brief second the sergeant's eyes softened. But then he jerked the musket from Bernardo's hands and he held it stiffly alongside his shoulder. Step by step, he went throught the Manual, demonstrating each order. "Let me see you do it!" The sergeant shoved the musket into Bernardo's hands.

All morning they worked. It seemed incredible that it could be so difficult.

But at the end of many days, the sergeant seemed satisfied that his student might have possibilities about remembering an order.

Then began the training in formations.

After that came the long marches.

"See that hill yonder?" the sergeant said.

"Yes, sir."

"March. On the double!"

Bernardo wanted to explain that the mountain was at least seven miles away and seven miles back. But he did not. He marched. The afternoon sun beat down, Bernardo's legs seemed those of an ancient man, the pack was filled with boulders, and the perspiration raced down his body in rivers.

He fell onto his bed, exhausted, muscles aching. How he slept! The morning came all too early with more brutal drills, long marches.

But he had asked for toughness. And he was getting his wish. He tried to comfort himself by remembering that he wanted to be the finest foot soldier in Chile.

The queer methods the sergeant had for hardening a man! Squirming on his stomach through underbrush and across fields, wading fords, sometimes swimming them, climbing inch by inch along cliffs where you felt for another finger grip. Bernardo would ask himself, "What foot soldier is going to climb a wall like this to fight an enemy?"

But he climbed.

And he sparred.

The sergeant seemed to Bernardo to be half puma and half tiger, the way he could send him spinning across the earth.

But there came a time when Bernardo could send the sergeant spinning. It seemed to please the tough sergeant. "Hit me harder!" he would order. "Harder!"

Bernardo forgot to count days, weeks or months. But at last came that memorable day when the sergeant said, "There is no finer foot soldier in Chile!"

"Then I can thank you, the instructor," Bernardo said, gratefully.

He had supposed cavalry training would be less demanding. It was just as difficult. Although Bernardo rode a horse well and could handle a sword competently, he now had to train his animal in maneuvers, as well as himself. He learned to take hurdles, each obstacle a little higher. He was grateful that it was not heavy armor he was wearing when he took the leaps, for he doubted if he could have accomplished them. How high and wide the adobe walls seemed when he first tried the hurdles, and yet simple enough once he learned. Riding hard and fast he learned to hit a target with a twenty-foot lance, and with pistols. He thought he was a good swordsman, but after two days of practice at swinging a saber as he raced at an imaginary enemy, he could scarcely move his arm.

Then he was commanded to take a squadron out; a company; a regiment.

Whenever he had time he wrote Mackenna about his progress and asked about tactics and strategy. He thought about nothing else, and meditated constantly on Mackenna's advice: act quickly. Attack before the enemy figures out your movements, or how he can defend himself. The element of surprise is valuable in warfare. Do what the enemy considers it impossible to do. Always be the aggressor if possible. Find the weak place in an enemy line and attack with your greatest strength. Shock the enemy. Make it sudden and vigorous. Remember that the Spanish officers are inclined to wait in attacking and are quick to retreat when vigorously attacked.

All this Mackenna taught Bernardo.

Then hundreds of sketches and maps of imaginary battlefields that Bernardo prepared, placing his right flank, left flank, center, his rear guard and outposts.

When he had passed all tests, he drilled troops until they obeyed with exactness.

At four in the afternoon one day, Bernardo rode into Los Angeles from Las Canteras. He was surprised to see in the Plaza a group of his men armed with lances and coletas. From the barracks of his regiment he heard shouts. Outside the door a formation was under way.

Bernardo hurried to the barracks' door. Inside, the men were arming themselves with lances.

"By whose orders are you acting?" he demanded.

They looked at him sullenly, without answering.

"Have you thought of the seriousness of your actions?" he asked, quietly. "This could be considered sedition. You know the penalty for sedition." He spoke with firmness, but without anger, for these men were his friends. He had trained them well. Always, they had been obedient to his orders, and he considered them as patriots working for the cause of freedom.

He waited, glancing along the line.

After a moment the men dropped the lances. They kept the knives.

Corporal Mariano Pino was holding a sword. He looked insolently at Bernardo. "No one enters the barracks except soldiers who want arms."

At that moment Bernardo's Second Company of the Second Squadron ran toward the barracks with lances to attack the men who were outside in formation.

Bernardo ordered them back to their barracks.

They obeyed instantly.

But as Bernardo moved toward the men in formation near the barracks' door, the line stiffened.

"If you have any grievance," Bernardo said without raising his voice, "present a petition of the wrongs. Your complaints will be heard, I promise you. If there are injustices, they will be remedied." He glanced down the line. "Have I ever broken my promise to you?"

Then the men yielded. They returned the arms to their places. All but Corporal Mariano Pino. He continued to hold a sword, threateningly.

There had been reports to Bernardo about Pino being a tool for Spanish Royalists. Quite possibly he had been in the act of planning a Royalist revolt. Bernardo ordered, "Give me your sword!"

The Corporal did not move.

Bernardo strode toward him. "Your sword," he demanded, still not raising his voice. With eyes on Pino, the upraised sword, Bernardo moved his hand as if reaching for his pistol.

Pino was watching Bernardo's hand, and for the moment had forgotten his sword.

In that moment, Bernardo leapt at Pino, grabbed his arm, struggled with him and wrenched the sword from his hand.

He ordered the Corporal to the guardhouse.

As he walked to his horse, he thought he detected a new respect from the men. But he was shocked that there might be Royalists among these soldiers whom he had trained. At a crucial moment they might refuse to obey orders. And how could he know which were traitors to the cause until the testing time came?

It was raining when he started for home. In torrents it cascaded along the slopes, pouring over dry pasture grass, weeping from bare branches. The land was sopped with the untidy downpour.

Gloomily, Bernardo watched the rain, thought of Corporal Pino, his insolence, the hatred in his eyes. For whom was he acting? "What enemy?" he asked himself.

CHAPTER XXIX

As HE dressed one morning early in January, Bernardo thought of the years he had been waiting for this day. Today, the people of his district of Laja would cast their votes for a deputy to represent them at the new National Congress. It would be the first time the people of Chile had a lesson in self-government.

Bernardo got into his uniform of lieutenant-colonel. As he brushed his hair, he saw strands of gray. He was only thirty, but he had lived twice that number of years, he told himself. Still, the troubles and work had been rewarding. Today, the results would be seen.

He left the house, happier than he had been since that time when, returning to Chile, he learned that his father had not died despising him.

His mother and Rosa were already dressed and waiting.

Rosa said, "You look handsome, Bernardo. But the uniform should be that of a general!"

A general? He smiled. Rosa did not know that generals were not made by pinning epaulets on their shoulders. She had always over-rated him, endowing him with qualities he did not possess. "I am only a good farmer," he said, "and content."

When Chile was entirely free, then he would have everything his heart desired. Everything, except Carlota. If only she were beside him today, on this important day for Chile. Perhaps sooner than he thought the country would be independent. He could go to Ireland, to Carlota, to bring her home.

Bernardo would like Rozas to be present and see these Chileans, feel their eagerness to share in government. For Rozas believed it was too early for the people of Chile to attempt self-government. They were unprepared, he said.

In the hall of election, the clerk was reading the instructions for the election of deputies to Congress.

The voting by secret ballot began.

How quiet the room was. How momentous the time. And how happy Bernardo was for the valiant and courageous Chileans!

He was thinking about his people when the clerk rose to announce the name of the new deputy.

"The deputy to the National Congress," he shouted, unable to control his excitement, "is Don Bernardo O'Higgins!"

Bernardo sat quite still. He thought, "It should be someone else. I have no capacity as speaker or statesman. My tongue never says what it should when I make speeches. Except when I am talking about Chile and freedom." He sat riveted to his chair, happy for the honor, but certain that he was not the suitable choice.

Someone began a speech about Bernardo's being a loyal Chilean who had sacrificed endlessly for the people. His patriotism had fired them with desire to be independent, and he merited all distinction, and he would take with him to Santiago and the Congress the entire confidence of the people.

This is the gentleman who should represent them in Congress, Bernardo thought, listening to the smoothly rolling phrases, watching the dark, animated face.

But he was speaking too eloquently. The words were fine, but the young man was allowing his imagination to run away with him. Bernardo was not all that! He was nothing more than a man who loved his country and his people. He had worked a little to help them. Thousands of others in Chile were doing as much.

The people crowded about him. He smiled, feeling embarrassed and yet enjoying their trust and affection. He must not fail them.

Watching the dancing in the Plaza that night, Bernardo thought of what the patriots had achieved without bloodshed.

Pray God it continues bloodless!

CHAPTER XXX

A STARTLING and shocking thing had happened. Captain Figueroa was marching to Santiago to take over the government for the Royalists! And day and night Bernardo had ridden to reach the capital ahead of Figueroa. Weary, exhausted, he arrived, strode into the Council Chamber with sword unsheathed. He laid it upon the table. "Command me," he said. "My life belongs to Chile!"

But the members looked at him uneasily. Rozas glanced with grave eyes toward the Plaza. He said, "Figueroa failed in his attempt. He was executed this morning!"

Bernardo stared at the Plaza. It was the first Chilean blood spilled for the country's freedom!

What a proud moment when the first session of the National Congress met that morning in July. He took his place in the hall, glanced at the tidy Spaniards, well mannered and polite, who knew little about government and yet were the government of Chile. And he thought what progress the patriots had made in spite of the inexperienced men.

But Rozas knew how to make addresses that stirred these members to vote for the important issues. His genius was in his ability to make involved statutes simple, to guide the timid with his wit and kindness.

Bernardo wanted to shout loudly with happiness when slavery was voted abolished, when the clergy was ordered paid from the Treasury instead of by tithes, when officers were ordered elected by vote, when salaries of government administrators were slashed mercilessly and the inefficient members dismissed, when some offices were dispensed with. He wanted to applaud loudly when the manufacture of guns was voted, and a military school founded.

Above all, when it was agreed that a newspaper was to be started.

But the program, limited as it was in Bernardo's opinion, frightened the conservative members of Congress. Bernardo made no speeches, leaving that to Rozas. For he and Rozas had agreed long ago upon issues to be presented at this first session of Congress. And then, Bernardo was no speaker. He sat that day listening to the conservatives plead for moderation. "Go slowly," they begged, back of their remarks the ancient fear of punishment by Spain.

One conservative member spoke of a ship that had arrived at Valparaiso with an order from the Spanish Regency to collect money due the Crown from Chile. This, the member said, was customary and routine business. He asked that Congress order the gold shipped at once.

For the first time during the session, Bernardo jumped to his feet. "This blind obedience to Spain!" he shouted. "The money belongs to Chile. If it is to be given to anyone, let it be to our peons and peasants."

There was a shocked and sudden stirring.

"The patriots are in the minority in this assembly," he continued, hotly, "but only in numbers. For we have spirit and we have energy to defend the right. We will act boldly to keep for Chileans this gold so necessary to our country at this time!" He looked around angrily at the startled faces and dropped into his chair.

The silence was tomb-like. Bernardo thought he knew what they were thinking. The quiet, mild-mannered Bernardo O'Higgins had dared to threaten them by force if the shipment of gold was ordered. And the stares of the conservatives were as fixed as the crystals on the chandeliers.

To his relief the members were impressed. He had expected a bitter fight over the question. Instead they yielded to his demand that the gold be retained, and the ship sailed from Valparaiso without the Chilean gold. He was glad it had ended so quietly.

And Juan Mackenna was jubilant. "Congratulations," he said, "both to you and Chile. Your first speech in Congress had the force and effect of a cannon ball. They were alarmed by your threat.

They cannot forget Figueroa and that bloody time, nor your drawn sword on the table before members of the council."

Mackenna was right. They had capitulated because they hated the idea of war.

"War cannot be avoided," Mackenna said. "War with the Viceroy of Peru is inevitable." His eyes were serious. "The only possible way to stop the cunning and trickery of the Spanish Royalists is to make war against them. The Spanish are superior to their enemies in the art of corruption. They will ruin the cause of the patriots unless they are forced to stop their underhanded intrigues."

Bernardo glanced at the vineyards, the peaceful mission and the quiet hills. But to the north in Peru were the Viceroy's troops which could reach Chile within days and begin warring against the patriots.

"The Viceroy can be stopped only with cannon," Mackenna said. "The conservatives of Chile see only the enormous power and resources of the Spaniards. They think a fight would be uneven for the Chileans. But there is no middle course. The powerful Royalist enemies in Chile will force the patriots to make war. It is their only hope of defeating the cause of independence." He paused, stared ahead. "Arbitration will not stop the Royalists and the Viceroy. And yet the conservatives of Chile would arbitrate rather than fight!"

Bernardo thought of Chile with less than three thousand trained soldiers.

"The Royalists understand only defeat by iron, lead, saltpeter, sulphur and muscle," Mackenna said, harshly. "We must lay aside metaphors and fine words. I would seize the chief Royalists in Chile and throw them into prison at Valparaiso. I would keep them there and continue the fight."

Bernardo asked, thoughtfully: "Mackenna, you would attack them at once?"

"I will tell you why, Bernardo. England will return the Spanish throne to the Crown if she succeeds in beating France. On the other hand, Napoleon will establish his brother Joseph firmly on the Spanish throne if he succeeds in defeating England. I think the French will win against England. Napoleon has two million men fighting for him. England has a couple of hundred thousand. Well, then, even if the English believe one Britisher excels six Frenchmen, certainly one Britisher is not the equal of ten Frenchmen. And when the French win and Joseph is firmly seated on the Spanish throne, they will throw their whole force against Chile."

The two sat in silence for a moment.

"If I did not understand how little help the Spanish army will give the English," Mackenna said at last, "I might think differently."

Bernardo did not doubt Mackenna. This able soldier was also a brilliant military engineer. He was entirely familiar with the science of war. And he knew men, the character of the English, French and Spanish. He was honest, looking without fear at hard facts and appraising them.

He studied the open countenance of Mackenna. "We must prepare for war, then," Bernardo said, earnestly. "You must lead us!"

Mackenna said kindly: "Others will not think as you do, Bernardo, that an Irishman should lead Chileans." His broad, generous mouth widened in a smile. "There are some with great pride of race."

"I know of no person in Chile, or in all South America, with your ability," Bernardo said. "Race should have nothing to do with who wins this struggle."

"The Carreras will oppose me." Mackenna studied the red hibiscus blossoms beside the road. "Captain Jose Miguel Carrera returned recently from Spain. I think he came home expecting to head the government of Chile. He has Napoleonic ideas without the ability of Napoleon."

Bernardo said in a shocked voice, "Rozas should continue to direct the government. He is a good patriot and his knowledge and loyalty are indispensable!"

This time Mackenna's smile was not pleasant, and his eyes were hard. "The Carreras will war against Rozas, O'Higgins and

Mackenna! These three stand between the Carreras and their ambition to seize the government and rule Chile," he said. "It would be the rule of tyrants!"

Bernardo thought of Jose Miguel Carrera, proud in his scarlet uniform, covered with gold braid, glittering with epaulets, and of his popularity with the troops because of his great wealth and his freedom in spending it. He had an attractive personality. He had always been spoiled by his family, taking nothing seriously except pleasures.

The Carreras! The Viceroy of Peru! The Royalists of Chile! The conservatives in the patriot group! All these to think about. Enemies within and enemies without. And war inevitable.

Bernardo glanced at the sunset. The sky had turned a strange, violent red. It was, he thought, the color of blood!

CHAPTER XXXI

In his bedroom at Las Canteras, Bernardo peered into the darkness, unable to sleep.

Disaster had followed disaster.

He went over them, one by one, all the events that had happened during the past few months since the formation of a National Congress.

One day while Rozas was absent, Jose Miguel Carrera had seized the government. His brother Luis had been given Juan Mackenna's place as commander of artillery. Mackenna was imprisoned and Rozas was exiled to Mendoza across the Andes.

And now the conceited, strutting Jose Miguel Carrera, in his scarlet uniform of the Spanish hussars with its layers of gilt braid, danced away the precious hours and days instead of preparing Chile for defense against the threat from the troops of the Viceroy of Peru. Daily the danger moved nearer.

Soon, blood would be spilled. And there was no leader. He thought of the able Juan Mackenna in prison in Valparaiso where the cold wind blew into his cell, the same wind that would bring the Viceroy's soldiers.

Bernardo thought also of Rozas exiled to Mendoza.

The two most important men in the country sacrificed because of Carrera's ambition.

A great leader was needed for Chile and there was none!

Morning came and he felt exhausted both in mind and body.

An hour later, Juan Tirapegui raced into the courtyard. He shouted as he sprang from his horse, "The Viceroy's troops have arrived from Lima! Concepcion has surrendered to them without firing a shot!"

Bernardo thought, heartsick, "Now, the blood begins to flow!"

War was here. And Carrera had no plan to defend any part of Chile. All the careful preparations suggested by Rozas and Mackenna were ignored.

With a grand flourish, Carrera had a gallows erected in the Plaza of Santiago as a warning to the Royalists. Then he departed from the capital and set up headquarters in Talca. He boasted that he would stop the Royalist general and drive him back to Talcahuano and prison.

At Talca, Bernardo offered his services to his country.

Realizing at last that he had only incompetents around him and that he needed soldiers with military skill, Jose Miguel Carrera released Mackenna from prison.

At headquarters everything was in confusion. There was not so much as a map of the territory on which the war would be fought. In the face of an advancing enemy of trained and hardened Spanish troops, the militia had to be drilled for fighting. A treasury had to be organized, stores collected and a commissary department established. There were no horses, mules, wagons, no muskets or uniforms, no supplies of any kind.

Carrera did not know the country, the roads, the haciendas.

But Bernardo knew. For this was Talca where as a boy he had roamed and played, and he was familiar with the land, with forests and vineyards, the rivers, fords and roads; he was acquainted with each hacienda and village.

He learned that the Viceroy's General had ordered a detachment of soldiers to Linares south of Talca to get horses. He longed for Mackenna who was now in Santiago. If Mackenna were here, Bernardo and he could take the Spanish soldiers at Linares. Bernardo began sketching the byways to Linares, the Maule river. By using a roundabout way along streams and through forests the enemy soldiers might be taken. How long would it take the Spanish to reach Linares? Bernardo knew the time required to reach

Talca. With thirty men, a clever patriot officer could take them.

Mackenna had said an officer should act when the enemy least expected an attack.

Bernardo gazed long at the tower of the church across the square. Move in quickly when the enemy was unarmed and relaxed, Mackenna had said.

When would the Spanish troops at Linares least expect an attack? Early morning? Breakfast?

If an officer and a few men rushed into Linares at eight o'clock in the morning while the Spaniards were at breakfast, he might take them without a struggle.

His pulse quickened. That was the method Mackenna would use to go after the Spanish soldiers at Linares. If an officer followed carefully what he had learned from Mackenna, he might succeed.

He returned to headquarters and asked permission to ride to Linares after the Spaniards and found Jose Miguel Carrera pathetically willing. For if ever a cock was trailing its gold feathers, it was Carrera. He was bewildered and utterly confused. He whined about the tremendous task of organizing for attack as if already he had not had months to prepare.

Bernardo was allowed twenty-seven men.

Shortly before eight o'clock they reached the gates of Linares and immediately moved to where the Spaniards were quartered. Bernardo and his men sprang upon the Spanish dragoons while they sat at breakfast, unarmed.

It had been almost too simple, Bernardo thought, as he marched the Spanish dragoons back to Talca. Lieutenant-Colonel Bernardo O'Higgins, who had no taste for warfare, had succeeded!

When he entered Carrera's headquarters Mackenna was standing there.

In his delight at seeing his old friend, he almost forgot to make his report. Carrera had to say sharply, "Colonel O'Higgins! What about Linares?"

How proudly Juan Mackenna looked at Bernardo as he related the action.

Bernardo was thinking that now Chile had a leader again. Even Carrera realized the importance of Mackenna as a leader.

Then, before Bernardo could visit with Mackenna, he was ordered by Carrera to retake the towns and villages in southern Chile now occupied by the Viceroy's soldiers. He gave him thirty men.

One after another, Bernardo took the towns, using the surprise tactics he had employed at Linares. At San Javier, the Spanish retreated into the houses and Bernardo had to order his soldiers to follow and drive them out. Because they were faster on their feet than the Spanish and could leap quickly and use the bayonet with surer aim and force, and could attack like savage Indians, they always succeeded.

At San Javier he lost two men. But the Spanish lost more.

As he marched, he kept thinking of his two brave soldiers who had given their lives for Chile. How quietly they had lain. He kept seeing their young, fearless faces, the precious blood seeping into the earth. He kept thinking of their families. He prayed for them, for himself and Chile as he marched against the other towns.

He advanced rapidly. And he searched everywhere for men to enlist with the patriot army.

This night he was stopping at the residence of a patriot, a superintendent of a large hacienda. The man said his workmen were eager to enlist and he hurried off to bring them.

Bernardo laid aside his dusty poncho, for he had been riding hard all day. He glanced about the long room furnished with three beds made of rough boards, the walls hung with pictures of religious martyrs, and at the rear of the room huge wine jars buried deep in the earth floor. Piles of cowhides, sacks of grain, large wagon wheels, were stacked against the adobe walls, and above he could see the reeds and through the spaces, the tiles of the roof.

Somewhere, he heard music and laughter.

Always music in Chile, he thought. Always singing and dancing and laughter. Life, death, war, but the music continued. For the Chilean could no more live without music than without food.

The superintendent returned. Soon the room was filled with

stocky, toughened, bright-eyed peasants in velveteen pants, their hose tied with faded ribbons, with worn ponchos, sashes bulging with their possessions—flint, knives, tobacco.

Bernardo looked into their eager faces. How gaily his people offered themselves to their country. He made his speech simple. If they would fight for Chile, he would furnish horses and arms. He would train them to fight well. They would drive the Royalist troops of the Viceroy from Chile's land and there would be no Bonaparte king to close Chilean ports again. There would be no more Inquisition. They would have plenty of land when the war was ended. They would be free men, like the North Americans!

"The Americanos!" a voice cried. "The Chilenos!"

They all shouted in glee. They pressed closer, anxious to hear more, to enlist and fight for their country's independence.

Bernardo thought, with such a spirit, Chile will be free. He had always known his people would rally to the defense of their country when the need was made known. Each man was his brother, and he loved them as brothers and would train them to be skillful soldiers, as Mackenna had trained him.

Within weeks his company of three score men had swelled to a thousand. He outfitted them from his slender resources, and marched them toward patriot headquarters with a proud heart.

He found that Carrera had done a stupid thing. He had laid siege to Chillan where the Viceroy's soldiers were quartered.

It was stupid, Bernardo told himself, standing in Carrera's tent that day, because Chillan had a rich store of provisions of all kinds that would supply the Spanish through months of siege. No one knew better than Bernardo the richness of the Chillan storehouses. Moreover, the Spanish troops were comfortable in well-built houses. They would suffer few inconveniences.

But here in Carrera's camp the patriot soldiers were poorly sheltered from the winter rains that had begun. They were inadequately clothed, poorly armed and half starved.

Bernardo explained all this to Carrera. Perhaps he was too critical, for Carrera replied with spirit that he knew what he was doing.

Perhaps Carrera did know. After all, he had fought with the Spanish in many engagements abroad. He had fought with Napoleon. Carrera might have some secret strategy that he had withheld from all of them.

And what did Bernardo know of military schemes and tactics and planning? He could follow instructions, but he had no ability at fighting a war. You had to have talent to succeed against the dragoons trained in the corps of the Spanish Viceroy. Bernardo had retaken a few villages, but Carrera had fought in actual battles.

He started to leave Carrera's tent.

"Before you leave," Carrera said, "and before you hear it elsewhere, your mother and sister are prisoners in Chillan."

Bernardo stared at Carrera.

"They were captured at your hacienda, hiding in a workman's cottage," Carrera said, quite calmly.

For a moment Bernardo was too stunned to speak. Then the feeling passed. He shouted angrily, "You've got to get them out of Chillan! I'll take troops into Chillan and bring them out!"

He glared at Carrera.

"Yes, O'Higgins," Carrera said, as if there was no danger at all, "we'll get them released shortly. Now don't worry. Don't get excited. There's no occasion for worry. I'm negotiating with the Spanish General to exchange them for prisoners of the Viceroy's that we have taken."

"But how soon?" Bernardo demanded, feeling anguished.

"They are all right. I investigated," Carrera said. "The Spanish have not mistreated them."

"Then make the exchange of prisoners, quickly!" he said, hotly. He turned and walked from the tent.

He stood, the rain pouring over him, and stared at the solid walls of Chillan. And then he thought. "Mackenna will help me! Tomorrow, I shall go to Mackenna!"

But on the following morning, Carrera lifted the siege as suddenly as he had begun it. With troops and officers he marched hurriedly south. His reason was that towns and villages taken by Bernardo must be protected. Then, one after another, because of his unmilitary tactics, Carrera lost the towns to the Spanish.

Night after night Bernardo and the men slept on the damp earth. For days the rain poured from gray skies.

He kept worrying about his family. The siege had been lifted by Carrera, but what about his mother and sister? Were they free and back at Las Canteras? Were they still prisoners? Had Carrera arranged for the exchange of prisoners as he promised, and if so why was there no word from his people?

Whenever he spoke to Carrera about the matter, he smiled and replied that everything was all right. The negotiations were about completed. For all he knew Bernardo's family might already be back at their house in Las Canteras.

A few days later, there still was no news.

Then, a week later, a messenger brought word that his hacienda, Las Canteras, had been burned by the Spanish.

For minutes he was unable to think. Then his shocked mind saw the flames rising higher and higher to destroy the home he loved, and the house his father had loved. The flames seemed to sear into his flesh.

CHAPTER XXXII

BERNARDO and the patriot troops led by Carrera had returned to the camp on the Itata River, near Chillan. It was early morning. Bernardo hurried to Carrera's tent to inquire about the release of his mother and sister, but found the General still asleep.

He returned to his tent. The unhappy faces of patriot soldiers looked at him questioningly. They no longer believed or respected their hero Carrera. They were discouraged and no longer wanted to fight.

He remembered how willingly the men had enlisted. They had dropped their work as muleteers, carters, as cowhands and farmers, to fight, and their spirits had been high. Now they sang little, laughter was seldom heard and they were deserting right and left.

They must have a leader to unify them and inspire them with fresh confidence. He should be an able soldier, that leader.

Bernardo walked on. Somehow, he told himself, the Council in Santiago must give the direction of this struggle to Mackenna. But how?

On the afternoon of October eighteenth, the patriots made camp near the river.

With his men, Bernardo prepared for the night at the summit of a high mountain overlooking the Itata River and Chillan. In happier days he had played in this stream. It seemed impossible that this remote mountain should be an encampment for soldiers, that his quiet Chillan was filled with Spanish enemies. That his beloved mother and sister were imprisoned there, in spite of Carrera's repeated promises to have them released. "God keep them!" he said.

He glanced unhappily toward Carrera's camp farther down the Itata. Tomorrow he would speak to him about the release of his family. For a moment he stared toward the road leading to a ford where guards had been stationed and then he returned to his labors.

Bernardo worked late over papers. The stars, when he looked at them, were close. He wondered if Dona Isabel and Rosa were looking at them, too.

He lay on his hard pallet, trying to rest and not succeeding. Then he heard many voices.

He was on his feet instantly, his sword in his hand.

He saw the troops of Carrera racing up the hillside in the greatest confusion.

"Where is General Carrera?" he shouted, running toward them.

"He has escaped," they answered. "The Spanish have taken the camp!"

As Bernardo ran, he saw the river covered with heavy mist and Spanish dragoons pouring over the palisade and into the enclosure where the men were camped.

The muskets of the Spanish blasted. About Bernardo patriot soldiers stumbled and fell.

"Brave Patriots follow me!" he shouted. Over and over the words were bellowed across the camp, the voice of a giant, ordering the Chileans to unite, to close in, to attack the Spanish with spirit and violence.

The men surged toward Bernardo and their muskets spat loudly, angrily.

Bernardo ordered a horse to be brought. When it came he raced along the line of patriots, giving orders, crying loudly, "Live, die with glory." The words of encouragement poured from him, and with each word another dragoon fell. The patriots fought with wild cries of "Viva la Patria!" And when one fell, another took his place.

Bernardo's horse was shot from under him. A bullet pierced Bernardo's thigh, but he felt no pain. He shouted, "Live with honor! Die with glory! Give no quarter!"

For three hours hand-to-hand fighting continued. For three hours Bernardo screamed encouragement to the men who were fighting like wild Indians, and as ruthlessly.

Suddenly the enemy fled, racing in confusion down the hill and plunging into the river to swim the ford.

The patriot soldiers pressed about Bernardo, and down across the river rolled their praises: "Viva O'Higgins! Viva la Patria! Live with honor! Die with glory! O'Higgins!"

The generous peasants! He could see the happiness in their faces, the tears in their eyes. His own were misting with joy at their success.

General Carrera arrived. "I was sleeping," he said, blithely. "A shot killed my horse. My men scattered. With the help of an aide I escaped by the river. I swam to the other side, and waited." He grasped Bernardo's hand. "It was magnificent," he said. "The finest soldier in Chile!"

But Bernardo knew Carrera. He was adept at flattery. Tomorrow it would be another story. Now, he was only relieved that he and his soldiers had not been defeated and taken prisoners.

Lying on his cot, the bullet removed from his thigh, the wound bandaged, Bernardo thought about tomorrow. There must be another commander in chief. Carrera must go. And Bernardo knew who the man would be. Juan Mackenna.

A few days later, when Mackenna arrived, he said, "I am proud, Bernardo. All Chile is praising O'Higgins."

Mackenna, like the peasants, was generous. One did a little to help and they made a great thing of it. But Bernardo knew his own limitations well enough.

"I've been asked by the Council and the regiments," Mackenna said, "to explain that we want you as commander in chief. I've come for your answer."

"You can't be serious," Bernardo said.

"The men believe in you. You have restored their confidence in themselves and in the cause. The Council has ordered you to take command. You cannot refuse." Mackenna walked outside the tent and took the reins of his horse. "I will report to the Council that you accept," he said.

Bernardo said, "Wait, Mackenna." He limped after his friend. "I'll have to think this over. You know I'm only a farmer. No one knows better than you that men must be born with military talent. It cannot be put on like a capota. I have no genius for that sort of thing."

But Mackenna was already mounted. His keen blue eyes were smiling.

"Look, Mackenna," Bernardo said, feeling a little desperate. "You yourself have often said that generals are not made by pinning gilt on their shoulders. Generals must have a canny genius for making war. The farm, that is where I belong. You are the one to lead us. You have the talent, Mackenna."

"Well, then," Mackenna said, briskly, "think about it for a short time. But you will have to accept in the end. And I shall be at your right hand, your general."

Watching his straight figure moving down the road, Bernardo thought, "The Council will understand when I explain that Mackenna is the one!"

He stared at the soldiers cleaning their equipment. Since that night on the Itata they had new spirit. They no longer had to be reminded they were soldiers. He was a sort of fighting man himself. Not the best, but an honest soldier like these men. But not a commander in chief. Certainly not a general. Not a man to direct an army through a series of hard conflicts. That took the genius that Mackenna had.

For two months Bernardo waited. Each time Mackenna asked for an answer, he said, "No!"

Then the members of the Council at Talca sent for him.

He sat with the three members in a room at Government House facing the Plaza. One of the Council, Jose Miguel Infante, was looking at his polished boots. He glanced up, studied Bernardo with serious eyes. "General O'Higgins," he said, "we have separated Jose Miguel de Carrera from the command of the Army of Chile. We have named you to replace him."

Bernardo glanced at him with a sense of hopelessness. "I am not the man to lead the Army!" he said.

"We have waited on you for two months." A shadow lay on the lined face of Augustin de Eyzaguirre.

The third member, Jose Ignacio Cienfuegos, was standing at a window grille. Without turning, he said, "You are too modest, General O'Higgins. You must accept for the country's sake."

"There is Mackenna," Bernardo said, stubbornly.

"Mackenna wants you to accept the appointment, as we do. You are Chilean. The soldiers want a Chilean. And you are the best soldier and officer in Chile."

This, Bernardo thought with annoyance, was not true. Mackenna was a better soldier.

But on January 26, 1814, when the rheumatism in his bones was like fire, and his body was weary with pain and loss of sleep from thinking about his unfitness, he accepted. He would do his best. That he could promise, faithfully. He would do the very utmost to succeed. He would even do more than he could. But he was not a general. That he knew!

They were wrong, but he would do his best.

CHAPTER XXXIII

THE HEADQUARTERS in Talca was in complete disorder. The military chest was exhausted and there were no funds for supplies. They had little food. And there was an ugly rumor that the Carrera brothers had helped themselves to forty thousand pesos which had been contributed for supplies and rations.

Night after night, Bernardo worked trying to bring order into the confused records. It was impossible to account for the money that had been spent since Carrera took office.

The task of raising more pesos looked hopeless, but Bernardo set about it. Some he supplied from his own diminishing resources. The Chilean patriots donated money, when they could, and animals and grain to be traded for muskets and ammunition. Bernardo sent officers throughout the country for horses and mules.

Order began to replace chaos. Men re-enlisted rapidly. A spirit of enthusiasm appeared, a stiffening of morale. Once again the patriot Army was a united, hopeful, singing group.

By candlelight one late Thursday evening, Bernardo read a message that had arrived by special courier.

The Viceroy of Peru had sent his finest general and heavy reinforcements of Spanish troops to Talcahuano. A formidable army of five thousand picked Royalist dragoons was marching toward Santiago.

Santiago was once again the seat of government, the Chilean Council having recently returned to the northern city from Talca. For months the Council had been located at Talca to be near the Army of Chile.

And Santiago was poorly defended.

If the Spanish general and his regiments reached Santiago, Chile would again fall to the Viceroy. His troops had to be stopped!

Bernardo started south with his soldiers. Then he and Mackenna learned that the enemy was marching for the River Maule, fifty miles away.

"If the enemy reaches the Maule and crosses ahead of us," Bernardo said, "he will move quickly on to Santiago and take the city."

Bernardo knew this country as well as his acres at Las Canteras. Alone, and with Don Juan Albano, he had traveled over all this area. Without looking at the map he knew the route taken by the Spanish, and it was the easiest. When the Viceroy's men reached the Maule, the Royalists in that district would help them to cross.

Even at the fords the river was swift, and the patriots, without balsas, would find their crossing slowed by having to swim the raging stream.

The Las Cruces was the nearest ford, and the most dangerous. There the Maule River was deep, extremely wide and the waters churned and eddied.

But the patriot troops by taking a short cut across fields, marshes, forests, might succeed in reaching the Maule ahead of the Spanish. Then at the ford where the enemy would cross, Bernardo and Mackenna could have embankments thrown up and, he hoped, by stiff fighting, stop the Viceroy's troops from continuing north to Santiago.

"We could move in this direction," Bernardo said, drawing a heavy line along the map. "It is much shorter than the route which the enemy is taking."

The patriots had been marching for better than an hour.

A scout brought word that the Spanish were still leading.

Bernardo thought of the Viceroy's regiments, hardened by years of training. But the patriots were a vigorous peasant army. They had been trained to endure hardship from childhood and they were tougher than any Spanish dragoons. Bernardo's men had both physical fortitude and a mental stamina inspired by their desire for a free Chile, to be a free people. The Spanish soldiers fought only for pay.

Bernardo glanced back at his soldiers moving with determined tread, a dark, silent mass, strangely quiet.

"How the men march!" Mackenna's face lighted with pleasure.

Ahead Bernardo saw the ford of Los Cruces.

He guided his horse down the steep wall.

Stumbling, sliding scattering earth and stones, his horse plunged, leaped the last several feet into the raging waters, sinking to its neck. The ice-cold water rose to Bernardo's thighs. He could feel his horse under him fighting the swift, eddying waters.

About him were struggling animals, pushing hard against the current, snorting in fear, but swimming gamely to reach the opposite bank. It seemed a long way off.

Then, at last, winded by the struggle, the horses reached the other bank of the Maule. Without pausing to rest, Bernardo and Mackenna raced on to Quechereguas, the place where the Spanish intended to make a crossing.

Mackenna gave a shout. He reached over and clasped Bernardo's hand in a hearty grip.

There where the patriots were to intercept the Spanish general and his troops, Bernardo ordered fortifications of earth, small trees and hides thrown up.

These peasants were accustomed to building adobe walls and digging irrigation canals. They knew about repairing roads that had been washed out, how to construct stout corrals for their animals. The men needed little instruction from him or from anyone to make a secure embankment for protection against musket fire.

When the Spanish general and his regiments reached Quechereguas, Bernardo and his men were prepared for the attack.

He would never forget this moment, the surprise and obvious annoyance of the Spanish general that his well-laid and secret plans had been discovered by the patriots and that he, the Viceroy's ablest officer, had been outwitted and stopped by a group of straggling Chilean peasants. And Bernardo could imagine the feelings of the general, who had already been repulsed at El

Quilo by Bernardo's troops, and again at El Membrillar by Mackenna. And now, when he was confident he had left the patriots
sitting at El Membrillar celebrating their victories over him, to
have them lined up and protected from his attack by strong, sturdy
fortifications, awaiting him, barring his advance to the capital of
Santiago.

He attacked like a madman, like an angry beast. He drove his
Spanish troops into battle relentlessly, sacrificing his men without
counting the cost. Fiercely, he blasted the fortifications thrown
up by Bernardo's peasant troops.

But the barricades defied him. The peasants mocked him, fighting just as well as they built and marched. With strong hearts,
clear eyes, sure aim, they returned shot for shot and blow for blow,
and better. They never misunderstood Bernardo's orders. And
like savages, they fought.

The Spanish general and his troops were forced to retreat.

Close at the enemy's heels the patriots followed, united in mind
and spirit against the enemy, pushing the Viceroy's fine dragoons
back, back, to defeat.

Across the camp that night sounded the guitars, the songs of
victory, the peasant voices rising clear and happy.

In the midst of rejoicing, Bernardo received a message from
the Council in Santiago. They wanted to confer with him at once.

The three members of the Council sat together at the long table.

"The country is weary of war and the land has been neglected
too long. Chile's commerce is at a low ebb. Our income has suffered and our funds are almost depleted. Soon the war between
France and England will be ended, and once again Spain will
have a Spanish ruler on the throne." Jose Miguel Infante paused.
He stared at his hands.

Jose Ignacio Cienfuegos said, impatiently, "Tell General O'Higgins frankly why we have called him to Santiago." He shifted in
his chair and looked at Bernardo with grave eyes. "The Viceroy
of Peru has offered Chile peace. He has promised that we will be
allowed to keep all the benefits gained by the patriots for the
country."

"We all are weary of conflict," Jose Miguel Infante said, slowly. "We can end it with honor, and gains."

Bernardo stepped nearer. The Viceroy was the instrument of Spain and he would never make peace, not a peace that would let Chile retain the benefits—open ports, the ships of all nations trading with the country; the monopolies ended; reduced revenues for the Crown and Church; a free press and public schools and libraries.

"Gentlemen," Bernardo said, his voice deeply serious, "we have defeated the Viceroy's army. Chile soon will be entirely free of the Viceroy and the Spanish Regency, even the Spanish King when there is one. Let us not act rashly, or foolishly. Let us accept no false offers from the Viceroy! He cannot be trusted!"

"We are going to accept the Viceroy's offer," Jose Miguel Infante said, his eyes still on his hands. "You and Mackenna must work out a suitable treaty and sign it for Chile. The Viceroy's general will sign for him."

General Gainza, Bernardo thought, whom I recently defeated!

He longed for Mackenna. With what angry retorts the able Irishman would receive this order! He said, "Gentlemen, you must not believe the Viceroy's promises. I beg of you, do not accept this false pretense of peace!"

For an hour Bernardo tried to reason with them.

But their minds were made up. Nothing he said would move the Council.

He returned to Talca with a heavy heart. The honored name of Bernardo O'Higgins would be signed to capitulation to the Spanish. It was a bitter blow. His mind revolted.

Mackenna paced the floor of Bernardo's office. "A trap!" he kept repeating angrily, his voice tight and tense. On and on he paced, and talked.

The Treaty of Lircay, it was called. It was signed on the third of May. By the terms of the document, Chile was to acknowledge the authority of the Spanish Crown; free trade would be permitted and the Spanish General Gainza and his troops would leave the country at once.

A fiesta for victory, Bernardo thought angrily, listening to the festivities in the Plaza of Talca. He glanced at Mackenna who was watching the scene glumly from a window grille.

"This is our greatest defeat," Bernardo said.

The only joyous result of the treaty was that all prisoners were released. Bernardo hastened toward Chillan to meet his mother and sister. He intercepted them, traveling with an escort, near the Itata River. Rosa began to weep. She said, "My brother, they have destroyed Las Canteras. Cannot you have anything in life except more and more disaster? Not even a home?"

But his mother looked at him with loving eyes. "You are safe, my son," she said. "We are all together again."

Almost before the ink had dried on the Treaty of Lircay, the Viceroy repudiated it.

Bernardo, at his residence in Talca, crumpled the message in one hand.

Then, as if this disaster was not enough, the officials at Santiago ordered Bernardo to the capital to protect the city and people from the Carrera brothers. They had seized the remaining funds and were terrorizing the citizens.

Leaving the greater number of his troops with Mackenna at Talca, Bernardo arranged a meeting with Jose Miguel Carrera on the plains of Maipú. Watching him as he neared, his face dark with hatred, was Jose Miguel, resplendent in a spotless uniform, his aides and guards surrounding him.

Bernardo dismounted. He said, "Carrera, the Viceroy, as you know, has repudiated the Treaty of Lircay. He has already shipped more troops to Chile. At any moment, thousands of Spanish dragoons will reach Talcahuano and again sweep north toward Santiago. Can you hold Santiago against six thousand trained and hardened Spanish troops?" He studied Carrera closely as he spoke.

He saw Carrera's face pale and become less arrogant. Perhaps he was recalling other tough Spaniards, against whom he had fought battles, and lost.

"This is no time for brother to fight against brother," Bernardo said, wishing that he and Carrera could forget differences and be friends. "I have no desire for position or glory," he continued. "I never wanted to accept the post of commander in chief. When this war is ended, as pray God it may be soon, I want only to return to my land and farming and quietness. I want no political position of any kind."

He paused. The dark, angry expression on Carrera's face had been replaced by a look of incredulity. But then, Carrera would not be able to understand a man without political ambition.

"Let us put aside our strife and fight together as friends for Chile." And he held out his hand. "Let us drive out the Spanish from our country. That is where true glory lies."

Carrera hesitated. He stared hard into Bernardo's face. What he saw seemed to satisfy him, for he stretched forth his hand. Momentarily, at least, Carrera had put aside hatred and was willing to be friends. "Then, for Chile, O'Higgins."

The Spanish reinforcements from Peru had reached Talcahuano.

Bernardo heard this and hastened to Carrera for a conference about their defenses. They stood near the River Cachapoal, where they planned to attack the enemy, for already the Spaniards were approaching.

Carrera appeared to agree with Bernardo about where the battle would be fought. He rode away.

Bernardo, with five hundred and fifty men, reconnoitered south to try out the position of the Spanish and to fortify cities threatened by enemy guerrillas. At Rancagua, he ordered trenches dug in the streets that entered from four sides, making a cross. The trenches were a protection against guerrilla threats.

On the River Cachapoal, where the battle was to be fought, he stationed defences at important fords where the enemy would attempt to cross. The ford of Cortes was to be defended by Luis Carrera, youngest of the three Carrera brothers.

Everything was moving smoothly as Bernardo had planned.

Then he received word that Luis Carrera had not defended the ford of Cortes. He had allowed the Spanish to pass the river without resistance.

Before he recovered from that staggering blow to his plans, an officer arrived in haste saying that another Carrera, Juan Jose, was barricaded in Rancagua by a few Spanish soldiers. He asked Bernardo for reinforcements.

These Carreras!—Bernardo thought, feeling desperate. But there was no time to waste in disgust or regrets. Before more Spanish reached Rancagua, he must go to Juan Jose.

Taking what troops he had, he reached Rancagua where Juan Jose Carrera embraced him tearfully. "I am your oldest brigadier. But you are the one to command," he said.

Bernardo thought if only the Carreras would stop quarreling among themselves and others about command. He ordered barricades of logs, stones, bales of dried beef. At the four entrances he had the cannon placed: three eight-pounders and nine forty-pounders.

Then he climbed the tower of the church to learn the enemy position.

He was startled to discover the town completely surrounded by at least five thousand enemy soldiers. They formed four thick columns at the entrances to the four streets. Looking down, Bernardo saw the streets formed like a cross. Saying a prayer, he descended.

He ordered two of the twelve cannon placed in each parapet. The others he ordered to the Plaza and the parade ground. The fusiliers he had placed in the crown of the churches and on the roofs of houses next to the parapets. A detachment of infantry was sent to protect the cannon behind the parapets. To each parapet he assigned a chief. The street leading south joined the church of San Francisco, and he ordered Captains Astoroa and Millan to that position. Captain Sanchez he assigned to the street on the north, that on the east to Captain Vial, and Captain Molina was stationed on the avenue leading to the west entrance. The cavalry in the large corral was in charge of Captains Freyre and Acquita.

Bernardo took his position in the hall of the Cabildo with his aides Astorga, Urrutia and Flores.

It was then about nine o'clock in the morning. The silence was too sudden, too deadly, a silence. He thought of the residents huddled in fear within their houses, in the churches, of the women he had seen kneeling in prayer.

He turned away from the picture of frightened women. He thought of his men in position and waiting. Everything ready for the Spaniards when they arrived!

A few hundred patriots against five thousand! But it was the spirit that fought and not numbers, and the patriots had an undying spirit, Bernardo thought.

The enemy came suddenly, from four directions, pouring toward the parapets.

At ten o'clock the cannon were fired on the Spanish columns and the rapid fusilade was returned. The first to attack was the column of Talaveras, one of the most formidable of the Spanish regiments. They came through the street on the south, nailing their bayonets in the grilles of the adobe houses and leaping the parapets.

A barrage of shellfire drove them back.

The slaughter on both sides was bloody and merciless.

That first attack lasted an hour. Then the enemy retired, improvised a barricade of adobe and furniture and placed their cannon. A shot from their cannon rocketed between Bernardo and the Surgeon, Moran.

A few more inches, Bernardo thought.

He mounted his horse again and rode from position to position, giving orders and encouraging his men.

The column of Talaveras attacked in the street of San Francisco, black streamers on their campaign banners. As they attacked they shouted, "Yield, traitors!"

Bernardo ordered the black banner of the patriots nailed on all the parapets and the towers of the churches.

At four that afternoon the enemy retired in disorder behind their parapets, after a terrific cannonading by the patriots.

The sun was setting. A long, orange-red glow lighted the gray heavens. Bernardo recalled that talk with Mackenna, the blood-red sky when he had shuddered to think of his countrymen shedding blood on this beautiful land. And now the blood was being spilled. It drenched the ground of Rancagua, the streets that formed the great cross.

He stared with sad eyes at the four streets making the cross. Once again a cross was a symbol of sacrifice for the liberty of men. Feeling anguish, he turned away.

The patriots were hopelessly outmatched, five to one, yet they fought better than the Spanish. But Bernardo thought of their water supply cut by the Spanish, of his dwindling ammunition, of his troops that had eaten nothing all day, and he remembered Jose Miguel and Luis Carrera and their fresh troops.

But he did not know if they were in Bodegas del Conde nine miles away or if they had been driven off by the enemy.

Still, he had to have reinforcements.

He scribbled a note to Commander in chief Jose Miguel, and signed the name of his brother Juan Jose who was in Rancagua with Bernardo. He asked him to come to their aid.

One of his soldiers volunteered to carry the note to the Commander in chief Carrera.

At two in the morning the soldier returned with a message from Carrera. "At dawn," the note ran, "this division will make sacrifices."

That was all. But it was enough, Bernardo thought. The morning would surely bring Jose Miguel and reinforcements.

The enemy was advancing again, and gaining ground. They set fire to houses and buildings as they marched. A blaze lit up the sky and there was a roaring like the approach of a tornado. Flames encircled the walls. The heat was intense. Embers were falling over the city, starting fires which had to be beaten out, for there was no water. The faces of all the men were blackened and scorched; their thirst was almost unbearable.

Bernardo's eyes were blistered and swollen. He could scarcely see.

Between the discharges of guns there was bleak silence, like death itself. Bernardo kept telling himself and his men that help was coming. Soon daybreak would come, and with it Jose Miguel Carrera with fresh troops.

The moment there was enough light, Bernardo climbed the tower of La Merced and with his glass looked eagerly along the road leading to Bodegas del Conde. At first he could see nothing because of his swollen eyes, but he made himself keep looking, and at last he saw blackened and ruined houses, burned trees. Far off the line of hills, further the Andes wrapped in grayness, the pale line of snow-capped crests.

His parched throat longed for that coolness.

He should be able to see troops if Carrera was coming. He should see clouds of dust yonder where the road passed the meadow, sent up by the galloping horses.

There was no dust; no horses; no armed division of men to help. His heart sank.

Carrera was not coming! Bernardo should have known. He had been tricked by Carrera before and once again he had been treacherously deserted.

The thought sickened him.

Hastily, he descended to receive another furious attack from the Spanish.

This was the fourth.

By ten o'clock on that Sunday morning the Spanish were coming from all directions with an advance that seemed irresistible.

Shouts of encouragement kept pouring from Bernardo's swollen throat. And his soldiers were fighting like demons. The enemy gradually became discouraged. Their fire slackened. Their death toll had been dreadful, as was Bernardo's. Fallen bodies cushioned the cannon and protected the breaches.

And over the wounded, the dead, the blackened bodies of living men, the destroyed city, was the brilliant sun.

Long ago Bernardo had ceased looking at the tower of La Merced. But his men kept glancing upward, trying desperately to hope, staring at the lookout whom Bernardo had stationed there.

Then a shout from the tower. "Viva la Patria!"

Quickly, Bernardo climbed the steps to the tower.

There along the road from Bodegas was a trailing cloud of dust. Beloved dust!—he thought. And this time, faithful Carrera! This time Bernardo had been wrong, and how happy he was to be in the wrong. For help was near, and his men, who had fought with the strength of thousands, had not fought and died in vain.

He ordered his officers to the parapets to await orders.

The shout of "Viva la Patria!" from his men when they heard the news drowned out the sound of cannon shot.

Bernardo watched the dust. He saw the advancing troops.

Then they halted, and turned.

That was strange, Bernardo thought.

Carrera had turned away! He and the troops were retreating.

The blackness of despair went over Bernardo. He descended from the tower with the grim news.

Colonel Osorio, commanding the Spanish, sent Bernardo a message. If General O'Higgins would surrender, he offered him personal safety, even Royal favor.

Bernardo sent his answer, "No!" He added that he would not accept even heaven from the King of Spain. He gave no quarter. He asked none.

Taking his banner, he ordered a black stripe sewed across it.

Then the Spanish poured out destruction and death, death and fire. The fire reached the house from which he and his men were fighting. All the ammunition was gone. Bernardo took even the silver coins from his pockets and used it for shot.

Two cannons Bernardo had ordered made from ox carts split after the second barrage.

From all sides the Spanish moved toward the house, raining

the fury of their guns upon house, walls, Bernardo's few remaining forces. About him lay the valiant dead.

Within minutes the Spanish would have scaled the walls, broken the gate to the courtyard where Bernardo was taking his last stand, and then shortly all of his men would be slaughtered.

But they would not wait to be murdered. They would make an attempt to escape. They would mount horses and then ride like demons through the Spanish lines. And if luck was with them they might escape. They might!

Already, the Spanish dragoons were scaling the walls.

Bernardo shouted to his men to mount horses. He ordered the foot soldiers to mount behind the cavalrymen.

Raising his sword high, he spurred his horse to a hard gallop, and leading his men, he slashed right and left with his sword, past the startled Spanish. Breaking through one of the squares near the house, he rode madly for an entrance gate. There he and his men clashed briefly with a few Spanish, who attempted an attack.

Bernardo and his soldiers fought off the Spanish. And he escaped.

He could hear his men riding furiously at his heels.

When he glanced back, he saw that already the Spanish had dropped behind, abandoning the chase. They would return and demolish the city of Rancagua. They would murder the people and burn every house, leaving nothing but death and smouldering ashes. The Spanish troops took their orders from Spain and from the Viceroy, to destroy utterly.

As he rode Bernardo planned his course. He would take a stand against the Spanish in Santiago. The Viceroy's regiments had been badly depleted. With fresh troops, Bernardo could defeat the Spaniards. They would yet drive them from Chile.

Hard and fast, he and his men rode toward Santiago, about fifty miles north.

He found it almost impossible to move along the streets of Santiago. Pack mules and carriages were everywhere, loaded with belongings of the fleeing residents, children crying, women lamenting as they hurried toward the safety of the mountains.

Bernardo searched for Carrera.

But all the Carreras with the government money and the troops were already racing for safety. Carrera had destroyed the valuable powder works and other plants. He had ordered all public records burned.

Bernardo sent an escort and horses to the Larrains, where his mother and sister were stopping. They were to follow him to Santa Rosa at once. "Tell them I'm riding after Carrera!" he said. "We must return and defend Santiago!"

Then, with his remaining men, he dashed through the city, across the bridge and headed for Santa Rosa, the last village before the Andes.

He would catch up with Carrera. He would talk him into returning with his troops to defend the city. Although Carrera had deserted Bernardo and the other patriots, he could not be a traitor to Chile. Because of Carrera's treachery, the patriots had been sacrificed at Rancagua and for that Bernardo could never forgive him. But he could in a measure redeem himself, by going back to fight the advancing Spaniards and save Santiago, and Chile. For if Santiago fell, Chile was lost!

Bernardo spurred his horse.   .

As he galloped into the Plaza at Santa Rosa, he saw soldiers, a line of horses tethered to a hitching rail. Nearby was a church.

Flinging himself from his horse, Bernardo called to the soldiers, "Where's Carrera?"

The soldiers straightened. They stared at Bernardo as if they saw a ghost. No doubt Carrera had reported Bernardo, and all the patriots trapped at Rancagua, as dead, as he undoubtedly hoped and believed they were.

One man said, "He is in the church."

Carrera, seeking absolution? Bernardo told himself it would take more than a church and lighted candles to wipe out the stain of Rancagua from that man's soul!

But there was a better way of asking forgiveness. That was by going with Bernardo to Santiago and forcing the Spanish troops back across the Maipú and out of Chile!

There, a little way inside the church door, Carrera knelt in the pious attitude of a supplicant.

Bernardo hesitated. Even a sinner should not be disturbed in prayer.

And then Carrera heard his step. He glanced up as Bernardo knelt beside him and his pale face went even whiter. His eyes, usually proud and insolent, were frightened and he seemed unable to move but remained kneeling like a wooden creature, momentarily stripped of his arrogance. He knelt, seeing, as he thought, the ghost of Bernardo.

Then his fear moved him. Leaping to his feet he rushed from the church.

Bernardo followed. He caught him by the arm. "Carrera!" He could feel Carrera tremble.

"We are going back!" Bernardo said, harshly. "You and I are going to save Chile! We can drive the Spanish out. Our country is not yet lost!"

"You would like to see me dead!" Carrera said, and his voice shook. "You and Mackenna would like to destroy all the Carreras. Only a madman would go back!"

Bernardo loosened his grasp. He recalled what Mackenna had said about the Carreras. And he had been right. They thought first of themselves in all things.

But still he persisted. All that day and the following day, and yet a third day he went from place to place with Carrera, pleading with him to think of Chile. "It will be three to four days before the Spanish reach Santiago," he said. "They will advance slowly, expecting an attack. If you love Chile, protect her with the last drop of blood."

Then word came that the Spanish troops were at the gates of Santiago.

Bernardo's heart and mind plummeted into darkness, like a stone falling into a bottomless pit.

CHAPTER XXXIV

THE BRICK house near the top of the Andes was fourteen feet square. A curtain of cowhide hung at the door. Once there had been a door. The small windows had been shuttered. But long ago both had been used for firewood. Now and again, above the storm, there was the sound of snow sliding from the arched roof.

Here on the crest of the Andes, remote from civilization, there was no such thing as time.

It had not been snowing when Bernardo and his family began crossing toward Mendoza City. Now, except for this house, one of twelve built by his father years before, everyone within its walls might be frozen.

The Spanish Colonel Osorio was ruling Chile for the Viceroy, and all the gains of Chile had been abolished. Those patriots who had not escaped had been imprisoned or shot.

Bernardo was doubly grateful to his father. Without the houses here on the Andes, it would have been impossible to attempt the trip to Mendoza at this season of the year. Always another reason for thanking his father, he thought.

He stared at the remnant of a small fire in the center of the room, at walls blackened by smoke from many fires. The crosses scratched in the sooty walls were monuments for those who had perished by falling. "God rest their souls!" he said, softly, thinking of the precipices.

The crosses, the blackness, the smell of smoke.

Bernardo could not forget Rancagua, the brave men who had fought and died within those streets that made a cross.

The treacherous Carrera! The traitor to Chile, to his own flesh and blood!

It had been more than a miracle that any had escaped.

The embers of the fire lighted the faces of soldiers and muleteers. Next to Bernardo sat his mother and sister, huddled in ponchos and sheepskins. He hoped they were sleeping. For night had dropped over the mountains, the storm wailed outside, slow hours stretched into what seemed eternity.

They had walked all the distance from Santa Rosa to this house. When the storm abated and morning came, they would move on, toward another mountain house.

If the food lasted they would ultimately reach Mendoza.

He thought of the time when these houses had been kept stocked with provisions. That was in his father's day. There had been, he understood, cabinets filled with dried beef and maté, sugar and other necessities, as well as wood for fires.

Dejectedly, Bernardo leaned against the wall.

Above his despair, one thought burned into his mind. Chile must be retaken. A thousand times he had said it as he climbed the ice-packed mountain. And each time another voice within asked, "How? How? How can Chile be retaken without men and with this mountain between Chile and Mendoza?"

Except for Carrera, he thought, they could have held Chile. Still, what was the good of thinking about the past. He must look ahead.

To what? he asked himself.

His thoughts moved to Mendoza and Buenos Aires and recalled the names of Lodge members there: Fretes, Terrada, Jose San Martin and others.

One small ember looked up at him like an inquiring eye. A little hope no larger than the bright coal glowed in his mind. He thought, "Out of the ashes, Chile must rise again, and be free."

He would, he must, win the help of the patriots of Buenos Aires in sending an army to Chile. For the people of Buenos Aires had been more fortunate in gaining and holding their freedom than had Chile. And the reason was that the Viceroy of Peru could not fight both Chile and Buenos Aires without armies from Spain to help. It was one thing to ship troops to Chile and another to transport soldiers around Cape Horn and up the Atlantic Coast to fight the patriots of Buenos Aires.

Bernardo looked hard at the ember.

If an army could cross the Andes from Mendoza, that would be a way to recapture Chile!

But the only accessible route for an army was the Planchon Pass near San Carlos in the south, which passed through Pehuenche Indian territory. The Indians would attack, and spread the word to the Spanish. Even if the troops got through Planchon, they still had to fight their way for two hundred and fifty miles or more north to Santiago. Before they reached the capital, the Spanish army would have moved south and reinforcements sent by the Viceroy would pour in from the ports.

The most direct route, then, to Chile was the Uspallata route which he was traveling, or the Aconcagua Pass farther north, which was higher and more rugged. It was madness even to think of bringing five thousand soldiers and provisions, muskets, ammunition, heavy cannon, thousands of horses and mules, across these northern passes. It would mean climbing to a height of thirteen thousand feet!

He thought of the miles of treacherous snow and ice, of soaring vertical cliffs and narrow paths. Freezing storms came suddenly with blinding force.

And how could cannon be brought along precipices and up towering jagged rocks?

The fire died out. Bernardo stared into the blackness.

Hannibal had crossed the Alps with men and animals.

But these mountains, higher, steeper, were more treacherous than the route taken by Hannibal.

The screaming of the wind was Bernardo's own despair.

Still, Hannibal had crossed the Alps and that had been a miracle. And reason did not enter when a miracle was worked.

Perhaps—by a miracle—it *might* be done.

This house and other shelters on the pass were something of a miracle, for without them the journey would have been impossible. Without them, Bernardo would by now have faced a Spanish firing squad, and God alone knew what would have happened to his mother and sister.

But the houses had been built. And by his father all those years ago, with roofs vaulted to protect them from the heavy snowfall, with thick, secure walls of brick and limestone. It was as if his father had been ordered to prepare the way for the patriots of Chile to make their escape, so they might return and free Chile.

Had not his father always protected him? Tonight, he seemed close.

As night wore on, he worked out plans to bring cannon and equipment up cliffs, across chasms. But he was not the mechanical genius that Mackenna was. He would consult Mackenna. He might be able to figure out something practical.

At daybreak a fire was built. Once again they were off, breaking a track through the heavy snow.

More mountain houses. More nights with too many people crowded together. Then the last house at Punta de las Vacas.

The Uspallata.

And at last Villavicencio in a deep canyon closed in by high, jagged mountains, the last stop before Mendoza City. From here on the journey was easy. More hovels, only a few feet high, with roofs of reeds, but they seemed like palaces after the mountains, the storms and the freezing cold.

Juan Mackenna arrived from Mendoza with Antonio Jose Irisarri, a cousin of Mackenna's wife. They brought clothing, provisions and mules. Never had friends been more welcome. And now Bernardo could plan for returning to Chile.

The city of Mendoza had taken the refugees to its great heart, Mackenna said. General San Martin, governor of the province, had arranged for a house for Bernardo. He and his lady Dona Remedios sent a welcome.

In Bernardo's heart was hope.

For General Jose San Martin, a patriot, was waiting with a welcome.

It was a little like coming into paradise, reaching Mendoza that bright morning after the dismal crossing. Bernardo, riding through streets lined with trees, saw comfortable homes, gardens. Mules and cargo wagons moved without haste, the drivers calling lazily to their animals as if there were no war within thousands of miles. Once, Bernardo thought, watching, Chile had been serene.

His heart tightened.

Everywhere familiar faces from beyond the mountains, from Chile. He was grateful to the Mendozans who received them as brothers. Once this province and city had belonged to Chile, and the people had taken the refugees to their hearts and into their homes as if they still belonged here.

Bernardo studied the long, handsome face of General San Martin. He did not look like a hardened soldier who had spent twenty years in rude barracks and on the battlefield. His manner was easy and graceful, like a man accustomed to the drawing room. He might be Bernardo's age, his hair black and strong, his nose arched proudly. With penetrating eyes he studied Bernardo as if there were many questions he would like answered.

Watching him, Bernardo thought of Chile again, bound by the ancient evils, of the long struggle for liberty which must not be forsaken in this desperate hour. The hearts of his people were still fighting for their homeland. This patriot, San Martin, was a soldier to accomplish the miracle of getting troops to Chile, he told himself.

There was talk of Chile.

"Tell me about it," San Martin said, briskly, and he glanced in the direction of Chile, "about Rancagua."

Bernardo thought of Rancagua for a moment. Talking about Rancagua would not help. Only a gathering together of a strong army and a return to Chile to drive the Spanish Royalists from his homeland would help. But San Martin had asked, and he must answer with a brief summary of the battle.

He told the tale as simply as he could. "It could have been a victory," he said. "Even after Rancagua, our troops could have taken a stand near Santiago on the plains of Maipú and stopped the Spaniards." Then, he was silent, thinking how gallantly the Chilean patriots would have fought had not Carrera deserted.

San Martin stopped his nervous pacing.

"That is past," Bernardo said, his eyes resting on the tall, slim figure before him. "I must return to my country and retake it! All the losses must be regained." He studied San Martin who was eyeing him intently. He thought of that dream he had dreamed in the mountain house of the Cumbre, while the wind howled outside; the dream of a desperate soldier. "Would it be insane to attempt to march an army of five thousand men across the Andes to Chile?" Bernardo waited eagerly for the answer.

San Martin continued to stare at Bernardo. He did not answer at once. The quietness of the mountains seemed to reach into the room. "It could be done!" San Martin said slowly.

"You have given me hope," Bernardo said, gratefully.

"It can and it will be done!" San Martin's voice was strong and his black eyes shone with a brighter light. "It is impossible! But we will do the impossible!" he said.

Bernardo said, "I will serve under you, San Martin, if necessary as a foot soldier, to save my country. For Chile must be free!"

He saw the curious, almost distrustful look San Martin gave him. He did not seem to understand. Then he said, quietly and with astonishment, "It is a novel experience to discover a general who is willing to serve as a foot soldier, even to save his country!"

"For seventeen years I have been working for the independence of Chile and the colonies," Bernardo said. "Since I was a very young boy I have wanted my people free. It is my only ambition!" Then he added, hastily: "The Uspallata Pass and the Aconcagua routes would be best. They are nearer Santiago."

A wild, eager look came into San Martin's fine eyes. These mountains were giants compared to the Pyrenees, he said. But in crossing the Pyrenees with General Ricardos, when he invaded France, San Martin learned about taking soldiers across difficult passes. "The men of wisdom will say that we are fools to attempt such a march," he said. "The Spanish will say it is impossible to bring an army across the high passes. But we will make the crossing, and swoop down upon the Viceroy's troops in Santiago with the swiftness of condors." Then he looked at Bernardo with disturbed eyes. "It will take many thousands of pesos," and he gave a hard laugh. "For months I have badgered the government in Buenos Aires to finance an invasion of northern Peru. And without success."

There would have to be money. Bernardo looked thoughtfully at San Martin. And the money would be raised somehow. Both for freeing Chile and Peru. He did not quite know where the pesos would come from. But he would delegate Juan Mackenna to go to Buenos Aires and speak with friends of the Lodge—to Fretes, whom Bernardo had known in Cadiz and who was in Buenos Aires, and to Terrada. Somehow, the funds would be forthcoming.

He enjoyed Juan Mackenna's look of astonishment, then delight, the stunned, incredulous expression of Antonio Jose Irisarri, when he passed on to them the news.

The poplar leaves along the Alameda of Mendoza danced like gold. Bernardo said, "Mackenna, will you and Irisarri go to Buenos Aires at once? To speak with Fretes about financing the liberating army."

For hours they discussed plans.

Everything was falling into a pattern again, Bernardo thought.

Soon Mackenna and Irisarri were on their way across the pampas, going toward Buenos Aires.

Bernardo rode with them for a few miles, giving the final instructions. They were happy again to be hopeful, to have a course of action, to be working for their homeland. They could even laugh a little as they rode under the brightest sky Bernardo had seen in months, could even speak of the vineyards and crops. But always they returned to talk of finances for the expedition.

"God with you!" Bernardo said at last and reined in his mount to watch his friends ride on. At last he turned and rode back to

Mendoza, but his mind continued to follow the straight, vigorous figure of his friend Mackenna.

He could not do without Mackenna, the general, the soldier, the engineer, the tactician. Now more than ever with this march across the Andes he would need Mackenna's guidance and knowledge.

A few days later as Bernardo was returning from the headquarters of San Martin, he saw Luis Carrera ride along the Alameda. He thought, "The traitor!" He stared after him.

Carrera was going toward the east. Bernardo wondered if he was traveling to Buenos Aires on some business for his brother Jose Miguel.

Jose Miguel thought that he and not General San Martin should be the chief here in Mendoza.

How Bernardo despised the Carreras!

A letter had reached Bernardo from Buenos Aires. He glanced at the handwriting, hoping it was from Juan Mackenna with good news about the financing of the expedition. Then he saw that it was written by Fretes, and he thought, "It is good news and Fretes is giving me all the details."

He read, "Juan Mackenna has met with a sudden and violent death in Buenos Aires!"

The room reeled and the walls came toward Bernardo, but the words were still there. He clung to the table and waited. After moments the walls straightened. A sickness went over him, and coldness. There was a gripping pain in his heart, like a fist closing over it.

The chair a few steps away seemed miles off.

Unmoving he stood, his eyes fixed on the message that lay crumpled in his hand, his mind repeating over and over that it could not be true. Not Mackenna! Death seemed to hang over Bernardo. He wanted to die, too!

After a long time he felt his mind move away from the thought of the grave. How had Mackenna met his death? The letter from

Fretes did not explain. Nor why Mackenna had been killed. Could he have been thrown from a frightened horse? Not Mackenna, who could control the wildest animal. Why had not Fretes told Bernardo everything and not left him in doubt? Was he asking that Bernardo come to Buenos Aires? And for what reason?

He tried to straighten, but his shoulders felt tired and old. He must write Fretes at once and demand an explanation. There were many things to be done. It was painful even to think.

But he made himself think.

Someone must take over the labors of Mackenna. Someone must pick up the work of raising funds for Chile that Mackenna had been forced by this disaster to drop.

Painfully, Bernardo thought about it.

He must control his grief and not succumb to utter despair. He must go on, as Mackenna had when the blows came. Had not his friend always said that blood and death were partners in the struggle for liberty and freedom? Mackenna never feared the risks. He went forward to meet them. His answer to danger and trouble was to challenge them and defeat them or be defeated! Mackenna had fought with his whole being for Chile since first he reached the country. He had suffered the humiliation of neglect and hatred because he had been a friend of the Viceroy, Don Ambrosio O'Higgins. For the cause he had suffered the humiliation of prison, of loss of rank. And he still went on. He had given his time and energy to train Bernardo, to direct and guide him, to stand against the enemies for the sake of Bernardo!

And now that right hand had been taken.

Again grief swept over Bernardo with such force that it threatened to engulf him. He could not go on.

But he must go on. He fought against the blackness. For a long time he struggled.

Gradually, he could control his anguished thoughts, could think more clearly and with some calmness.

Someone must take over the labors of that strong hand on which Bernardo had relied these many years.

For minutes he stared at the crumpled note.

He would go to Buenos Aires and carry on Mackenna's work. It would be what Mackenna himself would have asked.

And he would find out how Mackenna had been killed.

It might mean long months in Buenos Aires. Bernardo would have to take his mother and Rosa.

And later, when the money had been raised, he would return to Mendoza to help General San Martin as he had been doing.

He stood, feeling painful emptiness, coldness throughout his body and mind, wondering how to begin. For there was no man in the world competent to fill the void left by Mackenna's death!

CHAPTER XXXV

THE DESERT, the pampas. Hundreds of miles of wasteland to Buenos Aires. This was the fourteenth day from Mendoza. Days of fast riding through sand storms, through the heat of the sun, and yet not quickly enough for Bernardo.

And at night the wakefulness, thinking of Mackenna. Day and night burdened by the thoughts.

Now they had reached another post house and were waiting for fresh horses. He watched the Indian guide run across the corral, his trousers flapping, spurs rattling. He was trying to hurry as Bernardo had asked, but he seemed to take a long time.

At last the horses arrived.

Then off once more, galloping hard across the empty plain, hurrying to Buenos Aires.

The worst part of the journey was behind them. Soon they would reach their destination. Bernardo knew how hard it must be on his family. They had not complained about anything, accepting the heat, lonely vastness of the empty pampas, the twisted, shadeless desert trees, the uncomfortable trail, the ground for a bed without a murmur. And asking no questions.

It might have been easier if they had complained, or asked the questions, he thought.

Then, at last, Buenos Aires.

They reached the house of Fretes, friend and patriot.

"What of Mackenna?" Bernardo said. "How did he die?"

Fretes' eyes filled with tears. He said, "That noble soul! In a duel. His opponent was Luis Carrera!"

"Carrera!" Bernardo stared as if Fretes had struck him a hard blow.

How could it be? Mackenna was a better shot, more clever with the sword than any Carrera! Mackenna would not let himself die at the hand of a Carrera. There was some mistake. There had to be!

"There is little to tell." Fretes came to him. "One witness saw three horsemen pass his residence. One heard what might have been musket shots. A servant discovered the body of Juan Mackenna lying in a field one morning. The man whose servant found the body took it to the door of the Town House and notified the authorities. Luis Carrera was arrested. He admitted nothing. His friend Jose Maria Benevante, who came with Carrera to Buenos Aires, told the same story as Luis."

"Benevante?" Bernardo said in a shocked voice. He recalled the hatred of Benevante for Juan Mackenna and his threats that he would like to stick a dagger into the breast of Juan Mackenna, Bernardo O'Higgins, and all who opposed the Carreras. There had been angry words between Benevante and Mackenna over the Carreras. And Mackenna had upbraided Luis Carrera over funds belonging to the Chilean government.

He thought about it now, the bitterness of Mackenna over the evil doings of the Carreras and their friends. But it was not bitterness for what they had inflicted upon him, but what they were doing to Chile. They were acting treacherously toward their country. Mackenna loved Chile with all his heart.

Now he had given his life for the honor of Chile. But why had not someone helped him that night? What had happened on that remote field far from the city? What about Benevante?

Bernardo would speak with Irissari.

At last, worn out by the journey, by his sorrow, he slept.

He awakened early, pushed aside the scrim curtains of the bed, opened the wooden shutters. A little gray light filtered into the room.

He dressed and walked out into the patio. A few dried vines brushed lonesomely against the wall. Leaving the garden, he hurried toward Irissari's dwelling.

"Bernardo!" Irissari rushed forward. "I am glad you have come."

In his room, Irissari pulled a chair forward for Bernardo and ordered maté.

"Tell me about Mackenna," Bernardo demanded. "Fretes says it was a duel with Luis Carrera."

"It was impossible to stop the quarrel," Irissari said. "It began the moment Luis Carrera arrived in Buenos Aires. From then on the bitterness between them increased. I begged Mackenna not to fight Carrera. But you know Mackenna, how he hated all the Carreras. And how tenaciously he clung to a course that he considered just. He had rather die than yield one iota of honor."

He stared at Bernardo and his eyes darkened.

"The morning of the twenty-first, I saw Mackenna's servant preparing shot. Later, I heard Mackenna ask Captain Vargas if his pistols were in good condition. You know how particular Mackenna was about having his guns in order. In the afternoon I went out. I returned in the evening. Mackenna called to me that he was going to ride to see Commandant-General Don Guillermo Brown. I did not see him leave." He paused for a moment. "He was killed that night by Carrera, in a duel."

They sat quietly.

Irisarri said at last, "I have a transcript of the testimony by witnesses if you care to read it." He went to a table and brought the sheaf, bound in a folder.

Slowly, Bernardo turned the pages. He paused to read Captain Vargas' testimony: "He had heard it said that Don Luis Carrera was in a boarding house practicing shooting the pistol with shot and that on one of the walls may be seen the marks; that he also had heard that on that night he road on horseback and that on the person of the arrested was found a button stained with blood. . . . There had been a duel. . . . "

Bernardo passed on to the testimony of Lieutenant Don Joaquin Villalva, who said he had been notified by a cowhand that at the back of the farm of Conde was a body violently done to death and covered with blood. He had taken the body and a halter found at the same place to the doors of the Cabildo.

The testimony of Luis Carrera!

He read eagerly.

The judge accompanied by his secretary had gone to the barracks where Colonel Don Luis Carrera had been detained. Carrera said he was ignorant of the cause of his arrest. Asked if he knew Jose Maria Benevante, he said he knew him and came in his company to Buenos Aires and lived with him in the same house but did not know his present whereabouts. Asked if he had had any fight or enmity with any resident in this capital he said he had not had any quarrel with anybody and he had enmity with all who had it with him.

He was asked about his actions on the day and night of the twenty-first. After having breakfasted with Colonel Benevante and Don Tomas Taylor, the owner of the inn, he unloaded and cleaned his pistols, he shooting one at the wall of the patio, and Taylor shooting the other. He and Taylor had ridden that afternoon to the Mackinley farm, but he had ridden ahead to the house of Miller to pick up a letter which had arrived for Carrera from Mendoza.

Was it from Jose Miguel Carrera? Bernardo asked himself. And what did the letter order Luis to do?

He read on. Each moment of the day and evening had been accounted for. It was too perfect, too carefully worked out. When the judge asked if he knew Brigadier Don Juan Mackenna and where he was at that moment Carrera said he knew him and had heard that he had died, he did not know how. The bloody button? Carrera explained that, too. He had cut a finger with a table knife at luncheon on the previous day, and the same afternoon when he placed the bit on his horse he again injured this finger with one of the buckles.

The testimony of Benevante echoed the details of Luis Carrera's testimony: breakfast together, playing billiards, a ride in the afternoon, visiting with friends in the evening.

He was about to close the folder when his eye caught the name of Captain Vargas. Vargas had given additional testimony. This time, he admitted that he was the second for Juan Mackenna and had witnessed the duel and Tomas Taylor had acted as second for Carrera.

And yet, Bernardo had the feeling that certain vital details were missing.

"The case is closed now and Carrera exiled, the witnesses scattered." There was a pained look in Irisarri's eyes. "Yet I was told by the Dominican, Padre Amaro of the cloister of Santo Domingo where the body of Mackenna was prepared for burial, that there were two wounds, and one of them could not have been made by a pistol shot."

Bernardo's hands felt suddenly cold. "Where is this cloister?" he said, rising. "I must speak with the Padre."

He found the cloister, next to the Church of Santo Domingo in the heart of the city, and spoke with Padre Amaro about Brigadier Mackenna.

The Padre, ponderous like his voice, said, "When the Brigadier's body was being made ready for burial, we discovered, in addition to a bullet wound, a hole in the breast the size of my middle finger. A three-sided hole, as if it might have been made by a pike, a spear of some kind."

In a shocked voice, Bernardo asked, "Or by a dagger?"

He recalled Benevante and his threat. First a dagger and then a bullet, to stop the heart that refused to be stopped by a pistol shot from Luis Carrera? And were the seconds too frightened of being implicated to tell the whole truth?

A great sorrow filled Bernardo's heart. He thanked the Padre and crossed to the church of Santo Domingo where the funeral services had been held for Mackenna.

In the church he knelt under the English banners, mementos of that British defeat when the people of Buenos Aires learned their strength and unity and a way to freedom. He thought of Juan Mackenna lying under English banners that marked a loss by the British. The flags were symbolic of the rising tide of South American liberty, and Mackenna would appreciate their meaning, and be enormously pleased.

As he knelt, Bernardo swore to avenge his friend's death. He would search out Luis Carrera and Benevante and repay them for their treachery to the noble friend of Chile.

The church was quiet, like Mackenna's tomb.

And the voice of Mackenna seemed to come to him from the tomb. "Vengeance?" Mackenna seemed to be saying in that loved and familiar voice. "The only vengeance for me is to have Chile free of tyrants, from the Carreras as well as the others! Rededicate yourself to this cause we have sworn to defend with our lives and fortunes. You have my work to do as well as your own. This is how you can avenge my death."

Then there was silence in the gloomy walls of the chapel, below the banners.

Kneeling he prayed for wisdom, for strength to continue without Mackenna. For continue he must.

He prayed for his country to be free again. And that it might be free forever. However he could best serve Chile, let him serve.

Now he must labor for himself and Mackenna in this cause! He must fight with two hearts!

CHAPTER XXXVI

BERNARDO stared at the adobe wall of the house he had rented in Buenos Aires a year ago. He had moved here although it was too small for his family, for it was all he could afford from his dwindling funds. It had been a place to work, and they had managed by doing little entertaining. He had thought when first he came here that within weeks he would be returning to Mendoza to work with San Martin recruiting a liberating army for Chile. Daily, Chilean patriots came to this house, or sent letters to him offering their services.

They waited to serve. He waited.

The other Lodge brothers in Buenos Aires had labored as tirelessly as Bernardo to interest the government in financing an army for Chile. Certain officials disagreed and balked. They wanted the army to protect and defend Buenos Aires.

Bernardo reached for the newspaper. The war between England and France still raged.

But this news was months old and the war might have ended by now. Spanish warships might be sailing for South American ports, bringing seasoned troops to fight the colonists. Each day the chances of retaking Chile became less. Gloomily, Bernardo studied the paper.

An hour later, an order arrived from Director Colonel Don Ignacio Alvarez Tomas, his good friend. Bernardo was ordered to Mendoza as second in command under General San Martin. He had been given five hundred pesos a year for his living.

"The waiting is over," he shouted to his mother and Rosa.

"I'll start packing at once," Rosa said. She darted off. He heard her giving orders in her clear, decisive voice. Sometimes, he thought, Rosa was the best general of them all.

"When we reach Mendoza," his mother said, "I shall make bandages for your expedition. And small cigars for the soldiers. How many will you need?"

How many cigars?—he thought. And how many muskets, how many lances, pikes, swords, saddles and mules? He began writing down the items and what would be required for five thousand men. He added scalers for the mountains and scrapers to clear away ice, and rasps, spades, shovels, hatchets, tents and food. How many cattle to feed thousands of soldiers? How much maté? Every soldier would want tobacco and wine.

The heavy artillery. How would cannon be taken across the mountains? He thought of Mackenna, the engineer.

Mackenna was not here. Bernardo must figure it out for himself. It was impossible, but it had to be done! And when he reached Mendoza there would be a way.

He picked up a fresh sheet of paper and his quill. With a vigorous hand he wrote across the top of the page, *"Plan of Organization of Forces and Plan of Invasion of Chile."*

This time, his mother and Rosa would cross the pampas in a carriage. Don Antonio Jose de Escalada was making a visit to his daughter and to his sons who were serving under San Martin. He invited Bernardo's family to ride with him.

Off they went, one end of a gaucho's lasso attached to the carriage, the other to the girth of his saddle. The shouts of the guide sounded across the flat land as he headed for Mendoza.

Bernardo rode beside the carriage. It was good to be on the march again. He thought of his father, who had crossed this same route from Buenos Aires to Mendoza and on to Chile those many years ago. He had slept in these same post houses of mud bricks, eaten of the native Indian corn and onions and red watermelons that ripened around each dingy hut. On the seventh day of the journey, at Achiras, there was a vineyard. Las Canteras came to him here suddenly in this small hillside of grapevines. San Luis on the ninth day and steaks for breakfast, while the governor studied their passports and sent them on their way with wine from his own vines. Then at the River Desaguadero a deep ford, the water rising to the axles of the carriage. And, at last, the province of Mendoza and acres of cane, fig and orange trees and hedges of mimosa. To the west the eternal Andes.

Here, in the heart of this pleasant land, the liberating army would prepare for an attack against the Spanish in Chile and the people of Mendoza would give to that force all their strength and their resources and courage.

At last, he was making a fresh beginning, after the wearing months of waiting. Now there would be both finances and men for the regiments. Now the troops could complete their training.

The hacienda owners of Mendoza had promised that when needed they would free their slaves who had asked to serve in the liberating army.

And tomorrow the work of preparing for the crossing of the mountains would begin. He must train his soldiers well, better even than he thought he could. For they soon would attempt a climb that no army had ever before attempted. The men had to be toughened both for the Andes and for attacking the hardy and ruthless Spanish regiments. In Chile, the Spanish had a force of seven thousand six hundred and thirteen regulars and eight hundred militia.

To make up for the superior numbers of the Spaniards, San Martin proposed to use strategy instead.

It was evening at the house of San Martin and he and Bernardo were playing chess.

San Martin leaned back in his chair and glanced at Bernardo with bright, restless eyes. "In Yapeyu, on the Uruguay River, where I was born," he said, "we went to bed each night wondering if that would be the time the Guarani Indians would attack. I was raised on talk of Indian raids, and I still dream of them." Leaning forward he moved a chessman. "I was thinking of the Pehuenches to the south," he said. "We must anticipate what the Indians will do."

"They are solidly with the Spanish." Bernardo studied the

board. "And it is my father's doing. Many chiefs and braves visited my hacienda, Las Canteras. From those that had known my father, I learned that the Araucanians would fight with the Spanish if they fought with anyone. To them my father, Don Ambrosio O'Higgins, was the king of Spain! His promises of what Spain would do for the Indians had always come to pass. He promised that the Crown would protect them, and it was done. They needed provisions, clothing, and my father saw that they were provided with what they needed. He tried constantly to civilize them and teach them Christianity and make them into peaceful citizens and good farmers."

"It is fortunate then," San Martin said, a smile on his dark, eager face, "that the liberating army is not entering Chile by way of the Planchon." And he glanced at the chessboard as if it were the Pehuenche country. "We will spread rumors about the patriots," he said. "The Indians will be informed that the liberating army wants to cross into Chile through the Pehuenche land and by the pass of Planchon. They will be asked to keep this information a secret." He smiled again. "It will not be kept a secret, for the Pehuenches are certain to inform the Spanish."

San Martin made his move on the board.

"After all," he said, and chuckled, "what other way could an army of any size enter Chile? Certainly not by the terrible Aconcagua or the Uspallata!"

Bernardo studied the face of San Martin. "It is a clever piece of planning," he said, admiringly, "and moreover it will work. The Spanish will concentrate their greatest force at the Planchon Pass. They will place soldiers at the pass of the Portillo, also in the south. In the north, the dangerous passes which they think impossible to be crossed by an army will be guarded only by a token picket."

"I have arranged a conference with the Pehuenches," San Martin said. "We will meet with them when our troops are thoroughly trained and prepared to march."

February would be the best season for crossing the mountains by the difficult northern passes. Or January if the troops were ready. December through February was summer in this part of the world, the best season for traveling across the Andes. Bernardo made his move.

"From now until time for the meeting with the Pehuenches," San Martin continued, "the ladies of Mendoza should collect old finery, the sort of thing the Indians like—embroidered dresses, glass beads, bright handkerchiefs. I will also take them gifts of bridles, spurs, wine and dried fruit." He glanced up from the board. "A hundred and twenty goatskins of grape brandy and three hundred of wine should be enough, don't you think?"

Bernardo agreed that it should be ample. "The Indians never drink until a conference is ended," he said. "They have too much intelligence to take wine before important meetings. But afterward! That is a different story!"

And he remembered the large pits which the Indians dug in the earth and lined with bullock skins like the vats Bernardo used for making wine. Into the earthen bowl the Indians poured a mixture of brandy and wine. Then, seated around the edge of the pit, they began spinning tales of their skill with the lance, relating deeds of their ancestors and themselves. And as they told the tales, they drank.

San Martin said, "I will take a troop of calvary to the conference, and at least two hundred militia."

"That will impress the Pehuenches," Bernardo agreed. "They like a colorful and noisy show."

In September, San Martin rode south to the Indian territory near the Planchon Pass.

After they had gone, Bernardo walked with Friar Luis Beltran, who was in charge of the arsenal, back to his workshop. It was a large rambling structure. Here endless miracles were being performed by the modest Friar. Until the formation of the liberating army he had lived quietly in a cloister, where he operated a blacksmith shop.

Now he had put aside the role of priest and had joined the patriots' cause. He was a genius. It was almost as if Beltran had appeared magically when he was needed, and Bernardo repeatedly gave thanks in his heart for him. He had worked out the most intricate machines with a skill that Juan Mackenna would call miraculous. Whatever tool or machine was needed by the liberating army came out of Beltran's workshop. How were the heavy cannon to be carried over the precipices?—he was asked. "With specially constructed wings," he said. He would give wings to the cannon and to all the heavy equipment.

The Friar called for mules to demonstrate to Bernardo how cannon would be carried. Each piece of ordnance would be swung between two mules. A pole would be fastened to the packsaddle of each mule, the gun suspended from the pole. One mule would move ahead, the other would follow.

He had cables of hemp to lift and lower the equipment along the steep cliffs. A portable capstan had been manufactured to help raise and steady the guns. And for carriages, there would be narrow sleds made of dried bullock hides.

The noise in the place was deafening. Beltran was making thousands of horseshoes for mules and horses. It would be the first time horseshoes were to be used on the animals.

He would like Juan Mackenna to step into this arsenal Bernardo thought. He could imagine the pleasure with which Mackenna would examine each invention. And he could also hear his friend say, smiling as he spoke, that when a project was important and right, the way somehow opened.

Bernardo returned to his desk. For hours each day, when he was not training his men or busy with a thousand other details, he wrote letters to patriots about enlisting in the liberating army. He kept the Buenos Aires Lodge brothers advised. Today, the mail was heavier than usual.

There was no time for relaxation and scarcely time for meals. He had trays brought to his desk. When he wanted rest, he could take a nap on his sofa.

San Martin, too, often went without meals and rest. This overwork did not alleviate the illness that attacked him. Too often San Martin coughed blood and still refused to rest. He had not the strength nor the constitution of Bernardo.

More than one officer had spoken to Bernardo about San Martin's taking opium. Their eyes looked troubled as they asked, "Where will it end?"

He could not answer them. He only knew that San Martin endured the suffering until the pain was beyond endurance and then he resorted to the drug.

San Martin had returned from the Pehuenche country exhausted but elated.

He described the affair in minute detail, instead of resting as Bernardo urged him to do. His eyes were too bright, and his cheeks highly flushed. He had overworked. The sham battles, the firing of blank cartridges from the cannon of San Carlos fort by the patriot cavalry, the capering horses, the war cries, the palaver at the great table—he described it all. "They granted us permission to pass through their country," he said, at last.

And by now, Bernardo thought, the secret which San Martin had entrusted to the Pehuenches was known to the Spanish in Chile. It was running from mouth to mouth that the liberating army now training in Mendoza under San Martin and O'Higgins would soon enter Chile through the pass of the Planchon.

There was further good news a few days later. The Spaniards had divided their army, moving the greater number of troops to southern Chile near the Planchon Pass, certain that the attack of the liberating army would come that way.

San Martin's ruse had worked. Bernardo was jubilant.

One morning in January, he sat with San Martin checking the details of the march. "The roads have been cleared in the mountains, but we cannot control the weather," San Martin said.

Bernardo knew how quickly a blizzard could sweep over the Andes, blocking all paths. He had been in such storms when he crossed from Rancagua.

Provisions had been stored every thirty miles along the passes, should there be storms to delay the troops, with militiamen to guard them. But it was impossible to lay in enough fodder for eleven thousand nine hundred horses and mules and seven hundred oxen.

"Five mountain ridges." San Martin stared at the map. "Even in midsummer the cold will be intense. Some of the men will not survive the cold. And there will be accidents."

"I will warn the men again and again," Bernardo said, the responsibility lying heavy on his mind and heart.

"Then, once we reach Chile," San Martin said, "the Viceroy's toughest regiments to be defeated. For we cannot retreat up the side of a precipice!"

Bernardo thought, we shall not need to retreat!

On January sixteenth, the night preceeding the march, he was unable to sleep. Time and again he tried. The anxiety pressed too hard. He kept rising and going to a window to stare at the Andes. They looked three times their usual height. And the snow —what a lot of snow! He had never seen the mountains so heavily covered with snow at this time of the year.

He thought of Chile across that barrier. He paced the floor thinking of tomorrow and Chile.

The seventeenth dawned. Heading his division, Bernardo moved down the Mendoza Alameda between four rows of poplar trees, to the square.

San Martin held aloft the new flag which Dona Remedios had designed—clasped hands, a liberty cap, the crests of the Andes embroidered in blue and white. From many thousands of throats shouts went up that the flag would be defended to the death!

Here, in Bernardo's division, was Don Pedro Ramon Arriagada who had been twice arrested and sent to Lima to be arraigned by the Inquisition. And Manuel Bulnes, Manuel Ruiz, Apolinario Puga, Toribio and Martin Reyes. Yes, and Tirapegui. His good friend, even in Chile, had fought with the patriots.

With affection he studied the faces of his soldiers, among them hundreds of blacks who had been freed by their owners to fight for Chile. He thought of the Negro woman Maria, at Fretes' house in Buenos Aires, and her gratitude for what the patriots of Chile had done for her people. And Bernardo thought, "We shall do much more for them, and for all South American slaves!"

Then General Miguel Solar started off toward the Andes and shouts followed him.

Bernardo followed with his division.

Another roar went up from the watching citizens and the soldiers. It was a stirring sight.

On all sides troops and equipment on the move: mechanics, tools, implements to clear the mountain passes. The militia waited, in charge of spare mules and transport.

The priest, Luis Beltran, now an officer of artillery, whose genius had invented wings for the cannon, was ready to march with Colonel Las Heras, head of the artillery. The Padre stood quietly, his eyes seeking each piece of artillery, as if they were members of his parish.

Beltran and his crew had a cable bridge and grapples, a field train carried a hundred and ten rounds per gun, five hundred thousand musket ball-cartridges and a hundred and eighty mule loads of spare arms. In the mule packs were provisions for fifteen days for an army of five thousand two hundred men. More than a hundred loads were wine, a bottle a day for each man.

Bernardo saw Lieutenant-Colonel Freyre, his old friend from Concepcion, with his three hundred men, who would cross into Chile by the Portillo Pass in southern Chile. They would enter near Talca. With them went a hundred and twenty mules and the same provisions carried by all the army: jerked beef seasoned with chilies, toasted Indian corn, biscuit, cheese, onions, garlic. Garlic was important. It was supposed to cure mountain sickness.

Ahead towered the many ridges moving toward Chile. Bernardo with his division went toward the pass of Los Patos and Mount Aconcagua, the route assigned to him, the highest in these mountains.

Men went ahead to clear the route, but the Los Patos Pass was unpredictable. There would be high winds, storms, paths that zigzagged on the rim of great cliffs.

Bernardo's men marched in single file. Far behind them now

was Mendoza. They reached one height. Others stretched ahead, seeming never to end. Condors hung motionless above as if waiting for man or animal to fall, when they would swoop down.

He sent orders back along the line that his men were to remember his words about caution. He halted the march early. When men were exhausted, then accidents happened.

For three days they had marched. The ascent grew steeper, higher and harder. At times there was only space for the feet of the mules. The animals looked neither to right nor left, but straight ahead, moving with uncanny precision.

Bernardo glanced down in the yawning chasm. The river was like a thin white string. Quickly, he lifted his eyes. The path was so narrow that, seated in his saddle, one of his legs hung over the gorge.

Again, he ordered his men to be careful. He heard his order echoing along the line, resound through the bottomless canyons. He stared at the ears of his mule. That night they made camp on a mountain where the wind howled mournfully. It was impossible to sleep for the cold. He kept thinking, if the men did not sleep tomorrow there might be fatalities.

It was mid-afternoon of another day when two of his soldiers went hurtling over the cliffs. He saw and cried out, his instinct calling on him to rush to them and try to save them. It was sickening to stand helpless, knowing he could do nothing.

They marched on but he kept hearing the screams in his mind.

That night he lay thinking of brave men too exhausted to be cautious. And he thought, "More patriots dying for Chile."

When he rose the following day he could scarcely stand. Every bone in his body ached. He felt as ancient as the cliffs and staggered when he walked, like a drunken man. He sat down. The dizziness passed, and he felt better. He made himself mount his animal. His legs were like slabs of stone, his head was burning with fever.

Higher rose the path until it was almost perpendicular. Then they inched along and breathing became more difficult. His men were affected with mountain sickness, a constriction of the chest.

Several mules were lost again, and provisions.

At night the men stumbled to the ground, gasping for breath, blood spurting from their nostrils and mouth. Weakly they cried, "Viva la Patria!"

Bernardo's lips were so swollen that he had to make a tremendous effort before he could be heard. His face was swollen, too. So were the faces of all of them.

More days of marching.

More days of mountain sickness, of men reeling and falling to the ground, to writhe in pain as they tried to breathe.

On the thirteenth day the entire mountain ahead of the line seemed suddenly to erupt like a volcano. An avalanche of boulders thundered down the mountain and across the path.

They could not advance.

It was impossible to go ahead.

The boulders waited, ready to crush any soldier who dared step into the path to remove the debris.

For minutes, Bernardo stood there.

"Nature is against us, sir," one of his officers said.

"Bring me tools!" Bernardo said. "We are going to clear the path or die trying."

Cautiously, they worked. Any moment the boulders might fling themselves upon them.

The debris was cleared. Every man and animal passed in safety under the threatening rocks.

They quickened their steps. The ordeal seemed to have given them new strength. Up they struggled over the peaks. And always along the line came the shout, "Viva la Patria!"

The priest Luis Beltran and the heavy guns were moving at a snail-pace somewhere along the pass of the Uspallata.

Again Bernardo thought of Hannibal who had passed over the Alps with war equipment. But the Alps were not comparable to these hideous and monstrous Andes. No army had ever passed over mountains at this height!

The patriots had Beltran to thank for wings for the cannon. Let the wings fly well!—Bernardo thought. His own shoulders seemed to be pulling on the heavy artillery.

On they moved.

The passage had been planned to be made in fifteen days. Bernardo marked off the fourteenth day on his calendar.

Time after time a voice inside him whispered that his men would never last out the march to Chile. And time and again he silenced the voice with "It will be done!"

Back along the line he sent encouragement. "Soon we shall reach Chile. We defy the heights of Aconcagua, for our country's sake! We can defeat the Spanish and be free men! On, brave patriots!"

Then, suddenly, the cascading waters of a river. A guardhouse in a narrow ravine. The advance guards had destroyed the Spanish patrol. Farther on a spreading valley, a hillside of wild flowers, and rolling toward him from the west, Chile!

And an army had crossed the Andes! The impossible had been done! Shouts from his weary men.

Bernardo stood filling his eyes with the land.

CHAPTER XXXVII

On the eighth of February, Bernardo's division met San Martin and Solar at Chacabuco as agreed.

They were waiting for Las Heras and his artillery, due to meet them on the fourteenth, six days away. Meanwhile San Martin wanted everyone to be well rested after the difficult and grueling march across the Andes. Bernardo believed a short rest and a hurried march to Santiago would have been wiser.

There was no question but that San Martin needed rest. The long, tiring march had left him pale and exhausted, his hacking cough worse than it had been in Mendoza.

Bernardo watched him with anxious eyes and was troubled. He should be in bed. He refused to remain there, but sat with Bernardo and Solar planning the attack against the Spanish which would begin as soon as Las Heras arrived.

It was February twelfth, four days since the divisions had made the juncture at Chacabuco. In another two days Las Heras would arrive. Bernardo, San Martin and Solar were standing together on a height to study the plain and discuss their course.

Lifting his telescope, Bernardo swept it across the valley below and looked toward Santiago. He saw red roofs of houses, clumps of trees, spreading vineyards and corn, a placid, sunny land. And then, far off, something more. He peered at the moving objects, thinking he must be mistaken. It looked like a great company of horsemen and it was coming toward this mountain.

It could not be the Spanish. They had sent the greater part of their troops to southern Chile where the liberating army was reported to enter.

Then Bernardo saw the Spanish standards. "The Spanish, at least three thousand!" He tried to sound calm.

The tired eyes of San Martin looked at him in annoyance. "It cannot be," he said, wearily. But he took the telescope and stared. "There cannot be three thousand," he said, crisply.

"At least that many," Bernardo said stubbornly, as certain as if he had counted them.

San Martin glanced at Solar, as if he wanted his estimate. He seemed undisturbed by the sight of the oncoming Spanish.

Solar studied the columns for a long moment. He said, "General O'Higgins is correct, there must be at least three thousand." There was an anxious note in his voice.

Pulling about him his black cape, San Martin said, "You both are wrong." He turned away.

They would be trapped on this height with the Andes behind them. San Martin himself had said the liberating army could not retreat up a mountain. Where was that foresight San Martin had displayed in Mendoza, when he had been the capable and enthusiastic tactician and strategist? There was that night before Mackenna rode off to Buenos Aires, the last time Bernardo had seen his instructor and friend alive. Mackenna remarked about San Martin's genius. Then he stared into the poplar leaves along the Alameda. "Strategy has won battles," he said. "It has also lost battles. For the action of the enemy can upset the best-planned strategy. Then the fine plans must be abandoned for a course that will bring victory." Mackenna had paused and looked thoughtfully at Bernardo. He continued, "The Spanish follow patterns too closely. They do not like innovations or change. And a pattern can sometimes be disastrous when it is used blindly. It produces inertia. When there is a pattern and inertia, the mind is not functioning. Remember, the most important thing in warfare is to think faster and act faster than the enemy!"

Bernardo felt as if Mackenna stood beside him speaking the words. Mackenna was urging him not to delay.

"General San Martin," he said earnestly, "we shall be trapped here, and defeated. Give me permission to attack!"

He saw the shocked but relieved expression on Solar's face.

"The artillery is not here!" There was harshness in San Martin's voice. "My plan, as you know, is to wait for the artillery! This has been the arrangement from the beginning. It will arrive on the fourteenth as scheduled. That is two days away!"

Bernardo was silent. He glanced back toward the plain and saw the marching Spaniards. They came on, steady and determined. "I beg you, General, let me attack!" he said.

San Martin did not answer.

Bernardo turned and stared at the Andes. He saw his men as they had marched during the terrible crossing, saw them marching in spite of mountain sickness with blood spilling from nostrils and mouth onto their clothing. Many of the men had died from exposure and exhaustion. And many had fallen. He saw the soldiers falling into deep canyons. Their screams would always haunt him. Too many had been lost.

Were their lives to be thrown away? Was their great sacrifiec all for nothing? The dangers and suffering endured to reach Chile, to fight for Chile, to win independence for all of them? What would they say to waiting two days for artillery, while the enemy trapped them on this mountain?

The patriot soldiers would ask to fight without artillery! They would fight with knives, spears, lances, clubs, muskets, bayonet, any sort of weapon, and they would fight to the death rather than wait and be trapped.

And soon the three thousand marching Spanish would have reinforcements from southern Chile.

"Let me attack, at once!" Bernardo demanded his voice determined, for if San Martin refused, he meant to act without permission.

Then under the black cape, the shoulders of San Martin moved. "You may advance," he said.

Already, it was three in the afternoon. Bernardo had been pleading for this moment since morning.

In his tent he studied the map. A Royalist detachment was bivouacked on a hill with a ravine to protect it from the road. There was also a small detachment of Spaniards on the mountain. If Solar advanced a mile to the right he would cut off the retreat of the advance detachment. The Spanish on the hill would be in no position to resist his brigade. And if San Martin moved to the front at the moment that Bernardo attacked the front line of Spanish now advancing across he plain, the day would belong to the patriots!

It was with an anxious heart that Bernardo left his tent. He looked west. The sun was a brilliant red as it had been that night he and Mackenna first talked of this conflict's being bloody. And it had been bloody. Too much blood had been spilled. And now, more was to be given.

He prayed that it would not be patriots' blood!

Leading his men, he rode off. Where the ground leveled off he advanced more rapidly.

Ruthlessly he attacked, his mind hearing the orders of Mackenna. "Strike where the line is weakest! Strike hard and quickly and surprise the enemy. Give them no time to think or plan. Confuse and scatter their lines. Attack swiftly, with your greatest force!"

With shouts as wild as the battle cries of Indians, his men fought. Long months they had been training for this chance to wipe out the stain on their country's honor.

Time and again, the attacks.

The Spanish line broke, scattered. They tried to reform. But Bernardo's men closed in. There was relentless musketfire.

Bernardo's men were driven back.

They attacked again, fighting furiously hand to hand.

The ground was strewn with the wounded and dead.

Behind him was a roar like an avalanche. Across the field came San Martin's troops, the flying and fluttering of the blue and white patriot banners, the welcome reinforcements Bernardo so badly needed.

Once more the Spanish lines were attacked. The Spaniards turned suddenly and raced for protection toward a vineyard, leaving arms, ammunition and baggage, their dead and dying in hundreds.

The cries of "Viva la Patria!" roared across the plain, as the patriots pursued and slaughtered the Spanish.

CHAPTER XXXVIII

SAN MARTIN refused to be named head of Chile.

So now O'Higgins, against his wish, was Supreme Director.

For two hours the speakers in the Santiago Plaza praised the heroes. Now it was Bernardo O'Higgins they were lauding as patriot, hero, the finest general in Chile, the most fearless soldier; an unassuming and modest man.

Then the speeches were over. The crowds broke into cheers and a procession moved about the Plaza. A group of children sang patriotic songs.

Bernardo turned with relief from the adulations.

His first act upon taking office would be to reopen the public schools closed by the Spanish. There would be education for every child. They would be trained in civics and in the future the country would have young people capable of administrating a liberal government. And once again there would be a newspaper; first one, then many. Newspapers and books and libraries. He already had a long list of books to be ordered from abroad for the libraries and schools. They covered every subject. He wanted to install in the schools the method of instruction developed by the English Quaker, Joseph Lancaster.

The tasks ahead were enormous. He knew someone else who could fill the office better than he. Casimiro Albano, his boyhood friend from Talca, for example. Bernardo glanced at Casimiro.

His friend had been educated in the priesthood. He had wanted a good education and so he joined the ministry, but he had also embraced the patriots' cause.

Now Casimiro leaned toward Bernardo and said, "This victory will encourage Simon Bolívar to continue his struggle."

Bernardo thought of Bolívar when, in 1815, he had been forced to flee from the Spanish in the north. How bitter a moment that must have been! He recalled his own feelings after Rancagua when he fled from Chile. "All the patriots will be encouraged," he said.

The patriots of Chile were sworn to help and would help all the countries of South America to freedom. He would work constantly to bring it about. If, in his position of Supreme Director, he could hasten liberty for all the colonies, then he gladly accepted the responsibility. Independent completely, Chile would help others to build free states, for they all were one people. The achievements of one were the accomplishments of all, and no patriot in any colony should claim that he, alone, was liberator.

That evening, at the banquet held at the beautiful residence of Don Pedro Chopitea, there were more speeches, and toasts. During a momentary lull, Bernardo, sitting next to San Martin said, "It is now three days since Chacabuco. Shouldn't we follow the Spanish? They will hole up in Talcahuano and the liberating army will not be able to pry them loose."

With the Spaniards holding Talcahuano, the Viceroy could pour more and more reinforcements into Chile.

But San Martin seemed not to hear.

Bernardo persisted with his questions.

At last, as on numerous other occasions during these three days, San Martin smiled pleasantly. He said, "Enjoy yourself a little, Bernardo. There is plenty of time. Soon I will order the men south. Our men deserve this relaxation." And his eyes were bright and laughing. "Do you think of nothing but fighting?"

Bernardo lifted his glass.

But in the south Ramon Freyre was waiting at Talca for these liberating troops to join his force of three hundred and move ahead to stop the escaping Spanish forces. Each moment the remnants of the Royalist army that had escaped from Chacabuco and the Spanish dragoons stationed in southern Chile to stop the liberating army from Mendoza, were nearing the safety of the port of

Talcahuano, where two strong forts would help protect them from the patriots. Meanwhile the Viceroy of Peru would hear of the defeat of his dragoons in Chile and would send soldiers to Talcahuano to strengthen his depleted army.

The liberating army should have pushed on south the same day it reached Santiago. They should have driven on, fighting until the Viceroy's soldiers had been defeated.

He could not force the liberating army to march, for that was the responsibility of San Martin as commander in chief. But as Supreme Director of Chile he could begin plans for a navy.

The South Sea must be swept clean both of Spanish warships and merchant vessels, and he would organize a navy to drive them from these seas.

At present, Chile had no ships. Where would he begin?

Mentally he walked aboard all the vessels on which he had sailed, staring at cannon, measuring length and breadth, counting the number of seamen, wondering about sailing speeds and tonnage, and the purchase price of ships. There might be an American or an English ship in Valparaiso harbor that he could buy. Even a merchant ship might be refitted and sent into the South Sea to capture Spanish vessels for a navy for Chile.

Along the table he saw Arriagada, his neighbor from Chillan. He motioned to him that he wanted to speak with him.

Arriagada leaned across the back of Bernardo's chair.

"I was thinking of a navy for Chile," Bernardo said. "Will you ride to Valparaiso? There just might be a ship that the patriots could buy."

"I will leave at once," Arriagada said.

Bernardo looked at him gratefully. Here was a man who understood the importance of immediate action. Even in the early days of this struggle in Chile, long years ago, Arriagada had never waited.

Bernardo must have a navy chief. An admiral would be needed for Chile's fleet, once there was a fleet. Where could he get a capable admiral, a competent naval officer?

At his desk in the Palace, three days later, Bernardo spoke about the problem of getting ships and men to Jose Rodrigues-Aldea who had been preparing estimates for him.

"It will take an enormous amount of money." Jose Rodrigues-Aldea placed the figures before Bernardo. "These are the rough estimates. I will work out complete details for you. Ten ships will cost better than a million pesos."

A million pesos? It would be a difficult job to raise half that sum. But it had to be done. And how? He studied the figures. If there was a vessel in Valparaiso that could be purchased, it would cost, say, one hundred thousand pesos, plus repairs and refitting with additional guns. New ships would cost much more. And besides warships, Bernardo would need cargo vessels for transporting soldiers and supplies to Peru.

He had promised San Martin that the vessels would be purchased and equipped and that Chile would supply at least twenty-five hundred to three thousand men to fight with him in Peru. Bernardo had promised to have all this within eighteen months.

The time seemed suddenly much too short.

If only there was a financial wizard in Chile, Bernardo thought, feeling the push of time. But where in Chile would he find such a person? Here men could figure income and taxes and tithes but little more. Bernardo did not know of one man outside of Jose Rodrigues-Aldea, who had made the estimates for him, who could do this much. He thought it was something of a miracle that Rodrigues-Aldea had worked out the rough figures.

Jose had no experience in such matters, having been educated to be a lawyer, but he had an aptitude for finance. And Bernardo was forced to use what material was available.

Colossal mistakes of all kinds would surely be made by men inexperienced in managing a liberal government. And this Bernardo had explained to all the men he had appointed. They had agreed with great earnestness they all would do the best they could. They would be charitable with one another, would discuss their mistakes, and correct them.

"Jose," Bernardo said, "how would you go about raising a million and a half pesos for Chile?"

Thoughtfully, Jose stared at the sheets before him. At last he said, "Why not ask Chileans to contribute their personal property, such as jewels, plate, money and property? It is their cause and their country. They would gladly help. And perhaps England or the United States would lend money. We have bought guns and ammunition from both. We could arrange a sort of trade agreement with them. Could we impose an additional tax on products exported and imported?"

"I see you have given the matter thought," Bernardo said. He was both surprised and grateful to find a Chilean who looked ahead and thought of Chile's future. Jose Rodrigues-Aldea would do for his Minister of Finance.

That same day Bernardo wrote to the United States government and ordered a frigate and other vessels of war, to be armed and equipped, together with arms and stores needed by the Chilean forces.

To his and San Martin's friend Don Ignacio Alvarez Tomas, in Buenos Aires, he wrote about sending an emissary of the Chilean government to England to make inquiries about a naval officer, capable of commanding the navy. He did not mention that Chile had no ships. He suggested that the emissary approach Lord Thomas Cochrane, an admiral in the British navy. And if Cochrane refused, the agent should find another suitable officer, Bernardo wrote.

For years Bernardo had heard of the daring exploits of Admiral Cochrane, a radical and a thorn in the side of the British conservatives. Cochrane fought against inequalities, and a righteous cause was for him a challenge.

If Lord Cochrane would accept command of Chile's naval force, as yet unformed, how fortunate for the country. If he would not, then somehow another capable man must be found.

That same day Bernardo's mother and sister arrived with an escort from Mendoza.

As he greeted them, Rosa said with a curtsy and mock ceremony, "Your Excellency," and her face lighted with pleasure.

"You succeeded in getting across that dreadful Los Patos route safely," his mother said, and her eyes were filled with happy tears.

Proudly, he walked beside his mother into the official residence. Here in this Palace, except for that ancient Spanish law, she should have lived long years ago as the wife of Governor Ambrosio O'Higgins.

Rosa trailed behind them, peering into each room and, with the instinct of the housekeeper, suggested changes and improvements.

A few nights later San Martin came for a farewell dinner with Bernardo and other guests. He was leaving for Buenos Aires in the morning. Placing his hand on his sword he said, "My hand, my sword, my life will be given to the freeing of South America. I will yet wrest the flag of Pizarro from the Palace of the Viceroy of Peru. It is the banner under which the Incas were conquered. Its possession has always been considered a symbol of power and authority!" He drew himself up proudly and glanced around with an imperial air.

San Martin was welcome to the flag of Pizarro.

But it was San Martin's nature to be dramatic.

Before the flag of Pizarro could be taken, the patriots must conquer twenty-three thousand Spanish troops and take both Lima and Callao and the Spanish ships.

He watched the tall figure of San Martin, the lively eyes, heard the flow of words about training more troops for the fight in Peru. And he thought, "Where can I get warships, quickly, and where will the million and a half pesos come from to pay for them? Where are the officers, the sailors, to man them? And an admiral?" He must have a capable admiral.

Chile had none of these. Bernardo had to find them. And in eighteen months. It was an impossible task.

But bringing an army across the highest pass in the Chilean Andes had seemed impossible, too. Yet that had been accomplished, and in less than a year.

Somehow he would get ships. By the time the troops were trained and ready to sail for Peru, Bernardo would have a fleet of warships and vessels to transport an expeditionary force of six thousand fighting men!

He must succeed, and he would!

CHAPTER XXXIX

THE NEWS from Talcahuano was bad. Bernardo read the dispatches from the liberating troops fighting near the port, and realized that there must be improvement, and at once.

He paced the floor of his office.

After Chacabuco the patriots should have hastened after the fleeing Spanish. Except for a few captured en route to Valparaiso, all had escaped, while the patriots celebrated. The Spanish had holed up in Talcahuano. Now for weeks the liberating forces had been trying without success to drive them out.

He decided he would go to Talcahuano, to do what he could to help in defeating the Spanish.

The once isolated Talcahuano was now a chief danger spot for the patriots, since the Viceroy of Peru, and ultimately the Crown, could disembark thousands and more thousands of trained soldiers to fight against the liberating army. They could come in overwhelming numbers to attack the patriots. From Talcahuano, too, the Spanish forces would move swiftly south to Concepcion and take the city, thus controlling all of southern Chile, and then march north to Santiago. Then the Viceroy would again be in possession of the country.

Two days later Bernardo and his people entered Concepcion where they would remain the night before traveling on to the patriots' encampment which was midway between the city and Talcahuano.

The cathedral bells were ringing. During peace or war, they sounded at eventide, and everything waited until they ceased.

A woman on horseback stopped beside him. Her hair, lighted by the afterglow, was red and gold, and it carried Bernardo back to an evening at Las Canteras and a girl dancing too wildly. Her name, he remembered, was Dona Rosario Puga.

She glanced at Bernardo. Her eyes were large and bold; and her smile was distracting.

He touched his hat, said, "Good evening, Dona Rosario," and rode on.

At Government House, Bernardo took supper with Colonel Ramon Freyre, now governor of Concepcion.

Freyre had been a retiring person, but promotions, a little honor, and the position of governor had made him ambitious. It had come to Bernardo's ears that Freyre believed himself neglected by the patriots in Santiago and that he wanted to be in the capital as Supreme Director, and that Bernardo's political enemies in the north were attempting to promote Freyre.

At dawn, Bernardo rode to the camp near Talcahuano, four miles away.

The encampment was spread over a rolling hillside. His Chief of Staff, General Brayer, a Frenchman, had joined the army after Chacabuco. He came forward to greet Bernardo. They had breakfast together about nine o'clock.

Then Bernardo examined the position of the patriots.

He could see the Spaniards digging deep trenches on the land side of Talcahuano. He thought, "Those forts built by my father are as impregnable as Gibraltar." It was going to be difficult to get the Spanish out when they were protected by the castles. And he recalled the last time he had sailed into the port on the ship from Lima.

The rocky fortresses had looked down on him and he had remembered Gibraltar. These looked as immovable. And he recalled that Dolphin had described the thickness of the walls, the vast storage space, the number of cannon and other equipment.

"We will starve them out," General Brayer said. "There are ten thousand people living in Talcahuano. They cannot get food after their present supply runs out."

Bernardo did not like to wait. It might be better to start an immediate campaign and blast until the fortifications were shattered. He stared moodily at the forts, wishing his father had not built so strongly and well. It would be difficult to destroy the defenses of Talcahuano.

Slowly, he returned to the camp.

A letter came from Dona Rosario Puga. She invited him to a party at her house in Concepcion. A little relaxation from thoughts of war would rest him, she suggested.

He wrote her a note of thanks. He was sorry, he could not accept.

Then he was busy for days both in Talcahuano and in Concepcion, and he forgot about Rosario Puga.

In one week she sent him two more invitations. She asked if he remembered that once he had thought her the best dancer in Chillan? Did he remember that he danced with her at Las Canteras in the old days?

He interrupted his work to write her a hasty reply, telling her that he had forgotten neither her dancing nor that she had visited him and his family at Las Canteras. It had been most enjoyable dancing that evening. "Forgive me," he added, "but I cannot accept your invitation much as I would enjoy an evening with you and your friends. Once this war is over, we all shall dance again."

In his mind he could still see Rosario as she danced at his hacienda, her small feet strapped in sandals, the skirt of her green dress swaying to the music of guitars and drums. There had been a wildness about her, and an impudence, too.

Since that time he had heard that Rosario Puga had married. There had been some gossip about her and her husband being separated. He had not been interested enough to ask the reason, or even if it were true.

He thought about it. And about Rosario's bright hair, her grace. Sometime he would see her again, when there was once again the peace they all longed for, and freedom for Chileans.

Victory seemed a long way off still. He had moments of deep discouragement. He felt weariness, the need for some rest. And, turning, he looked toward Talcahuano, thinking of the fortresses, the trenches, the guns mounted ready to blast when the patriots attacked.

Another message had come from the Puga girl.

This time, she said, she was riding to Talcahuano to bring him a message of importance. He did not want her at the camp. Yet, if the message was really important, he should know what it was. She might have news that could not be sent safely by a courier.

He decided to ride and meet her. He would leave her at the gates to the city, and return to camp immediately.

She had explained in her note that she would arrive at camp about three o'clock that afternoon. Bernardo rode away in time to intercept her two miles out.

When she saw Bernardo she reined in her horse. She came slowly forward. "I did not expect an escort," she said, smiling.

"You should never ride without an escort," he said.

She laughed. Her eyes were impudent, teasing. He had a sudden desire to seize her and kiss her. "We can talk as we ride back to Concepcion. I will go with you to the gates," he said.

"Only to the gates?" And again she laughed, as if the idea amused her. "Then, let us talk here," she suggested. "There on the hill in the shade."

Bernardo glanced toward the hill, thinking that he should not take the time. Still, if he made excuses he would appear even more unfriendly.

Already Rosario was riding ahead, climbing the slope, going toward the broad shade of trees.

He followed. He tethered the horses to the branch of one of the trees and came to where she was seated on the clean, dry grass, her hands clasped about her knees. He dropped beside her and looked toward the marsh, at wild fowl feeding among the reeds and occasionally soaring off into the pale, sunny sky. He thought, how pleasant to rest from thoughts of war for a moment, here beside Rosario with the bright hair, the small waist, the white flesh. The dancing Rosario, he thought, looking at her feet, small and neatly shod.

She leaned toward him. Her shoulder brushed his sleeve.

He stiffened, but he did not draw away. "You had something to tell me?" He tried to sound casual, glancing as he spoke at her face close to his sleeve.

"Every patriot wants to be useful," she said. "You need someone to spy for you in Concepcion. Can I help?"

If only she would not look at him with such inviting eyes. And if her head was not so close, her lips as bright as wild red fuchsias, and if only she had not spoken of loneliness or of wanting to help him, then it would be easier to answer quietly. When he spoke his voice was too tense. "If you learn anything of importance," he said, "I shall always be glad to hear it."

With a light laugh, she laid her head against his shoulder. "Then I shall tell you when I learn of something of importance."

Bernardo looked off at the marsh. But his lips were eager to kiss the fuchsia-red mouth, the warm skin, the hair. He told himself he should break this spell and take her back to the city. But a more insistent demand called to his desire. The urge was hypnotic and although his mind spoke, he ignored reason, letting the flood of his senses, her nearness, sweep over and through him.

With a swift movement she turned and kissed him, and as she did her arms moved with softness around his neck. She whispered, "Bernardo!" in a voice honeyed, entreating, that was as beautiful as a chord on a low-toned instrument.

Her lips were nectar-sweet.

He yielded to her seductiveness entirely. He dropped beside her to the grassy couch which gave back the crushed odor of wild flowers. The perfume of her white skin was more fragrant than oleander. He kissed her, embraced her, possessed her.

There were other days, other meetings. It was no good promising himself that he would break the spell she had cast over him. It held him hypnotically. He told himself that she was married and that he was an adulterer, but he was drawn to her again and again, pulled irresistibly by her seductiveness.

A letter came from her one day, after their meeting of a week earlier. It was brief. She said simply that it was over. She would see him no more.

He crumpled the note in his hand, held it tightly.

Perhaps she had decided to return to her husband. He sincerely hoped that was the cause of this brief message. He trusted that Rosario and her husband had settled their misunderstandings and would be happy. He stared at the note.

Long ago, Bernardo told himself, this should have happened. And if the picture of Rosario Puga did not leave him immediately, in time he knew he would forget. For he had never loved her. There was only one love for him and that was Carlota.

He destroyed the letter and went to his desk and threw himself into his work. Here at his work was where he belonged. He should never have forgotten.

CHAPTER XL

ONE of Bernardo's spies brought word a few days later that soon the Spanish in Talcahuano would capitulate. They lacked provisions, guns and ammunition.

Bernardo continued his watchfulness.

He received word one afternoon that a vessel was moving toward the port, and he hurried to the heights overlooking Talcahuano.

The vessel was flying the colors of the United States. As a decoy the Spanish had hoisted patriot flags from the forts and the ship entered the trap. It meant that provisions and supplies intended for the Chileans would be seized by the Spanish. It would allow them to continue their resistance against the patriots' troops.

Hastily, he returned to camp. He would plan to catch the Spanish off guard. As they began the attack Bernardo could imagine the startled Spanish springing from their beds, the wild confusion along the beach of Talcahuano.

There was loud, brisk musketfire from both patriot and enemy lines.

The patriots charged boldly and entered the enemy lines at two places. Soon, they had possession of important batteries. They spiked the cannon, continued hand-to-hand fighting in the trenches.

When daylight came the parapet was covered with bodies of both Spanish and patriot soldiers and still the bloody fighting went on.

Shortly after dawn, Bernardo saw boatloads of escaping Spaniards moving toward the United States' vessel. It would be ordered to take the refugees to Callao.

Soon the victory would be the patriots!

Then a letter came from General San Martin, camped at Las Tablas, near Valparaiso. It advised that the Viceroy had sent reinforcements and supplies to Talcahuano. The ship was due almost immediately. Bernardo was ordered to retire his troops at once and make a juncture with San Martin at San Fernando.

The waste, Bernardo thought. But he ordered a retreat.

With his troops he started north.

He received word a few days later that the Spanish had arrived at Talcahuano.

The Spanish marched swiftly. They crossed the River Maule and advanced upon Talca.

Bernardo made the juncture with San Martin at San Fernando. On the nineteenth Bernardo and San Martin marched south to attack the Spanish.

The Spanish retired to Talca.

At sunset the patriot army took up a position at Cancharayada. San Martin said, "We will attack in the morning."

With a feeling of impending disaster, Bernardo urged that they attack at once.

But San Martin said: "Tomorrow!"

Bernardo noted the troops, resting but not out of formation. He glanced toward the mountains, thinking of Juan Mackenna in the churchyard in Buenos Aires.

There was a sudden blast of musketfire and the entire camp of the patriots was thrown into confusion and panic. As Bernardo ran forward, he felt a tearing pain in his arm. He kept running, calling orders sharply. Then he stumbled, fell and tried to rise.

Through his numbed mind he heard his voice calling to his men, but it sounded far off. He kept telling himself he must rise and rally his troops.

Then one of his officers called to him. "Are you badly wounded, General? We must ride fast. The Spanish are everywhere. I have horses."

Bernardo said, "The men?"

"Scattered. Everything gone!"

Bernardo tried to rise, succeeded on the third try. His arm and side were bleeding. He thought, everything gone!

On the twenty-fourth, Bernardo entered Santiago with General Quintana and Colonels Martinez, Necochea, Zapiloa and Melian.

The city was in confusion, the people in despair. For Monteagude of the Buenos Aires division had ridden into the city earlier and had terrorized them by the wildness of his report, saying the country was irretrievably lost, the Spanish advancing on the capital at a rapid march. O'Higgins had been killed, he said. Then he dashed on, riding toward the Andes and Mendoza to carry the word.

And now again the shops of Santiago were closed. The people clogged highways to the mountains and Valparaiso, hoping to escape the wrath of the evil Spaniards.

Bernardo held a meeting and organized a force for public safety. Within days a regiment of four hundred guerrillas was recruited and, armed with sabres and pistols, sent south to harass the enemy by attacking outposts among his rear guard.

His physician ordered Bernardo to remain in bed. The wounds were not healing properly and he must rest.

There was no time for that, Bernardo thought, and returned to his work.

San Martin and other officers arrived, the General trying hard not to appear downcast. At the Palace he received visitors and, sitting at Bernardo's side, explained over and over with forced cheerfulness about the disaster at Cancharayada. Some sharp skirmishing had taken place, he said, and he had proposed to attack the morning of the twentieth. He had posted sentinels, ordered the troops to refresh themselves, the horses were unsaddled, and mules unloaded. But the advance posts of patriots were taken prisoners or killed and under a tremendous fire of musketry the enemy entered the camp, throwing the patriots into confusion. Officers found it impossible to rally soldiers and many threw down their arms. The cavalry troops were mostly destitute of horses as the animals ran away in the confusion. Most of the artillery, baggage and clothing of the officers, the stores and money of the commissary department, were abandoned to the enemy. There was general panic.

San Martin looked hard at O'Higgins. General O'Higgins had been badly wounded. He should be in bed. They could be grateful that he had not been killed.

Bernardo said quickly, "Las Heras has rallied some of his men. He is keeping the enemy's advance guard in check. And we shall yet drive the Spaniards from Chile!"

The visitors had gone.

There was silence between him and San Martin.

Bernardo thought of the labors that confronted them. They must make use of the days before the Spanish, with better than six thousand disciplined troops, reached the capital. They must enlist and equip five thousand men, at least. And the men as well as officers must be inspired with confidence to face the ruthless enemy, and take the victory.

Already, the friends of the enemy here in the city were spreading fantastic tales about the strength and fearlessness of the Spanish regiments, hoping to undermine the morale of the patriots even more.

Bernardo said, "We should prepare a proclamation, reassuring the people that Chile will be defended. The recruiting has already begun. We should tell the people."

"I have already thought of that," San Martin said. "I shall prepare it immediately."

A camp had been set up a few miles from Santiago for training recruits.

Within nine days an army of five thousand had been recruited and was prepared to march, with fifteen hundred cavalry and eight pieces of light field artillery. Six of the cannon had been brought across the Andes.

And again, Luis Beltran was working his miracles.

Once more the people were roused, the patriot army inspired as never before.

Day and night Bernardo worked at details of the forthcoming campaign. Mr. Worthington, special agent to Chile from the United States, called to recommend North American and Swedish recruits.

He glanced at Bernardo's arm in the sling. He said, "Your Excellency, I hope you are looking after that injury."

Bernardo smiled. He would be all right, he said.

"I hear you fought bravely even after you were wounded at Cancharayada," he said. "A terrible blow, Cancharayada!"

How terrible no one would ever know. Bernardo thought, "This time there must be no waiting!" He asked Mr. Worthington to send the foreign recruits to him, thanked him for his help.

On April first, Bernardo learned that the Royal Army of the Viceroy was at Rancagua. Would that they might be trapped there as Bernardo and his men had been!

The Spanish came slowly north.

Two days later the patriot troops were prepared to march.

Bernardo ordered the women residents either to the protection of convents or across to Mendoza, his mother and Rosa among them.

On the fourth, the Spanish neared the plains of Maipú and at sunset the two armies were five or six miles apart.

Sunday, April fifth. Early the church bells called worshipers to mass. But today, Bernardo thought, there would be few in attendance for the men would be on the battlefield and the women praying in convents or on the road to Mendoza. There was the quietness of death in the Palace and the streets beyond. The scent of orange blossoms was heavy, almost too sweet. Now and again he heard the voice of a sentry.

The militia was guarding the city.

Dr. Craig came. He said Bernardo was in an exhausted state from overwork. His wounds were not doing well. He must remain in the Palace and not attempt to go to the battlefield. In his condition it might mean death.

The doctor departed.

With disturbed eyes Bernardo looked at his sword.

A dispatch arrived. He read eagerly: at dawn the enemy had attempted to occupy the road to Santiago to place himself between the patriot army and the city. Advancing in close column the patriots frustrated the maneuver by occupying the main road. The enemy took up a position on a hill near the Espejo farm, the Burgos regiment to the right, the infantry of Don Carlos to the left, between them troops drafted by the Spanish in the south.

Bernardo studied the report.

He hoped to God that there would be no waiting!

He thought of Juan Mackenna and his words of wisdom. His mind raced back over the years, the long, bloody years, to the losses, the gains, the losses again.

There must be no waiting!

Sitting there, he prayed earnestly with his whole heart that this might be the battle to end the battles, the one to bring freedom to all the colonies, the beginning of the end of tyranny in South America.

Then, lifting his head, he stared at his sword.

After a moment he crossed to the wardrobe. He took down his uniform and began dressing. He could not pull the sleeve over his wounded right arm, but he did the best he could. He threw a capota about his shoulders and picked up his sword.

Then the first gunfire began.

Hurriedly he left the Palace.

Placing himself at the head of the militia, Bernardo rode toward the battlefield.

The patriots' artillery on the right was firing upon the advancing left of the Spanish, when Bernardo reached the scene. The Spanish infantry descended the hill and was met by fire from the artillery of Colonel Blanco of the patriots. Each discharge was followed by destruction. Colonel Manuel Escalada with a small squadron of horse grenadiers charged the small hillock on which the Spanish artilery had been planted, and carried it.

Bernardo rode forward and flung himself into the battle.

From patriot soldiers rose cheers and shouts of "O'Higgins! O'Higgins has come! Viva O'Higgins!"

The Burgos regiment of the Spanish was retreating in disorder, the patriot troops advancing under heavy gunfire with the precision and determination of seasoned and disciplined soldiers.

Bernardo watched proudly. They were better than the crack Burgos regiment!

This was an important moment, he thought. If they held their position it might turn the battle in favor of the patriots.

The patriots' charged and the effect was startling. Almost at once the firing stopped, the Spanish and patriots crossed bayonets, fought wildly, neither giving an inch. Then, because of the smoke and dusk, it was impossible to know which was gaining, until at length the words "Viva el Rey!" died out entirely and across the field sounded shouts of "Viva la Libertad!"

Las Heras defeated the left wing of the enemy.

For a time the center action continued, but at last the line broke and the Spanish retreated toward the Espejo farm and the patriots followed.

From a window above the farm's gateway a white flag appeared.

But the patriots gave no quarter. The gate was blown open, the patriot troops charged into the courtyards. There was bitter fighting and terrible slaughter, the Spanish trying to escape through the orchards and vineyard. But they were butchered as they ran.

Off along the edge of the battlefield were the countrymen of Chile lassoing Spaniards who attempted to escape.

It was over. Thirty-five hundred Spanish prisoners were being driven toward Santiago and the battlefield was strewn with the dead—the patriots' own and the Spanish.

Bernardo rode to San Martin.

For a long moment they looked at each other.

Their hands locked in a firm clasp and they embraced!

Then the celebrations. In the Plaza the colors of Spain had been spread and above them a pillar symbolizing liberty. The bells clanged jubilantly, and from the church towers rockets were set off. In the streets was dancing and singing. The wild, happy Chileans!

Once more the adulations, which Bernardo disliked.

That night he listened to the shouts of revelers, gay music. But he was not thinking of the successes or the honors. He was thinking of that twelve-hundred-ton English ship recently arrived in Valparaiso. The Chileans had purchased it for one hundred eighty thousand pesos. It was too much money for an old ship that had been serving between England and India for years. But she had fifty guns, and she could search the South Sea for Spanish ships to form a navy for Chile.

He and the patriot army would clean out the watchdogs that guarded the castle at Callao.

One ship. Chile had one naval vessel.

But where could Bernardo find a captain to sail her?

CHAPTER XLI

THAT MORNING Bernardo, his arm still in a sling, was at his desk early when his mother entered followed by a servant. The Negro's face shone like the handsome silver service he carried, a massive set belonging to the Riquelme family. It was the heirloom his mother prized above any of her few remaining possessions.

The servant placed it on Bernardo's desk. His mother said, "It will help to pay for Chile's first battleship!" And she looked at Bernardo proudly.

He ran a hand along the smooth metal, engraved with a handsome design, recalling the happy occasions when this service had decorated the table. It had been used to celebrate Bernardo's homecoming to Chile after thirteen years' absence. It had brightened parties given to interest Chileans in the cause.

It stood looking at him, asking to share in the patriots' cause, and with great love he accepted the sacrifice, as he had others. They had poured in, rubies from fingers of Chilean women, diamonds from their ears and braids, emerald necklaces and bracelets that had come down from ancient times. Little and great, the contributions were given, and happily.

But none meant more to Bernardo than this silver service donated by his mother.

An hour later Captain George O'Brien arrived.

It was O'Brien who had been ordered to the port after Chacabuco, to capture Spanish fugitives who had swarmed toward Valparaiso. He had taken some prisoners. Among their baggage was found seventeen hundred doubloons, which were contributed to the public treasury of Chile. After the recent battle of the Maipú, O'Brien had taken thirty of his men and pursued the Spanish General Osorio. Informed that the General had gone toward Valparaiso, Captain O'Brien supposed he was boarding a ship for Peru. He took a short cut to the port. But the Spanish General had ridden to the River Maule. There, while his men slept, he had seized the best of the horses, taken twelve guards and crossed the Maule, fleeing to Talcahuano. His soldiers, left behind by their chief, had been imprisoned.

You could always count on Captain O'Brien's doing his best. He was a brave soldier, and a willing one.

And since Bernardo had not located a chief officer for the new warship *Lautaro*, he had sent for O'Brien, remembering that the Irishman had begun his career as a lieutenant in the British Royal Navy.

"You know more than any other man in Chile about warships," Bernardo said.

O'Brien looked at him in astonishment.

Bernardo explained. It was about the command of the new warship, the *Lautaro*. The Spanish blockade must be broken. The *Lautaro* must cruise about the South Sea and capture Spanish vessels to increase Chile's navy. "I want you to take command."

"It has been a long time since I was a member of the navy." The blue eyes of the Irishman narrowed. He seemed to be measuring the distance across the bow of a ship. After a moment he said, "I'll do it, General O'Higgins!"

Bernardo sat looking at Captain O'Brien, trying to recall how the English managed their warships when the Spanish vessel on which he was traveling had been taken as a prize. He remembered shots across the bow of the Spanish frigate. And orders from the British to surrender or be blown to bits. How many men had boarded the frigate that time?

There had been too much confusion, too much excitement. The English seamen had poured onto the ship.

"What about a crew?" O'Brien asked.

Bernardo said, "We will hire as many sailors from the merchant ships in Valparaiso as we can. The balance of the crew will be made up of peasant recruits."

O'Brien looked distressed. "I doubt if any Chilean peasant knows larboard from starboard."

Once they did not know about fighting battles either, Bernardo thought. He recalled the sturdy peasants, their eagerness to serve, the quickness with which they learned to handle firearms. And Bernardo had not learned the Manual of Arms until after he had formed two regiments. He smiled at the memory. "We must use what we have," he said.

"And officers?"

Bernardo was thoughtful. He had already planned that. "We will use army men," he said. "You should have one officer who can speak both Spanish and English, to translate orders. The Chileans do not understand English and few North American or English or Dutch sailors speak Spanish. How about young Miller?"

The Britisher, William Miller, was twenty-three years of age. He had joined the army shortly after the battle of Chacabuco. At Cancharayada he had used his head. It was Miller who helped transport the heavy cannon across the swinging Indian bridge when it threatened to fall into the river.

Yes, Miller kept his head, O'Brien agreed. And he understood and spoke Spanish.

Days later, Bernardo left Santiago for Valparaiso. He wanted to watch Captain O'Brien and his men sail the *Lautaro* out of the port to try to capture Spanish ships cruising offshore and blockading the harbor.

The old English Indiaman had been completely overhauled and refitted. Now she was the *Lautaro*, after the Lodge and the Araucanian hero. From the heights above Valparaiso Bernardo and the Governor of the port looked down at Chile's first naval ship.

Never had Bernardo seen a more beautiful object.

The day seemed especially bright, as if polished for the occasion. The *Lautaro* waited, her spars straight and proud.

He and the Governor rode on down the steep path, through the suburb of Almendral with its orchards and gardens, and on along the single street of Valparaiso that fronted the harbor.

Bernardo guided his horse out of the milling crowd to the beach where Captain O'Brien and his crew were entering boats that would take them to the *Lautaro*.

A hundred foreign seamen had been signed by O'Brien. They had deserted merchant ships to join Chile's navy. Captain O'Brien had also signed on two hundred and fifty Chilean peasants. Not one of the Chileans had ever been aboard any vessel and they had no conception of what a seaman was supposed to do. While Bernardo watched, they plunged into the water and with hoarse, wild shouts, began swimming to the *Lautaro*.

He thought, "They swim as they ride, as they use the lasso, as they fight. They will fight at sea as they have on land, with stout hearts and without fear, throwing themselves into the fray as if they were roping steers."

The tall, lanky William Miller came loping across the sand.

Days later, young Miller, assistant to Captain George O'Brien, brought Bernardo details of the first engagement of the *Lautaro*.

His young voice tense, his face struggling to hide his emotion, Miller said, "We were flying British colors as we approached the Spanish *Esmeralda*. She lay to with her topsails to the mast to speak with the supposed British ship. The *Lautaro* ranged upon the weather quarter of the enemy, when, having hauled down British colors, and hoisted the Chileno, she discharged her foremost guns. Captain O'Brien jumped on board with thirty men following. The marines kept up a steady fire from the *Lautaro's* forecastle. There was panic among the *Esmeralda's* crew. The Spanish ensign was hauled down. A jerk of the sea carried the vessels clear of each other, upon which the *Lautaro* lowered boats to send reinforcements."

Miller paused.

Perhaps he was thinking that even a green seaman should have known enough to secure lines to keep a ship from drifting, Bernardo thought. His heart went out to the young fellow.

"The *Esmeralda's* crew rallied, seeing only a handful of patriots on deck. They shot Captain O'Brien!"

His voice trailed off. After a moment he said, "His last words were, 'Never leave the ship, my boys, the ships is ours!' "

Sorrowfully, Bernardo thought of O'Brien, the loss of a good friend.

When Miller spoke again, he said, "The *Lautaro* lost the *Esmeralda*, but returning to Valparaiso, she took another, a Spanish vessel en route to Callao with fleeing Spanish from Talcahuano."

Bernardo stared at the tanned face of Miller. Captain O'Brien would be pleased, he thought, that now there were two ships for Chile. But the life of so brave a soldier was too great a price to pay.

Then Miller was gone, before Bernardo could commend him for his share in the action. But Bernardo would not forget.

Another vessel, and the blockade lifted! Bernardo wished that O'Brien could be here in Valparaiso to share the success. He walked across the courtyard of the governor's residence, mourning the loss of O'Brien.

For many weeks Bernardo was in Valparaiso thinking and talking ships, ships, ships, figuring the cost of them and the expense of repairs.

And time. There was always the pressure of time driving him.

Jose Rodrigues-Aldea worked hard to raise the money to pay for the vessels. It took such a lot, much more than they had figured.

Bernardo had four refitted ships by October of that year: four naval ships for Chile and a total of a hundred and thirty-six guns.

Shortly afterward, he learned from Buenos Aires that a convoy of ten Spanish transports was bound for Chile with twenty-eight hundred troops to fight against Chile. Most of the Chilean troops were with San Martin being trained for the invasion of Peru. If the Spanish convoy reached Talcahuano, they would have reinforcements. Again the country would be threatened by invasion!

The convoy had to be stopped before it reached Talcahuano.

How could it be stopped? Bernardo had only four ships. Four ships, against ten well-manned Spanish warships! He felt smothered.

He studied the gray sea.

If the Chilean ships hoisted Spanish colors as they approached the Spanish frigates off Talcahuano, they might take the convoy, one by one. But they would have to work out a code of signals to be used by the Chilean ships. With a system of signals the patriot ships could communicate and carry out a unified attack. First, take the Spanish commodore's vessel and seize the written orders. Then signal to the other Spanish ships of the convoy as they approached the rendevouz and give them faked instructions. Bernardo knew the meeting place. It was included in the message from Buenos Aires. The location was the island of La Mocha, south of Talcahuano. The convoy would be a month making the voyage from Buenos Aires to La Mocha.

While the Chilean ships were moving south, the green naval officers would have time to train their even greener seamen.

Bernardo and the Governor, on the heights above Valparaiso, watched the four Chilean warships sail.

When they were out of sight, the patriots' Commodore Blanco would open his orders. He would learn that his destination was the island of La Mocha in the archipelago near Chiloe and that he was to search for the Spanish frigate *Maria Isabel*, daily expected around Cape Horn with eight to ten transports.

Now it was up to Commodore Blanco, who was skillful at keeping officers and men working in harmony. He had a sense of order and timing and he was honest and reliable. These qualities were as important in handling a fleet as was navigation. And he knew as much about seamanship as any other man in Chile, although that was saying little enough.

God go with them!—Bernardo prayed. For only God could help Chile now.

A heavy gale was blowing. In the usually quiet harbor of Valparaiso the waves were running high and Bernardo, watching the sea, wondered how the ships were taking the gale. And what about officers and crew? A gale such as this would be a severe test even for seasoned mariners.

The days passed.

Waiting out the time, Bernardo was disturbed and troubled. It would be nothing short of a miracle if it succeeded. Let it be a miracle; he prayed.

One morning as he worked at his desk in Valparaiso, he heard loud, excited cries beyond the fort.

A voice shouted, "The fleet!"

Rushing up the steps of the fort, he saw from the ramparts the magnificent sight.

Lined up and moving into the harbor were thirteen ships! He counted them again and again.

From the street below rose a loud roar of victory.

Already the ships' guns were saluting! The cannon of the forts answered.

Thirteen ships, Bernardo thought as he stared, almost disbelieving. But the colors of Chile were flying from each of the masts. Thirteen was a fleet that any admiral would be proud to command.

The miracle had happened. And Chile had the navy she needed to move against Peru and the Viceroy.

CHAPTER XLII

In Santiago, Bernardo received other news, startling and alarming news, from Dona Rosario Puga Soto Aguilar. Bernardo's child was a son, the message said, and the child was with the priest at St. Isidore.

His son! And he had not known about the child. Why had he not been told? When he had attempted to see Rosario after she reached Santiago, she had refused to see him. He had learned only that she had not returned to her husband.

During the months that followed, he had almost forgotten about Rosario.

And now this!

Feeling desperate, he stared at the window grille.

If you loved a woman, you wanted children. You wanted a son—sons and daughters. Rosario should have spoken to him of the child. And yet, why should she? She had never loved him. And he had never pretended to love her, not like Carlota.

Then, he thought, a child and without a name. A child nameless and a mother who does not care for him. Bernardo from the first moment had the affection of his mother and his grandfather. He had been wanted and loved by his father.

A child needed most of all a mother. Without Dona Isabel, Bernardo's life would have been desolate. In his darkest moments he had been certain that his mother loved him. He had believed and then known that his father loved him. It had always steadied him.

With a troubled mind he stared into the street.

For an hour he stood there, not knowing where to begin nor where to turn, but certain that he must acknowledge the child, care for him, love him always.

He could think of only one course.

Quickly, he walked along the corridor to his mother's room, and tapping at her door, he entered. Dona Isabel was writing in a diary that she filled with unimportant items about Bernardo, the things he did that seemed to please her.

He would not please her now, he thought, wondering how he would begin.

Lovingly, he studied her dark head, scarcely touched with gray. He glanced about the room, at the tidy chest, a portrait of him, one of his sister, the pincushion of lace, the curtains pulled back letting in sunlight.

She closed her writing case and her hands lay folded over it. And she smiled.

The linnet in a cage near the window called softly.

He stood just inside the door where he had stopped, dreading to speak, not wanting to rouse the old memories of that time years ago.

But at last he said, "Mother." The words stuck in his throat.

He blurted out the message. "My son. Mine and Dona Rosario Puga Aguilar's son, is at St. Isidore." His voice broke. "I have just learned. I knew nothing about a child until now."

For some time his mother did not stir. Then, with great gentleness, she said, "What name have you selected for your first born?"

He could not speak. He had known she would understand. How could she do otherwise? But the compassion and kindness in her voice was almost more than he could endure.

At last he said, "I had not thought of a name. But I like the name Demetrio. It shall be Demetrio O'Higgins. That is my son's name."

Her small hands laid aside the writing case. She went quickly to her wardrobe and from it took a black wrap. She opened a drawer in her mahogany chest and shook out a mantilla and arranged it on her head. Then she faced him, and her eyes were calm and without sorrow. "I will go at once to St. Isidore, to the priest," she said, her voice like music. "Demetrio, my grandchild, will be my charge."

That day Bernardo's son was christened Pedro Demetrio O'Higgins by the priest of the church of St. Isidore.

Bernardo tried once again to speak with Rosario, this time about their son. But as on the other attempts, he failed. She refused to see him.

That night he looked down at his child's face, at small fists, the sunny hair, and thought of times when he had felt keenly the stigma of being born out of wedlock. He would never forgive himself for bringing dishonor on a helpless child. If he could have married Rosario, he would, for the sake of this infant. But the church would not permit divorce. And Rosario would refuse, for she was interested in another Chilean, a young and wealthy man.

Bernardo had given the child his name. He would keep him with him always. He would try to be a good father to Demetrio!

CHAPTER XLIII

BERNARDO returned to the Palace, from an inspection trip to the plains of the Maipú, in low spirits. His plan for installing an irrigation canal was meeting serious opposition both from officials and residents. He wanted the barren waste land turned into farms. The farm owners would be assessed to pay for the canal.

When the expeditionary forces were on the way to Peru, he would push his plans for the canal.

His secretary brought him a letter from London.

Glancing at the postmark, he read the letter and his spirits soared. Lord Thomas Cochrane accepted Bernardo's invitation to command the new Chilean navy. He would arrive in November on the English ship *Rose*.

Bernardo thought of the Spanish defeat at Maipú when Chile had not possessed any ships. Today, only a few months later, the country had a fleet of thirteen. And Bernardo thought with gratitude of the accomplishments of Blanco, Miller and the untrained Chilean sailors who took practically the entire Spanish convoy.

A navy and a skilled commander. It was better than he had hoped. He had not thought a genius like Cochrane would accept the commission to Chile. But he had. Now the Spanish could at last be driven from these seas and never again would the soldiers of the Viceroy and the Crown overrun Chile. This was a day that brought total independence for the country much nearer.

Soon San Martin would have the troops trained and prepared to march. Bernardo had kept his promise to San Martin, and here was a fleet to transport six thousand soldiers to Peru.

Then, before many months, the friends in Peru would be independent. Soon all South America would have broken the bonds that strangled liberty.

He recalled the stories he had heard of the brilliant Cochrane— bizarre adventures, his angry speeches in Parliament, his inventions and his determination. In one blow he would cut out Spanish warships that hugged the castle of Callao, and this would enable San Martin to advance on Lima and encircle Lima with the liberating army. The two cities, Callao and Lima, would be taken in one concerted action by the patriots' army and navy.

Peru was close to complete freedom, as was Chile.

Bernardo notified the Santiago officials of the good news. He began arrangements to receive Cochrane. An attractive and comfortable house would be ready for the admiral when he arrived. There would be celebrations both here and at Valparaiso.

San Martin and the friends in Buenos Aires were delighted that Cochrane had accepted the post as Admiral of the Chilean Navy.

Then, on November twenty-fifth, Bernardo rode to Valparaiso to meet Lord Cochrane.

The new commander in chief of the naval forces of Chile reached Valparaiso on the twenty-eighth and was welcomed by Bernardo at the Governor's residence.

With his Lady and escorts, Lord Cochrane entered and came forward to greet him.

Bernardo was surprised at his apparent youth. In years he was a little older than Bernardo. He was slender and he carried himself well, which made him appear taller than he was. His eyes were fine, arrogant, and he appeared well aware of his capacity without being offensive. He spoke with pleasing elegance, and quickly. After talking with him for a few moments, Bernardo understood how it was that Parliament, where Cochrane served as a member from Westminster, had both enjoyed and deplored his cutting wit.

Cochrane said, "Is it a fact that in April your country had not one warship, Your Excellency, and that now you have a fleet of ships?"

"Yes," Bernardo said proudly.

"Then, I shall enjoy working with you," Cochrane said. "You do not wait on events. You make them happen. And that is my method!"

As Cochrane spoke, Bernardo glanced around the room at the smiling faces of Chile's ministers. How long would they smile at this firebrand?—he asked himself.

Zenteno there, Marine Minister, would he have understanding and grasp of Cochrane's plans? Until a few months ago Zenteno had never set foot on a warship, perhaps not even a small coastal steamer. He had migrated across the Andes with the fleeing patriots. He had fought loyally and could be trusted not to betray the patriots. He had worked at any honest employment after the escape to Mendoza, while waiting to return with the liberating army to Chile.

That was nothing against a man, to work with his hands. Many patriots had served in menial positions to earn a living while waiting for Chile to be retaken. What was unfortunate, Bernardo felt, was that there were few educated and experienced men in Chile with talent for government. Zenteno at least had some education. He could interpret law, and he had picked up a little about naval affairs. No man in Chile knew much about navies. Zenteno was the official that Lord Cochrane would consult about details.

Lawyers, tradesmen, priests, farmers. These were the men who constituted the government. Casimiro Albano, raised on a farm and trained for the priesthood, was president of the Congress. A priest, Camillo Henriques, was editor of the first Chilean newspaper. Bernardo O'Higgins, farmer, soldier, was Supreme Director of Chile.

Bernardo returned to the capital.

On the fourth of December, Lord and Lady Cochrane and their young son came to Santiago. They arrived at night with a small escort of cavalry and went to the house that had been prepared for them. There was no fanfare. Few of the residents were aware that Cochrane and his family had arrived. The Admiral seemed a little disappointed.

But on the following day, and for days after callers crowded into his residence.

A dinner for Cochrane was being held in the courtyard at the Palace. Bernardo glanced about the table, and thought that here were the prettiest women of Chile. Senora Blanco with her dark beauty was as handsome as blonde Lady Cochrane. But his mother was the most beautiful of them all. Her carriage was regal, she wore her gray and silver dress well, and her earnest manner of listening with interest to her dinner partner, Lord Cochrane, was charming. And Rosa, not beautiful but attractive and poised, with pretty manners, won all about her.

Happy night. Happy Chile. He was almost a contented man, because the future of his country seemed certain. He listened to the laughter, watched the dancers. Senora Blanco was dancing with Lord Cochrane.

"*Cielito, mi cielito.* Heaven, my little heaven," Senora Blanco sang, as she danced with Cochrane.

Dinners. Fetes. More dinners. Now Lord Cochrane was giving a dinner. When would they get down to navy business, Bernardo thought. But this was the Chilean way of entertaining. It must be endured.

Lord Cochrane had welcomed his guests wearing the plaids of his clan.

Again he was dancing. He had learned the Chilean steps quickly. The hem of his pleated kilt swung with the rhythm, his feet moved like those of a youth.

This Britisher, Bernardo told himself, would work as intensely as he danced. And a man of that sort, a worthwhile man, accomplished great deeds and helped the world progress in spite of those who cried peace when there was no peace. Miranda had been such a one as Cochrane. Mackenna was another. They had been misunderstood and hated. They had been feared for their fearlessness.

Cochrane was singing the words of the song as he danced, like a Chilean. The pianofortes tinkled, guitars and zithers whined, the drums throbbed and castanets rattled.

Faster the music and faster the feet. Faster swayed Lord Cochrane's kilt.

Bernardo smiled as he watched. He had not enjoyed himself so much in years. His heart warmed as he stared at the dancing Cochrane.

The largest of the ships in the Spanish convoy, now a part of Chile's fleet, had been renamed the *O'Higgins*, and given to Admiral Lord Thomas Cochrane for his flagship. He would sail for Peru in February.

At Bernardo's country house a mile from Santiago, he and Cochrane were speaking of the expedition.

"In February," Cochrane said, "I shall attack Callao during carnival time, at the height of the excitement. Everyone will be heady with wine, even the guards at the castle will be relaxed and not so watchful. There will be only a token force guarding the Spanish warships moored in the harbor."

Cochrane studied the silver bombilla of his maté cup as if it were one of his cannon. "By the way," he said, glancing at Bernardo with a pleased expression, "the figures you gave me about Callao are correct." He added, humorously, "Of course you knew they were."

Bernardo had given the Admiral the figures shortly after he reached Santiago. "The Spanish have two frigates," he had said, "two brigs of war, twenty-six gunboats and some armed merchantmen. And the Callao fortifications are manned by a hundred and sixty-five guns."

He thought of the nights he had lain awake, thinking of those fortifications of Callao. How many times he had tried to think out a method of getting ships out of that harbor, and had given up because Chile had no fleet, even if he had a plan. It was his business to know the number of vessels and guns, he thought. For he and

San Martin, in calculating the men, provisions, equipment for the expedition, must know what they were attacking and the strength they would need.

"My plan," Cochrane said, "is to fly the flag of the United States, using the names of two American frigates which are expected in those waters in February. A packet will be addressed to the Viceroy of Peru. It will contain faked dispatches from the Spanish Ambassador at Washington. The packet will be delivered to the first Spanish government boat that hails us."

It was a good plan. Bernardo, recalling Cochrane's tilts with Mr. Worthington of the United States, was amused that he would use the North Americans as a blind. He recalled that when Mr. Worthington visited Bernardo at Christmas time, the American had spoken of Cochrane's attitude. "A spirit of jealousy toward the United States," was how Worthington put it.

Worthington was right. Cochrane wanted to shut out the Americans from trade with South America. He wanted everything for England.

Yet, Mr. Worthington had been one of the first foreigners to give a contribution to a fund for purchasing the *Lautaro*. It had come out of his own pocket. He had encouraged Bernardo in buying the first ship for Chile's navy. He had surmised that the United States would recognize Chile before any other nation gave her recognition. "The Americas belong together," he said. "We should stand together."

And they would stand together, as friends and neighbors. Bernardo had said as much to Mr. Worthington, asking him to carry that message to President Monroe in Washington. "If the United States will recognize Chile, Mr. Worthington," Bernardo said that Christmas day, "it would be a great help. We would like to work together with your country."

The recognition had not yet come, Bernardo was thinking. He studied the handsome face of Cochrane. And he remembered a toast Cochrane had given at the dinner for him when he first met San Martin here in Santiago.

The dinner had been given in the Palace that had once been the

Bishop's residence before he was exiled. Cochrane had raised his glass. "May all South Americans be as free as England!"

Worthington had flushed, then smiled. He was on the point of rising when San Martin sprang to his feet. His restless, animated eyes went around the table until they came to Mr. Worthington. He held his wine glass high. "Washington!" he had said with spirit.

"The packet for the Viceroy of Peru, ostensibly from the Spanish ambassador at Washington, will serve to get two Chilean ships into the Callao harbor," Cochrane said. "The officers and men from these ships will board two of the largest Spanish warships. A Spanish corvette carrying sixty thousand dollars has been scheduled to leave Callao on that day. And our ships will seize both the corvette and the money."

"It is a good arrangement," Bernardo said. "And you are the officer who can execute it. I shall come to Valparaiso to watch you sail for Peru."

Cochrane paced the terrace with a quick step, looking thoughtful.

Bernardo said, "Are you getting the help you need in Valparaiso?"

"Oh, quite," Cochrane said.

Bernardo was glad to hear this. He had feared there might be difficulties with the Marine Minister.

The bay at Valparaiso was crowded with English and American ships. Bernardo could remember when only an occasional Spanish frigate touched the Chilean ports. Soon, with the South Sea cleared of the Spanish, there would be more foreign shipping. This was how he had dreamed it years ago when he promised the Chileans open ports and improved commerce.

This action of Cochrane's against Callao was the beginning of that better day for Chile.

He watched the activity on the bay, the ships of Chile preparing to sail.

Standing with him on the heights of Valparaiso were nationals from North America, England, France, Sweden, Holland, who had served with the Chilean forces. They were as eager for Cochrane's success as any native.

Up went the sails. Off moved the Chilean fleet, sailing gracefully into the South Sea, large white wings reaching for the clean air of free Chile. First the flagship *O'Higgins*, which carried Cochrane, then the others, one by one.

From the cliffs where the company watched, from the street below, rose loud cheers!

Then Bernardo received word that Cochrane's plan had not succeeded as he had hoped. He had failed to cut out the Spanish vessels at Callao, because the Spanish refused to respect the colors of the United States.

Bernardo thought, above his disappointment, Cochrane would make another try. He would succeed next time.

At the Palace, weeks later, he heard from Cochrane that the second attempt also had been a failure. This time the Spanish moored their ships to the walls of the castle with enormous iron cables.

He refused to be downcast. Cochrane was a great admiral. There would be a third time.

What worried Bernardo even more than Cochrane's failures was the refusal of the Buenos Aires government to finance the expedition to Peru to the amount of five hundred thousand pesos, which it had previously promised to do. San Martin was accused of withdrawing his allegiance from Buenos Aires. He ought to join their general instead of staying on the other side of the Andes to assist Chile and Peru, the government officials said.

And, because of the dissension, San Martin wanted to resign as commander in chief of the expeditionary force.

Bernardo promised to raise the money. He urged San Martin not to think of resigning. He owed it to both his officers and troops, Bernardo told San Martin, not to drop out at this critical moment. "Let the men decide," he said.

As Bernardo anticipated, San Martin was elected to the chief command by his officers.

Riding from his country house to Santiago one morning, Bernardo stared at the new irrigation canals which had been installed at his insistence and at great expense. There seemed not enough money for all the important needs. The Chilean treasury had been drained for the financing and support of the army and the navy. It had neither money nor credit. From Concepcion, Ramon Freyre was stirring up trouble and demanding money, talking about the neglect of southern Chile. And it was not a question of neglect, but simply a lack of funds. Freyre and others did not seem to realize that everything had gone into promoting the cause, and that independence of Chile must come first. They all had suffered, and would suffer more for this cause. For this expedition to Peru would cost a fortune. But it was as much to keep Chile independent as to give the Peruvians liberty.

At his office there was encouraging news. The Lautaro Lodge agreed to furnish two hundred thousand pesos of the five hundred thousand Bernardo and San Martin had asked for the expeditionary force for Peru.

A few mornings later there was news of another kind.

Cochrane had sailed south to Valdivia, two thousand miles from Callao, when he was supposed to be planning an attack against the castle of Callao. Without permission, he had contacted Ramon Freyre in Concepcion, had discussed with Freyre the means of expelling the enemy from the south of Chile and, taking the decision in his own hands, had moved to Valdivia with troops borrowed from Freyre.

It was insubordination!

But he could not dismiss him. The Britisher was needed. Before San Martin and the expeditionary troops could attack Lima, Cochrane had to cut out the Spanish warships defending Callao.

He had known from the start that Cochrane would be unpredictable. That was the chance he took.

But Bernardo had no doubt that Cochrane would take Valdivia, and brilliantly. And he would take it because the failures at Callao made it necessary for Cochrane's own selfrespect to accomplish the impossible without help. He had planned it alone; he would execute it with only the few troops borrowed from Freyre.

It was Freyre as much as Cochrane that concerned Bernardo. If Cochrane succeeded, and he would, Freyre would convince himself that it was his success as much as Cochrane's.

There would be more trouble with Freyre. He was already working secretly with a faction in Santiago to improve his position. He wanted to be located in the north. He blamed Bernardo that he had no place with the government in Santiago. He had ceased to be the unassuming and affectionate friend, and had listened to the enemies who wanted to undermine the present government. Now Freyre would believe he had Cochrane with him in his feelings against Bernardo and the government and he would make use of the occasion.

That had not been Cochrane's intention. Bernardo understood Cochrane's reasons for going to Valdivia. Freyre did not, and others would misinterpret it.

Word came at last from Cochrane. Bernardo read the report with growing concern.

"Sir: I had the honor to inform you, from Talcahuano, that, taking advantage of the opportunity which presented itself of communicating with Colonel Freyre on the means most effectual toward expelling the enemy from the south of Chile, and freeing the country from future incursions, I availed myself of the assistance of the zealous and active officer; who supplied me, on the 28th ult., with the troops and other assistance I required.

"The *O'Higgins*, *Intrepid* brig and *Montezuma* schooner sailed with a fair wind, and on the 2nd instant arrived at the preconcerted rendezvous, ten leagues to the southward of Valdivia.

"All the troops were then embarked in the small vessels; and leaving the *O'Higgins* outside, we stood in for the Aguada Inglesa, where we anchored at a moderate distance from the battery and fort of San Carlos. The troops were disembarked at sunset, but this was not effected before the castle commenced a fire upon us, and in consequence of the heavy surf retarding the disembarkation, the enemy gained time to collect a considerable force behind the precipices which line the head.

"Nevertheless, the marines of the *O'Higgins* and *Intrepid* with the military having reached the shore, put the enemy to flight, and pursuing them to the forts of Aguada Inglesa and San Carlos, immediately took possession of the fort. The second was taken by assault after dark, in spite of the efforts of the enemy to defend it. . . ."

Bernardo did not finish the report. He laid it aside. Cochrane had taken Valdivia. It was a brilliant act. It dispossessed Spain of her finest Chilean harbor.

He was delighted. And he was also disturbed.

For the ministers in Santiago and Valparaiso were furious with Cochrane and demanded his dismissal.

Bernardo quieted them as best he could. Then he ordered medals struck commemorating the taking of Valdivia. They read, "Long live Cochrane, the hero of Valdivia!" And he invited the Admiral to Santiago. He wanted to speak of reimbursing him and his men, to smooth over the insults which the ministers had heaped upon Cochrane.

At the country place, Conventilla, the pale and disturbed Cochrane paced the tiles of the terrace. He stopped suddenly before Bernardo. He struck that theatrical pose which was a part of him, and the handsome, arrogant face was stern, eyes angry. He had taken Valdivia, he said, fiercely. And alone. He had taken it to prove to himself that he still was Cochrane the seaman, the fearless sailor.

"I understand," Bernardo said. "Others do not."

He recalled that more than once he had stepped out of line himself. Sometimes that was how things got done. He recalled Chacabuco, when he demanded of San Martin to be allowed to attack. Yes, he had stepped out of line, but successfully. And there had been other times. For that matter every man in the Chilean government had acted beyond his jurisdictional authority more than once.

Right or wrong, they had all done it. In a struggle such as this, it could not be avoided.

He was endlessly grateful to Cochrane, although it meant serious trouble ahead with Freyre.

"There stands the castle of Callao," Cochrane raged, "positively leering at me. My rockets should have worked. Except that the charming Marine Minister and his assistants employed Spanish prisoners of war in Chilean jails to prepare the rockets. Any donkey should have known better than to turn that important work over to Spanish prisoners loyal to the Crown."

Bernardo said nothing. But he thought Cochrane was right. Any donkey would have known better. Cochrane forgot that Chile still was in swaddling clothes so far as government, ministers and technicians were concerned. The ministers often acted like donkeys. Bernardo, who had more advantages, often had.

"I'll cut the *Esmeralda* out from under that blasted fortress of Callao!" Cochrane's face was flushed with rage, and he continued to pace the terrace. "I'll stop the jeers of the Spanish at my failures!"

Bernardo said quietly that he knew Cochrane would succeed at Callao, as he had in other naval expeditions. It was only a matter of time, of planning, of waiting as patiently as he could. Bernardo had never doubted for an instant that Cochrane would succeed.

Cochrane stopped the pacing. He stared off into the distance at the plains of Maipú as if it were the South Sea, the harbor of Callao, the castle and the Spanish warships.

The expeditionary forces under San Martin were ready to move north to Peru. Without waiting on Cochrane to make another attack on Callao, Bernardo and San Martin decided to ship the forces, disembark them in the bay of Tarapaca, a few miles south of Pisco in Peru, leaving Cochrane to blockade Callao.

Now Bernardo would write the Peruvians that the expeditionary forces of Chile and the Buenos Aires troops were prepared to march against the Spanish Royalists of Peru and liberate the north.

Bernardo went to his desk at the Palace.

The friends in Peru must understand that when a patriot army entered their cities under General San Martin, it came as a friend to help and not as an army to conquer them. As he pulled paper toward him, he thought of that great land of Peru which independence would soon link with Chile and Buenos Aires.

Thoughtfully, he stared at the paper.

This message must inspire confidence and rouse the Peruvians to support the expeditionary forces. For minutes Bernardo worked over a beginning. He wanted to write about wiping out entirely the evils of Spanish tyranny. There would be no more domination, no more Inquisition. And the rights of free men would be theirs.

After an hour he began:

"In the tenth year of the South American revolution, and the three hundredth of the conquest of Peru, a people whose rank in the social scale has hitherto rated below its destiny had undertaken to break the chain which Pizarro began to forge with his blood-stained hands in 1520. The government established in Chile since its restoration having conceived this great design, deems it right that it should be carried into execution by the same person who having twice promised to save his country, has twice succeeded. An expedition equipped at the expense of great sacrifices, is at length ready to proceed, and the Army of Chile, united to that of the Andes, is now called upon to redeem the land in which slavery has longest existed and from whence the latest efforts have been made to oppress the whole continent. Happy be this day on which the record of the movements and the action of the expedition commenced! The object of the enterprise is to decide whether or not the time is arrived when the influence of South America upon the rest of the world shall be commensurate with its extent, its riches and the situation. O'Higgins."

The expeditionary forces were on the march for Valparaiso. Bernardo watched from the cliffs above the town. As the men passed, spectators shouted, bands played, and the flags of Chile, North America and England waved.

Bernardo glanced along the main steet of Valparaiso. It was

as colorful as a fiesta. Every mule, horse and wagon was decorated with myrtle and paper flowers. Church bells rang. The boats of fishermen were trimmed with banners and the green water was strewn with carnations and roses. He heard happy voices singing patriotic songs.

On August nineteenth, the first of the expeditionary troops embarked.

Bernardo saw Cochrane's flagship, the *O'Higgins*, as she moved around Angel Point going toward Peru. It was followed by the *San Martin* on which the General sailed. Chile's other ships unfurled their sails. Guns boomed from the fortress of El Baron!

His father Don Ambrosio giving his encouragement!

A dispatch had come from Lord Cochrane.

Eagerly, Bernardo read. On the night of November fifth, fourteen boats, under command of Cochrane, had left the *O'Higgins* and moved on the castle of Callao. The men wore white jackets or shirts and were armed with pistols, sabers, knives, tomahawks and pikes. They shouted "Viva el Rey!" to deceive the enemy, while they secured the *Esmeralda*. They took possession of all the Spanish ships in the harbor.

Cochrane had cut out the *Esmeralda!*

And Chile was at last the undisputed master of the coast!

But, although this should have been the signal for San Martin to move against Lima, Bernardo received no word that he had acted.

Bernardo wanted to be in Peru. He wanted to speak to San Martin and urge him to attack. Why did the General wait?

Then at last came word from San Martin. He explained that the Peruvians must be prepared before the liberating troops entered Lima. There must be a softening period.

November, December. Then January of another year. Then June, and still the troops of San Martin had not taken Lima. He was advised in August that in July the Spanish had abandoned the city of Lima.

Now, San Martin would act, Bernardo thought hopefully. Now was the moment the General had wanted.

He was elated when he received word that San Martin had been invited to Lima and had been elected Protector of Peru. With the General heading the government, the patriots were in control of practically all of South America.

Bernardo gave a dinner for the Chilean ministers to celebrate the great moment. Again, the fiestas!

Then came the exciting news that the United States had recognized the patriot governments of Chile, Peru, Buenos Aires and Colombia.

Learning of it that bright winter day, Bernardo hurried to a wall map of North and South America, looking with happy eyes on the enormous stretch of land and sea. Two great continents linked!

Chile a nation among other nations. Chile, a free country like North America. A little better than twenty years ago since Bernardo returned to Chile from Spain, and already the countries of South America had taken their place as free and independent countries. It seemed fitting, he thought, staring at the map, that the first to recognize the independent states of South America should be the liberated and free North America.

Proudly, his eyes found the long stretch of land along the coast of South America that was Chile. With a full heart, he stood looking at his country. His country, a free nation among nations!

CHAPTER XLIV

JUDGE PREVOST, United States Consul-General in Chile, was visiting Bernardo at Conventilla.

They were having dinner in the pleasant dining room, the doors open and the sun streaming across tiles and polished sideboards, the serving tables, gleaming silver and best porcelain. Everything the finest for an envoy from Chile's neighbor and friend in North America, Bernardo thought, watching the merry face of the amiable Judge, listening to his easy conversation.

He had mentioned a Mrs. Maria Graham, an English writer and artist, widow of a naval officer, who was in Valparaiso. She was a fine woman, the Judge explained, and a good friend of South America, unorthodox and advanced in her opinions. "You will like her. She is coming to Santiago on a visit and to gather information about Chile. May I bring her to call?" And Judge Prevost smiled, pleasantly. "She will be the house guest of the Cotopas family. You know them, of course."

The Cotopas family! Bernardo glanced off toward the garden, seeing again the scowling face of Jose Miguel Carrera, the weak face of Luis Carrera. Indeed he knew the Cotopas family. The Cotopas were related to the Carreras by marriage. One of the daughters had married the eldest brother, Juan Jose.

Bernardo felt his spirits sink. For whenever he thought of the Carreras, he remembered Juan Mackenna. And the memory always saddened him.

Judge Prevost was still speaking of Mrs. Graham. She was a friend of Admiral Cochrane. She was writing a book about Chile.

"You can give her better information about your country and the struggle for independence than any other Chilean."

"Mrs. Graham will be very welcome," Bernardo said. He would be happy to speak with an Englishwoman who was interested enough in Chile to want to write about it. He would be delighted if the British government were as interested in the country, enough so to grant it recognition, which had been long in coming. How much longer, he thought.

"Then on a Friday, perhaps?" the Judge said. "At the Palace? The Cotopas' house is not far from the Palace."

Mrs. Graham arrived at the appointed time escorted by the Judge. With them were two of the Cotopas ladies.

Bernardo and his mother and Rosa made them welcome.

Mrs. Graham was a handsome woman of about thirty-five with kind but inquisitive eyes, a clear and pretty English voice and an inquiring mind. She had the forthright manner of speaking that he admired in the English and she gave her opinions frankly.

"I attended school in Richmond," Bernardo said, and a flood of memories surged into his mind.

"I often visited Richmond," Mrs. Graham said. "My uncle is Sir David Dundas. Did you know him, by chance?"

Did he know Dr. David Dundas, Bernardo asked himself, his heart feeling the ancient pain. Would he ever forget that gentleman, the house, the old yew tree, the small study hung with blue, the polished fender and a blazing fire.

And Carlota sitting in the wingchair looking up at him with tearful eyes, the gentle eyes telling him of her love, eager to be told she was in his heart forever, his own beloved.

Mrs. Graham was looking at him, waiting for an answer.

"I knew your uncle very well," he said, as calmly as he could. "I spent many pleasant hours in his house near the old Richmond castle." And he paused a moment. "Did you on any of your visits meet a family by the name of Eeles? From Dublin."

She was thoughtful. "No, I don't recall the name," she said. "But

I was only a girl in my early teens at the time. And a scatterbrain. I remembered nothing." She glanced about the drawing room. "It is a room like those I visited in Richmond," she said, studying the carpets, draperies, the straight lines of rosewood and mahogany chairs, the tables. "I feel at home."

Bernardo listened but he was thinking of the Eeles home in Richmond, and of Carlota at the pianoforte, of Carlota singing for him, of his dancing with her.

And he wondered if his officer who had gone home to visit in Ireland had located the Eeles, for there had been neither word from him or from the Eeles family. "Look them up," he had asked his officer, "tell them that I shall be coming to Ireland one day. Ask about Carlota Eeles. If she is not married, I would like to know. Find out for me."

There had been no word about the Eeles.

Mrs Graham said, "I have heard about the Indian orphans that you have adopted," she said. "Could I see some of them?"

Bernardo sent a servant to bring them from another part of the Palace. He explained to Mrs. Graham that they were children whose people had been slaughtered in the war. "When the Indians go into battle," he said, "they take their families along. The Chilean government offers a reward for all persons, especially women and children, who have been saved after a battle. The children we educate to act as mediators between their Indian nations and Chile. They are taught their native tongue as well as Chilean."

"Will you ask them to speak the Araucanian tongue?" she asked, and she leaned forward in her chair, her eyes intent and serious.

Putting an arm about Maria, the daughter of a chief, he explained that the charming English lady was their friend and the friend of Chile. "The lady comes from England," he said. "England is across the great sea."

The child smiled at Mrs. Graham with round, dark eyes and when she spoke the Araucanian words of greeting, her voice was pretty and soft, like the language.

The child's eyes rested on Bernardo with affection for a moment, then she darted off.

Mrs. Graham spoke of the Chileans. "How indebted to you the Chileans are," she said kindly. "I hear only praise for your labors. You have done the impossible many times."

"Love of country inspires a patriot," he said. "Even ordinary men like myself are motivated by that." And he glanced at the Turkey carpet, thinking how little he had done and how much remained. "You may think us backward, Mrs. Graham," he said. "But the shackles of Spain were on Chile for three hundred years. In time more improvements will come."

The guests departed.

After Mrs. Graham had gone, Bernardo stood quietly thinking of Richmond, the memories which Mrs. Graham had revived. He called to Rosa and asked her to send a tray of the finest Chilean fruits to Mrs. Graham. "Send something that might not be found in England," he said.

Rosa prepared a magnificent arrangement. It rose like a pyramid, the lucumas, sweet limes and loquats, oranges and watermelon, topped by lime blossoms, jasmine, fuchsias and roses.

Two servants in livery carried the tray to Mrs. Graham at the Cotopas' residence.

For a long time Bernardo stood at the window in the drawing room, thinking of Carlota.

At last, he went to his desk and tried to word a letter to her. He would write of his love, of his constant affection for her. He would tell her there never had been and never would be another love for him, and he would ask her to travel to him in Chile if she still was free, and marry him.

But sheet after sheet of paper he tore up. Suppose she had married, he asked himself.

Perhaps, in time, there would be something from the Irish officer explaining about Carlota. Then Bernardo could write.

Bernardo was in conference with one of his ministers at the Palace one September day when he received word that San Martín had arrived in Valparaiso from Peru.

It was shocking news. He wondered why the General had returned so suddenly without advising him beforehand.

He sent a carriage to bring San Martin to his country place, for the message that brought word of the General's arrival said he had not been well, and a carriage would be more comfortable than a saddle.

San Martin reached Santiago and came at once to Bernardo at his country place.

As he stepped from the carriage he said, "I am sick to death. I am discouraged by pain, dissension, ingratitude. The people of Peru no longer need me. In Lima, I went about the streets in a disguise listening to what people were saying about San Martin, the Protector."

He walked beside Bernardo along the hall. "My friend," San Martin said, "Peru no longer wants or needs me."

Bernardo said, "Peru does need you, San Martin. A patriot like you is always needed. I am sorry you left Peru."

"You know," San Martin said, "I once thought that. I felt if Bolívar would help, we could keep the government and the people steady and root out the Spanish entirely. There were too many problems for one man who had battles to fight as well. I hoped, with a patriot like Bolívar to help, we could work things out."

A servant brought wine.

San Martin looked at it lovingly. "Mendoza!" he said, as if he wanted to be there. And he picked up the glass and held it against the light and stared at it. "So, I went to see Bolívar at Guayaquil, thinking we would speak together as equals and come to some agreement about saving Peru." His voice was unhappy, and his dark eyes sad. "Imagine," he said. "Bolívar sent word to me by one of his officers that the *Liberator* would speak with San Martin!"

He turned his glass, sipped the golden liquid. "The Liberator!" he repeated, and he sounded contemptuous. "Tell me, my friend, who liberated Buenos Aires, and Chile, and Peru? Who fought to bring five thousand soldiers across the Andes?" Slowly, San Martin set the glass on the table.

"Bolívar!" San Martin said, again. "It was the crossing of the

Andes by the liberating army that gave Bolívar confidence, and that gave the people courage to resist the Spanish. And it was the expeditionary force enlisted by you and me, and the navy of Chile, that liberated Peru."

Bernardo refilled San Martin's glass. "Does it matter, San Martin?" he said. "You and I know. The countries are free. That is enough."

"Bolívar will be known to future generations as the Liberator," San Martin said. "Because he insists that whenever his name is used or written he be spoken of as Liberator Bolívar." He rose and stood erect. "But I have the banner of Pizarro. When I reached Lima and the Viceroy's palace, I took the banner. Bolívar may call himself Liberator. But I have the banner!"

Bernardo thought, "Now what will happen? Will all the sacrifices for Peru have been in vain? Can Bolívar do without the tactician, the strategist, San Martin? How able is Bolívar?" Someone should be with Bolívar to help, for it was Peru and liberty that mattered.

"I am going to my farm across the Andes," San Martin said. "There I shall recuperate, and never fight again."

Scarcely was San Martin on his way when Lord Cochrane arrived in Santiago.

Bernardo saw him at the Palace, then at his country place.

At the dinner table at Conventilla, Cochrane was in an explosive mood. He poured out his anger and indignation. "I can talk to you, O'Higgins," he said, looking up from his dinner plate. "I am grateful enough, you may be sure, to find one man in Chile or Peru that will listen with intelligence and understanding. I have respect and affection for you." He looked at Bernardo with kindness.

Then suddenly his eyes flashed at some memory. "Did Freyre actually believe that because of the Valdivia episode I would desert you to go with him and his party? The man is an idiot!"

This was not news to Bernardo.

"You should have accompanied San Martin to Peru," he said. "Then things might have turned out differently. Now, there is only confusion and a threat of anarchy. And Simon Bolívar! Before he loosens his grip on Peru there will be anarchy," he said.

Then he was back to San Martin again. "San Martin needs someone to stand beside him and goad him to action. A fine soldier, an able tactician. But always waiting. Genius is useless if it is wasted on indecision. He should never have handled finances for the country. He refused to pay the navy. He said that should be paid by Chile!"

How the words poured forth! How the flaming, rocket-like mind of Cochrane lighted with anger, annoyance, with gentleness and affection as he raced from San Martin to Chile, to Bernardo!

And Bernardo could only listen. Words would not help now.

Then the visit was over.

Within weeks, Cochrane, too, had sailed for another land. He had been commissioned to command the navy of Brazil. Sadly, Bernardo thought of the friends that had fallen away. More and more his critics asked for changes, and the fledgling statesmen listened and attempted to satisfy everyone. And Bishop Rodrigues made the most of their desire to be all things to all men.

For Chile had been three hundred years under the heel of the Church as well as the Spanish Crown, and belief in the clergy was deep seated. Even Bishop Rodrigues, whom Bernardo had banished for his political intrigues, he had recently permitted to return because the people had asked for it. He had reminded the Bishop that as long as Bernardo was head of the government neither pope nor priest would possess temporal power and that if he did not act accordingly, he would be exiled again.

Already the Bishop had overstepped. Already he was plotting against Bernardo and his government. These high churchmen could not be changed in a moment. They had always considered themselves above the state, and the Bishop had already split the Chileans into factions. And he was spreading rumors about Bernardo, the army and navy, about public officials.

The Bishop wanted Spain to govern again and restore to the Church the riches taken from it by the patriots' progressive laws.

Lately, the gossip had been about Jose Rodrigues-Aldea.

And yet Jose had raised funds for Chile. No other Chilean could have promoted a million and a half dollar loan with the British government. He had paid for ships, arms, ammunition, for the wars, the peacetime industries. The ministers wanted Jose dismissed.

Bernardo had given the Bishop his chance. It began to look as if he would have to speak with him again.

One morning, arriving early at the Palace from Conventilla, Bernardo learned from his secretary of a secret meeting that was being held by some of the government officials. They were planning another form of constitution to the one supported by Bernardo. They had discussed the removal of Jose Rodrigues-Aldea, and the subject of replacing the Supreme Director had come up. Freyre had been mentioned to succeed Bernardo. It had been said by a spokesman at the meeting that Freyre wanted to march his troops to Santiago and take over the position of Supreme Director.

Bernardo listened, shocked into silence.

This was the work of the Bishop and his friends. And his colleagues had listened. Where was that pledged honesty and outspoken criticism they all had agreed to with such solemnity?

He went to his desk, sat staring at the blotter. He removed from his pocket a letter that had come from the people of Peru. They had offered Bernardo, for his labors in liberating Peru, the hacienda Montavlan. For weeks, Bernardo had carried the letter in his pocket, grateful for the appreciation and the affection that it contained.

He thought about Peru now. He thought of Simon Bolívar. Bolívar, a man who wanted to be called Liberator above all else. The brilliant soldier and patriot, a man who wanted freedom for South America as Bernardo and San Martin and the others had wanted it. They all had the same dream and hope. They all had worked tirelessly, without thought of reward, for the freedom of their countries. The names on that long list of patriots who had labored for freedom would never be counted; some had already been forgotten, but all were equally important. All of them, combined, were the Liberator. It was not the work of one man. One person could not have done it.

But if Bolívar wanted to call himself Liberator, Bernardo would not quarrel with him. It was a weakness. Let him have the weakness so long as the countries kept their liberty.

And Bolívar needed help in Peru.

Bernardo still was head of the Army of Chile. He would go to Peru and offer his services to Bolívar in any capacity. Give him a title or no title, low or high place, so long as the Spaniards did not return to rule any country in this land. And let Bernardo help to wipe out the threat of anarchy if it existed in Peru.

For as long as South America needed a soldier, Bernardo would help wherever, however, he could.

With hasty steps he walked along the corridor and to Government House where the officials were meeting secretly.

They glanced up in embarrassment as he entered.

"Viva O'Higgins!" one cried.

Others took up the words.

But Bernardo answered by ripping from his chest the broad ribbon, his badge of office. "There will be no talk of troops and bloodshed over me," he said. "You do not terrorize me by talk of sedition, by threats, secret meetings or cries. I despise death today, as I have scorned it on the battlefield. But if it has not been given me to consolidate the new institutions of the Republic, at least I have the satisfaction of leaving it free and independent, respected abroad and glorious in victory. I thank God for the favor he has given to my government. I pray that he may protect those who succeed me."

He turned and walked quickly away, to the shouts of "O'Higgins! Viva O'Higgins!"

He had scarcely reached his office when the ministers called on him. They urged him not to leave Chile. They begged him to reconsider.

"I am leaving Chile," he said. "I am going to Peru. It will be better," He saw that clearly now.

All new governments went through stages of development. The government of Chile was entering another phase, and he could help now by leaving. He would not bring bloodshed to his country by remaining. They would choose a new Supreme Director, and another, and another. In time, things would be steadied.

He was leaving them with love. He glanced around the room at the solemn, strained faces of men with whom he had fought on the battlefield and who had helped him form the government. He wanted to comfort them.

When they had gone he wrote his abdication.

"Firmly believing that during the present circumstances I have it in my power to contribute to the tranquillity of my country by retiring from the supreme command of the state," he wrote, "and having well deliberated on the subject, I have finally agreed with the inhabitants of Santiago who are here met, and are the only body with whom I can at the present crisis treat, that I hereby abdicate the supreme direction of the republic of Chile, and consign the provisional exercise of my authority to a *junta gubernativa*, composed of the citizens Don Augustin Eyzaguirre, Don Miguel Infante, and Don Ferdinand Errazuris, because there is not a national representation at present, unto whom I could verify my abdication; which representation the *junta gubernativa* must procure to unite, and form with the greatest speed in consideration that if the present doubts are not settled by the provinces the junta will cease, and the inhabitants of the capital will deliberate as to what steps it will be most convenient to take; and in order that they know what are or will be their prerogatives and faculties, a regulation stating this must be made by the committee . . . Don Juan Egana, Don Bernardo Vera and Don Joaquin Campino.

"Printed, published and circulated. Given in Santiago, January 23rd, 1823. Bernardo O'Higgins."

He proclaimed the newly elected government himself. Then he left them.

A letter had come from Ireland. It told Bernardo that Carlota was dead. She had never married, but to the end had remembered Bernardo with love.

His heart heavy, he read, then sat thinking of his dear Carlota. Throughout the years she had loved him, wanted him. The sweetness, the bitterness, he thought. Dreams came, then vanished.

He folded the letter and put it aside, feeling the grief, the loss.

After a long time he rose and went to Conventilla.

Rosa was packing. His child Demetrio played near her.

His wish had been to raise Demetrio at Las Canteras. He wanted to teach him riding, roping of cattle, the care of the vineyards. He watched the child playing with a toy horse.

In Peru, there would be horses, a hacienda, a home. Bernardo would have his family, his work for South America.

"I will ride ahead to Valparaiso," he told Rosa and his mother, whose grave faces tried hard to smile. "I will arrange for our passage to Peru. You will follow me to the port in the carriage. I will provide an escort for you."

Mounting his horse he rode off along the Plaza, past the library with books from England and North America, past the new school. He hurried on. At the monument near the breakwater built by his father, he reined in his horse and read the words as he had many times before.

All those years his father had worked for Chile. And his son had labored, too.

Then he touched the flank of his horse and cantered on across marsh, past haciendas, olive trees, peaceful vineyards. Once, he turned to look at Santiago, the Andes, staring at the mass of rock and snow, the blue and white that was like the flag of the liberating forces.

Across the land of his beloved Chile he hurried. He was leaving his country because of that love.

Toward the west, toward Valparaiso and Peru, rode Don Bernardo, son of O'Higgins.

SELECTED BIBLIOGRAPHY

SELECTED BIBLIOGRAPHY

I WOULD like especially to mention the scholarly compilation of facts and documents in the volume *El Marques de Osorno Don Ambrosio Higgins,* by Ricardo Donoso, a publication of the University of Chile, which is an indispensable aid to any writer or student of the life of Don Ambrosio Higgins.

ANTEPARA, JOSE MARIA, *South American Emancipation, Documents Historical and Explanatory, General Miranda for the South American Emancipation.* London, 1810.

DE AMICIS, EDMONDO, *Spain and the Spaniards,* translated from the Italian by Wilhelmina W. Cady. New York and London: G. P. Putnam's Sons, 1880.

BEALS, CARLETON, *The Long Land: Chile.* New York: Coward-McCann, 1949.

BIGGS, JAMES, *The History of Don Francisco de Miranda's Attempt to Effect a Revolution in South America, in a Series of Letters.* Boston, 1808.

BONNYCASTLE, RICHARD HENRY, *Spanish America 1794-1848.* 2 volumes. London, 1818.

BRACKENRIDGE, HENRY MARIE, *Voyage to South America, Performed by Order of the American Government, 1817 and 1818, in the Frigate Congress.* London, 1820.

BYRON, JOHN, *The Narrative of the Hon. John Byron, Containing an Account of the Great Distresses Suffered by Himself and His Companions on the Coast of Patagonia, from 1740 to 1746.* London, 1768.

CALDCLEUGH, ALEXANDER, *Travels in South America During the Years 1819-'20-'21.* 2 Volumes. London, 1825.

CAMPBELL, ALEXANDER, *The Sequel to Bulkeley and Cummins' Voyage to the South-Seas.* London, 1747.

CAMPBELL, JOHN, *The Spanish Empire in America.* London, 1747.

CARLSON, FRED A., *Geography of Latin America.* New York: Prentice-Hall, Inc., 1943.

CARVALLO Y GOYENECHE, VINCENTE, *Descripción Histórico and Jeográfica del Reino de Chile.* Santiago, 1875.

CAUGHEY, JOHN WALTON, *History of the Pacific Coast of North America.* New York: Prentice-Hall, Inc., 1938.

CHISHOLM, A. STUART M., *The Independence of Chile.* London: T. W. Laurie, 1913.

COFFEY, THOMAS, *In South American Waters, O'Higgins and The Freedom of Chile.* Dublin: M. H. Gill & Sons Ltd., 1924.

COFFIN, ISAAC FOSTER, *Journal of a Residence in Chile, During the Year 1822.* Boston, 1823.

DE LA CRUZ, ERNESTO, Editor, *Epistolario de D. Bernardo O'Higgins 1798-1823.* Santiago, 1916.

DAVIE, JOHN CONSTANSE, *Letters from Buenos Aires and Chile With an Original History of the Latter Country.* London, 1819.

DONOSO, RICARDO, *El Marqués de Osorno Don Ambrosio Higgins 1720-1801.* Santiago: Publicaciones de la Universidad de Chile, 1941.

DUNDONALD, 10TH EARL OF, THOMAS COCHRANE, *Narrative of Services in the Liberation of Chile, Peru and Brazil, from Spain and Portuguese Domination.* London, 1859.

ELLIOT, GEORGE FRANCIS SCOTT, *Chile, its History and Development, Natural Features, Products, Commerce and Present Condition.* London: T. Fisher Unwin, 1920.

ENCINA, FRANCISCO A., *Gestacion de la Independencia. Revista Chilena de Historia y Geografia.* Volume 89. Santiago, Chile, 1940.

EYZAGUIRRE, JAIME, *O'Higgins,* Santiago, Chile: Zigzag, 1946.

FALKNER, THOMAS, *A Description of Patagonia and the Adjoining Parts of South America.* London, 1774.

FITZROY, ROBERT, *Narrative of the Surveying Voyages of His Majesty's Ships Adventure and Beagle.* London, 1839.

GALDAMES, LUIS, *A History of Chile,* translated and edited by Isaac J. Cox. Chapel Hill: University of North Carolina Press, 1941.

GARNETT, RICHARD, *Richmond on the Thames.* London: Seeley & Co., 1896.

GOETZ, DELIA, *Neighbors to the South.* New York: Harcourt, Brace Co., 1941.

GRAHAM, MARIA, *Journal of a Residence in Chile.* London, 1824.

HAIGH, SAMUEL, *Sketches of Buenos Ayres and Chile and Peru.* 2 volumes. London, 1831.

HALL, BASIL, *Extracts from a Journal Written on the Coasts of Chile, Peru and Mexico in 1820, 1821, 1822.* 2 volumes. Edinburgh, 1824.

HANCOCK, ANSON URIEL, *A History of Chile.* Chicago, 1893.

Handbook of Latin American Studies. Cambridge: Harvard University Press, 1935.

HARRISON, MARGARET H., *Captain of the Andes.* New York: Richard R. Smith, 1943.

HIBBERT, EDWARD, *Narrative of a Journey from Santiago de Chile to Buenos Aires in July, August 1821.* London, 1824.

HILL, SAMUEL, *Journal and Log of the Ophelia and Packet 1815-1823.* Manuscript Room, New York Public Library, New York, N. Y.

HOLE, CHRISTINA, *English Home-Life 1500 to 1800.* London: B. T. Batsford Ltd., London, 1947.

DE LA PEROUSE, G. F. G., *Voyage Round the World 1785-88 by the Boussole and Astrolabe.* 3 volumes. London, 1807.

LECKY, WILLIAM EDWARD HARTPOLE, A History of England in the XVIII Century. 4 volumes. London, 1878.

MAITLAND, FRANCIS J. G., Chile: Its Lands and People. London: Francis Griffiths, 1914.

MANNING, OWEN, The History and Antiquity of the County of Surrey. London, 1804.

MANNING, WILLIAM RAY, U. S. State Department Diplomatic Correspondence of the United States Concerning the Independence of Latin-American Nations. Selected and arranged by William Ray Manning. 3 volumes. Oxford University Press, 1925.

MATHISON, GILBERT FARQUHAR, Narrative of a Visit to Brazil, Chile, Peru and the Sandwich Islands, During years 1821 and 1822. London, 1825.

MEANY, EDMOND STEPHEN, Vancouver's Discovery of Puget Sound. Portland, Oregon: Binsford and Mort, 1942.

DE MIRANDA, DON FRANCISCO, Fragment from an XVIIIth Century Diary. Compiled and translated by Jordon Herbert Stabler, with a preface by E. B. Cunninghame Graham. Caracas: Tipografia "La Nacion", 1931.

MEDINA, DON JOSE T., Colonial History of Chile. Santiago, 1878.

MILLER, JOHN, Memoirs of General Miller. London, 1829.

MOLINA, JUAN IGNACIO, The Geographical, Natural and Civil History of Chile. Translated from original Italian by an American gentleman, Middletown (Conn), 1808.

MOSES, BERNARD, South America on the Eve of Emancipation. New York: G. P. Putnam's Sons, 1908.

MOSES, BERNARDO, Spain's Declining Power in South America. Berkeley: University of California Press, 1919.

MYERS, JOHN, Myers' Life and Travels. London, 1817.

O'Higgins, Bernardo, *Archivo de don Bernardo O'Higgins-Archivo Nacional Chile.* Volumes 1-10, Santiago: Editorial Nascimento, 1946.

O'Higgins, Dictator of Chile. Temple Bar, London, Volume 115, 1898.

Opazo, Gustavo, *Maturana Origen de las Familias del Antiguo Obispido de Concepcion. Revista Chilena de Historia y Geografia.* Volumes 86, 87, 88. Santiago, Chile, 1939-1940.

Orrego, Eugenio Vicuna, *O'Higgins, Vida y Tiempo.* Buenos Aires: Editorial Losado, 1946.

Pan American Union Bulletin. Washington, D. C.

Porter, Captain David, *Journal of a Cruise to the Pacific Ocean in the Frigate Essex, years 1812, 1813, 1814.* 2 volumes. New York: Harper, 1822.

Proctor, Robert, *Narrative of a Journey Across the Cordillera of the Andes and a Residence in Lima 1823 and 1824.* London, 1825.

Raynal, G. T., *A Philsophical and Political History of Settlements and Trade of Europe in the East and West Indies.* London, 1798.

Robertson, William Spence, *The Life of Miranda.* 2 volumes. Chapel Hill: University of North Carolina Press, 1929.

Rodney, Caesar Augustus, *The Reports on the Present State of South America.* London, 1819.

Rolt, Richard, *A New and Accurate History of South America.* London, 1756.

Secchi, Eduardo, *Arquitecturo en Santiago.* Santiago de Chile, 1941.

Skinner, Joseph, Editor, *Present State of Peru.* London, 1805.

Staunton, Sir George, *An Authentic Account of an Embassy from the King of Great Britain to the Emperor of China.* Philadelphia, 1799.

Stevenson, William Bennet, *History and Description Narrative of Twenty Years Residence in South America.* 3 volumes. London, 1829.

SUTCLIFFE, THOMAS, *Sixteen Years in Chile and Peru from 1822 to 1839.* London, 1841.

DE ULLOA, DON ANTONIO, *and* JUAN, DON JORGE, *A Voyage to South America.* Translated from the Spanish in 1806. Dublin, 1758.

URZUA, LUIS ROA, *Casa Riquelme de la Barrera, Don Bernardo O'Higgins y Riquelme. Revista Chilena de Historia y Geografia.* Vol. 54. Santiago, Chile, 1927.

VANCOUVER, CAPTAIN GEORGE, *A Voyage of Discovery.* 3 volumes. London, 1798.

VICUNA, BENJAMIN MACKENNA, *Vida del Captain Jeneral de Chile, Don Bernardo O'Higgins.* Santiago, 1882.

VICUNA, BENJAMIN MACKENNA, *Francisco Moyen, or the Inquisition as it was in South America.* Translated from Spanish by J. W. Duffy. London: H. Sotheran & Co., 1869.

VOWELL, RICHARD, *Campaigns and Cruises in Venezuela and New Granada and in the Pacific Ocean, from 1817 to 1830.* 3 volumes. London, 1831.

WAY, THOMAS R. *Architectural Remains of Richmond, Twickenham, Kew, Petershan, Mortlake.* London: John Lane, 1900.

WILKES, CHARLES, *U. S. Exploring Expedition Years 1838-42.* London: Lea & Blanchard, 1845.

WILLOCK, JOHN, *The Voyages and Adventures of John Willock, Mariner.* Philadelphia, 1798.

WINTERBOTTOM, WILLIAM, *An Historical, Geographical, Commercial and Philosophical View of America United States and European Settlements in America and the West Indies.* 4 volumes. London, 1795.

WOODS, JOSEPHINE HOEPPNER, *High Spots in the Andes.* New York: G. P. Putnam's Sons, 1935.

ZAMUDIO, JOSE Z., *Fuentes Bibliograficas Para el Estudio de la Vida de la Epoca de Bernardo O'Higgins.* Santiago de Chile: El Esfuerzo, 1936.